Get started with

AutoCAD® Electrical

(Full version - Parts 1, 2 and 3)

An independently produced course with 18 hours of step by step lessons

James Richardson

Published by Musselburgh Press

www.MusselburghPress.com

ISBN: 0-9957492-2-1
ISBN-13: 978-0-9957492-2-1

To my Mam and Dad,

Contents

1. Introduction

1.1 Aim of this book

The Autodesk® AutoCAD® Electrical software is a powerful package but you cannot just turn it on and start producing schematic drawings. There is a lot more information controlling a drawing than just the lines you see on the screen. If you do not set up your project properly, these hidden structures will cause you problems.

The ideal solution is a formal training course. Unfortunately, not everyone has the time or money for that, particularly if drawing schematics is only a small aspect of your job. Should your boss give you a copy of AutoCAD Electrical and expect you to start printing out schematics that afternoon you may well give up, unfairly blaming the AutoCAD software for being too hard.

This book is intended to help people in this situation. Starting as a complete beginner, it will get you producing schematics in a couple of days. Not only will these look professional, they will be set up in a proper project structure and be based around intelligent symbols and databases.

Using the help files or a full reference manual, it is difficult to know which steps are essential and which you can skip. This book provides a linear course which you should work through from page one, as you would a novel. The early chapters cover essential set up to make your drawings work properly.

That does not mean you must finish the whole book to be able to use AutoCAD Electrical. You will be able to produce simple drawings after chapter 2 and by the end of chapter 8 your drawings will be better than many you come across in industry. The later chapters cover more advanced features. These are useful but you don't have to learn them if you don't want to.

1.2 How to use this book

In a typical reference book you might read half of the first chapter, then jump to chapter 10 which looks like it explains the thing you want to do. Please don't do that with this one. Instead work through it sequentially.

Chapter 2 gives some brief advice on installation, mainly covering the loading of manufacturers' component libraries. These notes are very short and it is assumed that any installation issues will be supported by either the software vendor or your company's IT department.

The rest of chapter 2 guides you through your first steps in drawing with the AutoCAD software. It explains how to open a drawing, draw some shapes, save your drawing and print the results.

One aim of this chapter is to get you drawing something and feel you are making progress. The other is to become familiar with the methods for scrolling around your drawing and for selecting and modifying objects. This is very important so take your time. After this chapter you will be able to produce single sheet drawings made up of basic shapes like lines and rectangles.

The next four chapters set up a blank project ready for your future drawings.

Chapter 3 explains how to group drawings into a project. Chapter 4 creates a title block which will form a border around your drawings. Chapter 5 uses this block to create a drawing template. Finally, chapter 6 explains more features of projects and builds a template project for you to copy.

1

A proper project structure and templates are required before you tackle the rest of the book. To make things as fast as possible I have included example information for you to type in, even suggesting filenames. You can tweak these examples to match your company's requirements or repeat these chapters later to make a customised template.

Chapter 7 explains electrical schematics. This is the bit you actually want to learn! Chapter 8 continues this by adding wire numbers, wire types and signal cross-references to your basic schematic. Chapter 9 introduces the **Terminal Strip Editor** which helps organise the large number of terminals that might be scattered across your drawings.

At this point you could stop learning and still use the AutoCAD Electrical software to a worthwhile extent.

AutoCAD has only a limited range of schematic symbols. Chapter 10 explains how to create your own and set them up properly. It also explains a little more about how the AutoCAD Electrical symbol libraries work. Chapter 11 describes the AutoCAD tool for generating connector symbols.

The next few chapters cover the database information which can be attached to your schematic symbols.

Chapter 12 explains how to assign location codes to represent a component's physical location. Chapter 13 covers from/to wiring reports and ways to control the physical order in which components are wired together. In chapter 14 we see how to group individual conductors into cables. Chapter 15 assigns manufacturers' part data to components and shows how to produce a bill of material from the schematic drawing.

Chapter 16 explains how to create a mechanical panel layout from your schematic. Chapter 17 continues this theme with the physical layout of terminals. These chapters also explain methods of printing scale mechanical drawings.

The book up to this point is based on point to point wiring of discrete electrical components. In chapter 18 we cover drawings for PLC based equipment. You can create PLC I/O modules using an automated tool, show your wiring as ladder rungs and include PLC address information in your drawings.

This book is completely self-contained and requires no external materials. You may however wish to visit the website **www.MusselburghPress.com** where you can download additional resources that may prove useful.

I hope this book gets you off to a flying start with your drawing software. If so please write a short review on Amazon. It doesn't need to be an essay, just a few sentences to let other readers know it is a genuine product.

Best of luck,

James

2. Getting started (1¾ hours)

This chapter explains how to open a new drawing and produce a diagram using lines, text and shapes. If you only need a block diagram or a quick sketch then this chapter will be enough to get you going.

Items covered:

- Install the required component libraries
- Open a new drawing
- Understand parts of the screen
- Identify the **command line**, **Project Manager** window and layout/model space tabs. Learn how to hide or show these items
- Change colours and other settings
- Create a simple drawing using lines, rectangles and text
- Change the properties of these objects
- Become familiar with methods of selecting objects in AutoCAD
- Understand layouts
- Print your drawing

2.1   Installation and libraries

Installation

This book is not intended to cover the installation process for the AutoCAD Electrical software. For a single PC it is relatively straightforward to download the files from Autodesk and use the installation wizard. For more complicated systems, with multiple users across a network, it is assumed that installation will be done, or at least supported, by your company's IT department.

Autodesk release an updated version of AutoCAD Electrical each year, usually around April. These are named AutoCAD Electrical 2019, AutoCAD Electrical 2020, etc. You can install more than one version at once. For example, you might install the latest copy to try it while still using the old one. They are installed as separate programs without conflict.

One aspect of installation which does fall within the scope of this book is the installation of the symbol libraries.

Changing component and symbol libraries

As part of the installation process, AutoCAD Electrical will install several libraries of electrical symbols. It will also install component data from various manufacturers.

These databases are large so you should avoid installing everything. After installation you may wish to change the items installed. To do this you need to close the AutoCAD Electrical software and run the AutoCAD installation wizard from within Microsoft Windows. The exact method and the appearance of the screenshots will depend slightly on your version of Microsoft Windows.

2

How to open the AutoCAD installation wizard in Microsoft Windows 7:

If you are using Microsoft Windows 7, click on **Control Panel** and select **Programs and Features**.

You will be given a list of the programs installed on your computer which you can uninstall or modify.

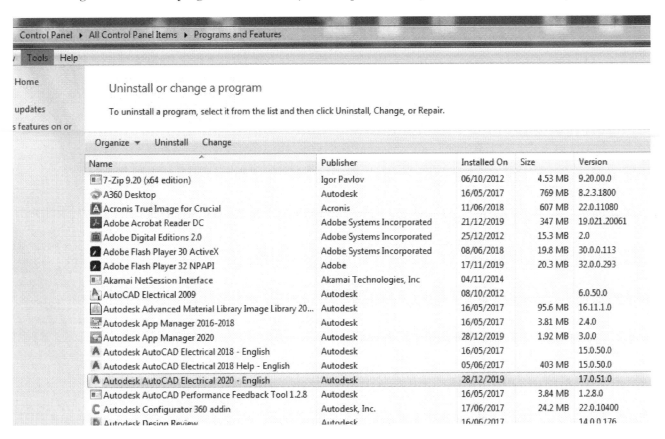

Left click the version of AutoCAD Electrical you are using, for example **"AutoCAD Electrical 2020 - English"**, to highlight it. Then either click **Change** at the top of the screen or right click the highlighted program and select **Change** from the menu that appears.

How to open the AutoCAD installation wizard in Microsoft Windows 10:

If you are using Windows 10 it is a little harder to find the **Control Panel**. The easiest way is to press the Windows button on the keyboard and type **Control Panel** in the search box that appears.

Within the **Control Panel** select **Programs** then choose **Uninstall a program**. This will bring up a list of programs for you to **Uninstall, Change** or **Repair**.

Highlight the version of AutoCAD Electrical software that you are using and select **Change**.

Using the AutoCAD installation wizard to change the installed libraries

After opening the AutoCAD installation wizard you will see the following screen.

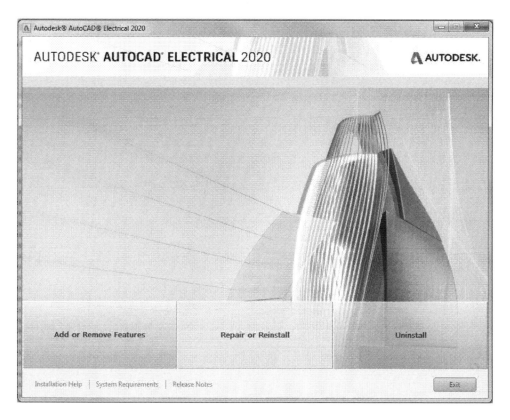

Click **Add or Remove Features**. You will see a list of manufacturers whose data is installed.

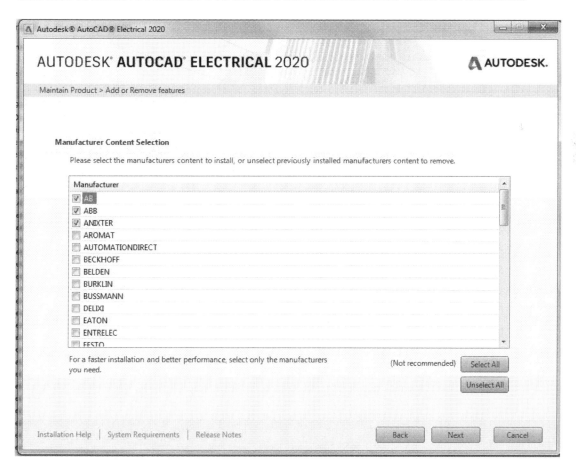

Change these manufacturers to include any whose components you expect to use. To match the examples in this book ensure **AB**, **LAPP**, **Telemecanique** and **WAGO** are ticked. Then click **Next**.

You must now choose which libraries of schematic symbols you want to use.

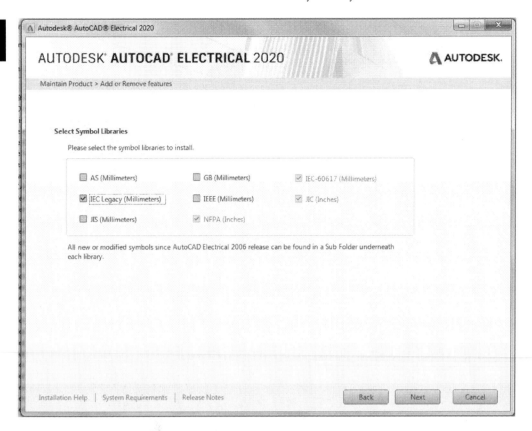

Tick any libraries which you intend to use. The examples in this book will use the **IEC4** library which is a metric (for drawings in mm) library based on the IEC-60617 symbols. This (and the related **IEC2** library) are included in the **IEC Legacy (Millimeters)** library which is ticked by default.

After choosing your libraries click **Next**. You will see the following screen.

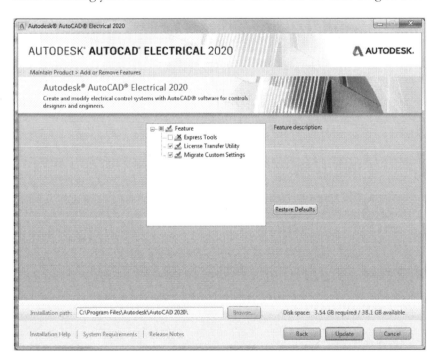

You can use the **Back** button to change your earlier choices and you can exit without changing anything by clicking **Cancel**. If you are happy with your changes click **Update**. The program will install the new data and then close.

Your individual projects will still need to be told to use any new symbol libraries. This is covered in chapter 3.

Repair / Reinstall

On rare occasions I have had problems with AutoCAD being unable to access a manufacturer's data, even though it had been installed. Should you encounter similar problems where you suspect the AutoCAD software is not working properly, you can use the **Repair** and **Reinstall** options in the installation wizard.

In my case the **Reinstall** option fixed the problem. The **Reinstall** process did not delete the template and drawing files I had created but I suggest backing up any important files just in case.

2.2   Set up the drawing area

Open the AutoCAD Electrical program on your computer.

When you first start AutoCAD, the screen will be similar to the image below. A quirk of AutoCAD is that many functions will not work unless you have a drawing open. Even things that do not act on a drawing, for example opening menus and dialogue boxes, will not work unless a drawing is open.

Our first step is therefore to open a drawing.

Open a new drawing

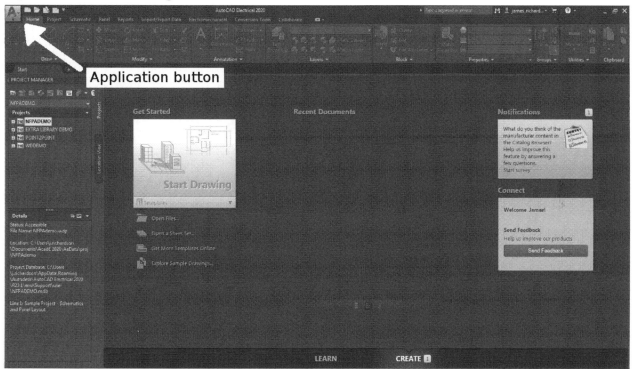

Click the large, red **A** at the top left of the screen. This is called the **Application Button**. A menu will appear. Select **New** from this menu. A dialogue box will open asking you to select a template for your new drawing. In later chapters we will create a custom template. For now we will use a pre-supplied blank template that comes with AutoCAD.

Select **acadiso.dwt** from the list of template files and click **Open**. This opens a metric template for a blank drawing. This template is suitable for use with the IEC electrical symbol libraries and is the one we will adopt in this book. There is also an imperial template, **acad.dwt**, which is set to inches to match the scaling of the **JIS** symbol library.

2

When working through this book please use the metric template, **acadiso.dwt**, for consistency with the example screenshots. If you wish to use inches, it is easy to change the drawing settings later, even starting from the metric template.

While the metric system is used for all of the examples in this book, points where you might choose a different setting for imperial (inch) measurements will be highlighted.

The diagram below shows the process to create your new drawing.

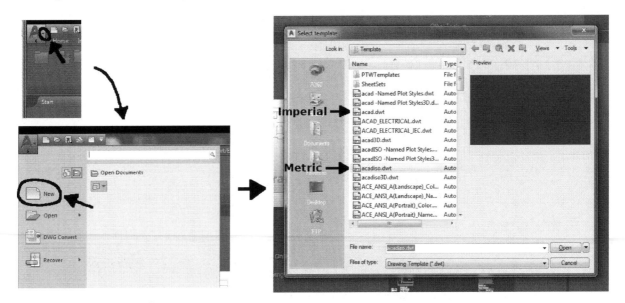

Note that by default, AutoCAD looks for templates in the **Template** folder:

C: /Users/ *Your username*/AppData/Local/Autodesk/AutoCAD Electrical 2020/R23.1/enu/Template

It is easiest to keep any new templates you create here although you can store them elsewhere. The value **R23.1** in this address will change for different versions of AutoCAD Electrical.

Problems displaying the file selection dialogue box

Occasionally you may encounter a problem with the above process. When you click **New**, instead of opening a dialogue box to select your template, AutoCAD will bring up a command line and expect you to type the filename and directory path. This problem can sometimes happen with other file selection dialogue boxes - **Open**, **Save** etc. It is caused by a bug setting a flag called the **FILEDIA** bit to zero and the solution is to set it back to **1**. Hopefully this bug will not occur on your first day of using AutoCAD, but if it does the solution is as follows:

At the command line (discussed below) type **FILEDIA** and press **<Enter>**. Then type **1** and press **<Enter>**. This should set the **FILEDIA** bit to **1**, telling AutoCAD you want to select your files from a dialogue box, not type them at a command line MS DOS style.

If you cannot see the command line don't worry. You could open it as described below but without a drawing open many commands, including **CTRL + 9** to open the command line, will not work.

In this case just press **<Esc>** to stop any half completed actions in progress.

Type   **FILEDIA**   **<Enter>**
then   **1**   **<Enter>**

Even though you cannot see the command line, it still operates and the commands will have the same effect.

You can now select **New** to create a new drawing and get the dialogue box as described above. Once **FILEDIA** is set to **1** it should stay that way but occasionally it seems to drift back to zero.

2.3   Understanding the AutoCAD screen

With your new drawing opened the screen should look like this:

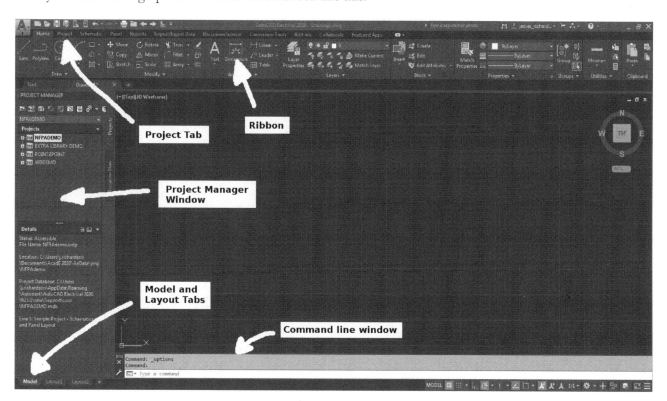

Ribbon

Along the top of the screen you should see the ribbon. This contains commands as handy buttons. Click on the tabs at the top of the ribbon to select which group of buttons is displayed.

The following tabs are used in this book:

Home

This has commands for drawing shapes and text and for adding dimension arrows. It also includes commands for manipulating layers in the drawing, changing an object's properties and grouping objects together.

Insert

This menu allows images to be inserted and also has tools to manipulate blocks.

Project

A project is a group of drawing files and will be discussed in Chapter 3. This menu has useful tools which operate on a set of drawings.

The **Manager** button, at the left of the **Project** tab, opens the **Project Manager** window if you have closed it.

Schematic

The **Schematic** tab is important for electrical drawings. It lets you insert components and wires, manipulate wire numbers and create new component symbols.

2

Panel

The **Panel** tab is used to generate mechanical panel layout drawings. It also contains a tool to make working with terminals easier.

Reports

This is used to produce a bill of material, wiring lists, cable schedules and other reports for your drawings.

Other tabs provide features beyond the scope of this book:

Import/Export Data

This tab contains commands to exchange data with other programs.

Electromechanical

The **Electromechanical** tab allows you to link your AutoCAD Electrical project to a 3D model in AutoCAD® Inventor®.

Conversion Tools

The **Conversion Tools** tab provides many features for modifying blocks, symbols and wires and for converting between different types of objects.

Add-ins

This allows you to interface with the Autodesk AutoCAD app store.

Collaborate

This tab allows you to share an online version of your drawing with other people. It also has a tool for comparing different versions of a drawing.

Featured Apps

This tab allows you to connect to the Autodesk AutoCAD App store and also see recommended apps.

To change which tabs are visible on the ribbon, right click on a blank part of the bar, level with the tab titles. A menu will appear. Move the mouse over **Show Tabs** to display a submenu as shown below. The possible tabs are listed with a tick beside those which are visible. Click the items to add or remove ticks.

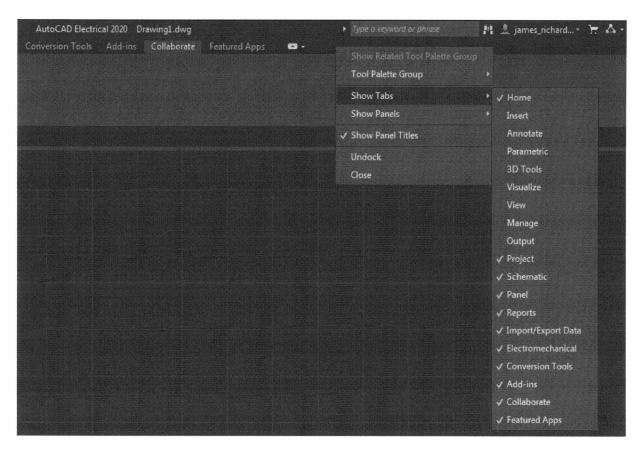

Ensure **Home, Project, Schematic, Panel** and **Reports** are ticked. Also add a tick beside **Insert**. We will be using these tabs in this book.

Catalog Browser

You may see the **Catalog Browser** window as shown below.

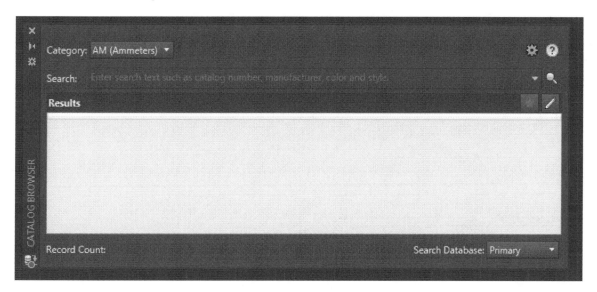

We will not be using this until much later in the book. Click the **X** in the top corner of this window to close it.

Viewcube

At the top right of your drawing you will see a compass and box. This is the **ViewCube**. It is used for switching between different projections of 3D mechanical drawings. For electrical schematics you will probably want to turn it off.

2

Do not click the **X** beside it. That will close your drawing, not the **ViewCube**. Instead, right click on an empty area of your drawing to open the following menu.

Select **Options...** at the bottom to bring up options for your drawing environment.

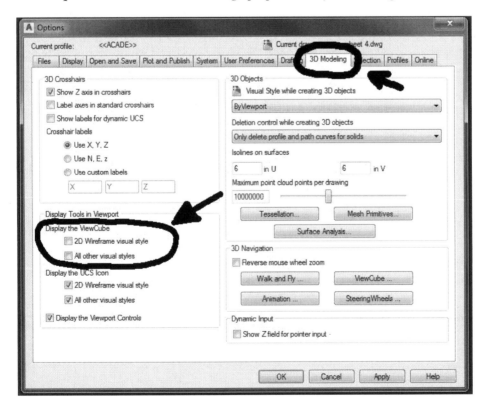

Choose the **3D Modelling** tab and untick the two boxes under **Display the ViewCube** circled above. Click **OK** and the **ViewCube** will be gone.

Project Manager window

This is a very useful window and you will probably keep it open most of the time. It is normally shown on the left of the screen although you can move it elsewhere. If you hover your mouse over its top right corner, an **X** will appear, allowing you to close it.

If this window is not open, click on the 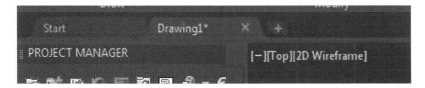 button in the **Project** tab of the ribbon to make it appear.

The **Project Manager Window** shows the projects you have open and which one of them is currently active. You can use it to manipulate the drawings within a project and to change properties for both individual sheets and the overall project.

Projects are discussed in chapters 3 and 6.

Drawing tabs

Each open drawing has a tab at the top of the screen with its name. If you have several drawings open you can jump between them by clicking these tabs. Currently you only have one drawing open. AutoCAD will have given it the default name of **"Drawing1"**.

Command line

While AutoCAD can be operated using a mouse, you can also enter commands via a text based command line.

You are free to mix the two. The graphical interface is intuitive but the command line may be faster for some tasks if you are an experienced user. It is also a good way to enter precise values, for example the radius of a circle or an angle of rotation.

Clicking the **X** at the left of the command line will close it. If it is closed then pressing **CTRL + 9** will make it re-appear. Note that the command line is always active. If you type AutoCAD instructions they will still have the same affect with the command line closed, you just won't be able to see what you are typing.

Model / Layout tabs

At the bottom left you will see tabs marked **Model**, **Layout 1** and **Layout 2**. These are important for mechanical drawings but we can make good use of them for electrical schematics too. Imagine the model tab as an infinitely large canvas on which you can draw your drawing. The layout tabs represent the sheets of paper you intend to print on. They contain windows looking at the parts of the model you wish to print.

You can create your drawing in model space then use the layout views to present it for printing, either on paper or as a **.pdf** file. More on this soon but for now be sure you can see the tabs and can switch between them.

2

If the **Model** / **Layout** tabs are missing then click the **Application Button**. Select **Options** from the menu that appears. In the **Options** dialogue box go to the **Display** tab.

Ensure the checkbox **Display Layout and Model tabs** is ticked.

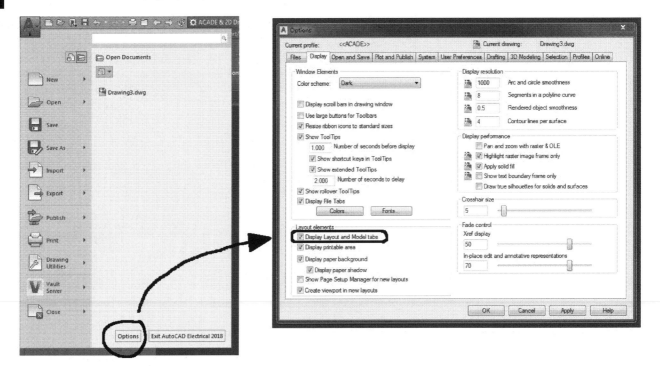

You can also access this **Options** screen by right clicking on a blank part of your drawing and selecting **Options** from the menu that appears, as we did when we closed the **ViewCube**.

Save your drawing

Before we go any further, save your drawing by clicking the **Application Button** and then selecting **Save**. You should get a dialogue box titled **Save Drawing As**.

Give your drawing a meaningful name and select the location where you want to save it. AutoCAD will probably suggest the Microsoft Windows **My Documents** folder but you can choose any location.

The file will be saved as a **.dwg** file.

Drawing space

Look at the **Model** / **Layout 1** / **Layout 2** tabs and be sure **Model** is selected (in bold compared to **Layout 1** and **Layout 2**. If necessary click the **Model** tab to be sure you are in model space.

By default the background colour may be set to white with light coloured menus. If you prefer you can select a dark background. This is easier on the eyes and will match the screenshots in this book.

Right click the drawing space and select **Options**. Alternatively click on the **Application Button** and select **Options**. You will see the same **Options** dialogue box we saw before. Select the **Display** tab again. Select the **Dark** colour scheme to make the menus and frame darker.

You may want to change the drawing background to a dark grey. To do this click the **Colors...** button. The **Drawing Window Colors** dialog box appears. This allows you to change colours of individual elements in the display. The **Restore current element** button on this screen is useful if you pick a horrible setting and want to get back.

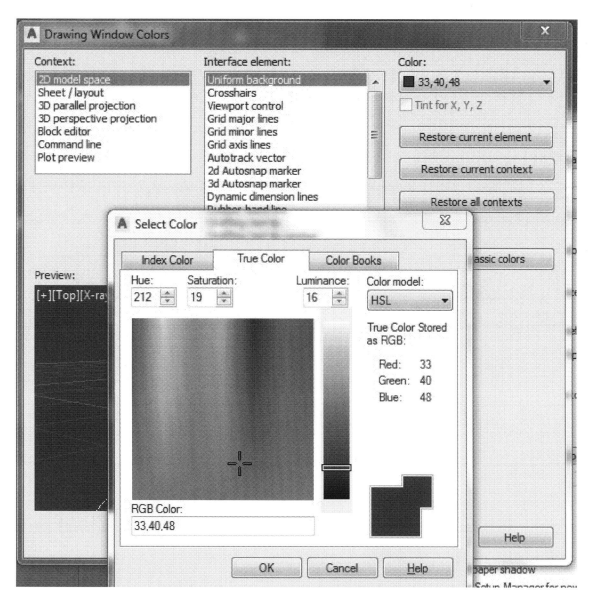

Select **2D model space** (In the box titled **Context**) and **Uniform background** (In the box titled **Interface element)** as the items you want to change. Under **Color** at the top right, click the drop down arrow. Various bright colours are presented. To choose the dark grey used in this book, choose **Select color...**

The smaller **Select Color** dialogue box will open. Go to the **True Color** tab and type the RGB value for dark grey directly (in the box at the bottom left) as **33,40,48** (separated by commas, not full stops).

Click **OK**. Then select **Apply & Close**. Finally click **Apply** and **OK** to close the main dialogue box.

2.4   Draw and manipulate shapes

Before moving to electrical schematics we will draw some simple shapes. This will get you used to the AutoCAD interface. It is also possible to draw parts of your schematic using basic shapes. This is useful if you are drawing a block diagram or to annotate your drawings.

Simple shapes can also be used for unusual components until you learn to produce custom symbols in chapter 10.

Draw a rectangle

Select the **Home** tab on the ribbon. Click the **Rectangle** button (see picture below) then click on the drawing area to mark the first corner. Move the mouse and click again to mark the second corner.

If you wish to draw a second rectangle you will need to click the **Rectangle** button again. AutoCAD does not assume you will draw a second rectangle.

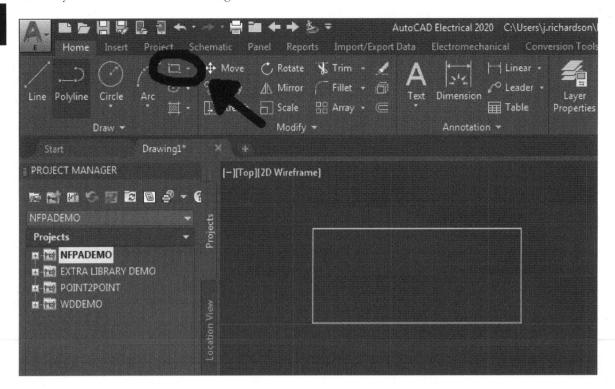

Understand the drawing area

The AutoCAD interface works best with a mouse which has two buttons (left and right) plus a centre wheel which can be pressed as a third button. Instructions in the book assume that you are using this type of mouse. It is recommended that you change your mouse if it does not have this function.

Move the mouse pointer over the drawing. Press the wheel down on the mouse and hold it as you move the mouse around. This turns the pointer into a hand which drags the sheet with it as the mouse moves. This is different to some other software packages but very intuitive once you get used to it.

Turning the wheel on the mouse (without holding it down) zooms in and out.

AutoCAD Electrical is based on the mechanical AutoCAD software. This has been developed over many years for producing scale mechanical drawings. Think of the canvas you are drawing on in model space as an infinitely large sheet of paper. If you keep zooming out you will see your drawing become a tiny speck on this huge canvas.

Points on this canvas are defined as an X-Y grid. As you zoom out you will see the origin (point **0,0**). From this origin the X axis increases to the right and the Y axis increases vertically going up.

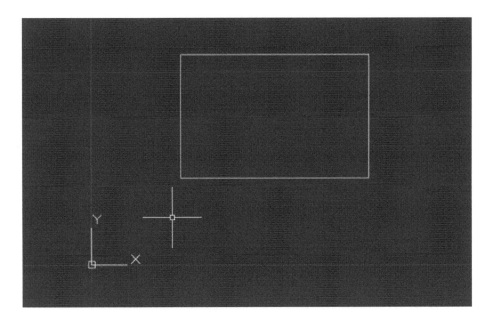

If you were producing a mechanical drawing you would draw in model space at a 1:1 scale. You would define your shapes in mm (for a metric drawing), including fractions of a mm if necessary. Even if your drawing was many km across this would not matter. Mapping parts of this drawing onto sheets of paper as one or more scale drawings would be done using layout space.

For electrical schematics the scaling is less important and there are several ways it could be handled.

In this book we will use a rectangular drawing border positioned in model space. Our schematic will also be drawn in model space, inside this border. We will then print each drawing on a single sheet of paper using the layout view.

Chapters 16 and 17 will explore alternative scaling methods for mechanical drawings.

Drawing grid, snap to grid and orthogonal

When drawing schematics you will often want to line shapes up with each other. Using the mouse it is easy to be slightly out giving, for example, a slight slope on a horizontal line.

AutoCAD can draw gridlines on the screen to guide you. You can either use this as a visual guide only or force the mouse to snap to the nearest grid point. The grid lines and snap function can be toggled on and off by left clicking the grid and snap icons at the bottom of the screen. When turned on they are highlighted.

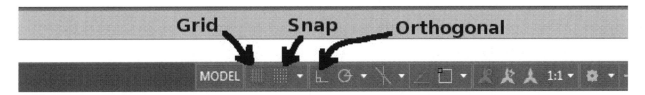

To change the grid settings, right click on the grid icon. Left click on the words **Grid Settings...** that appear when you do this. The window shown below will open. You can change the grid line settings and snap settings independently.

For a metric drawing I suggest setting the grid spacing to **10** and changing the snap setting to **2.5** to allow points a quarter of the way between grid squares as shown below. In your own drawings you might sometimes reduce the snap setting further to **1.25** for easier connection to certain components.

A related function is **Orthogonal**. It is toggled on and off by a button next to **Snap**. When enabled it forces the mouse to only move at 90 degrees to the previous point. The second point is either on the same horizontal line or the same vertical line as the first but never on a diagonal line. This helps with lining up shapes and keeping lines vertical or horizontal.

When using AutoCAD tools you can toggle these useful buttons on and off, even in the middle of doing other operations. As a default you will usually want **Grid** and **Snap** turned on and **Orthogonal** turned off.

Delete your rectangle

For consistency throughout this chapter we will keep our drawings within a space the size of a sheet of A3 paper. This will ensure your drawings match those in the book. The rectangle you drew may have been any size, depending on how far you were zoomed in or out when you drew it, so we will delete it now.

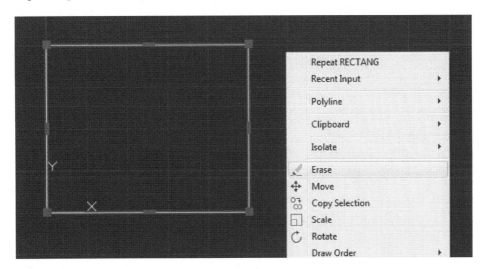

Select your rectangle by clicking it once with the left mouse button. It will be highlighted with small tabs at the corners and the centres of the sides. Right click on an empty area of the drawing with the mouse. A menu will appear. Click **Erase** in this menu and the selected rectangle will be deleted.

Drawing a rectangle at specified coordinates

Ensure you have the command line visible (Use **CTRL + 9** to open it if hidden)

Select the **Rectangle** button again from the **Home** tab of the ribbon. Instead of clicking the drawing area, define the first point by typing **0,0** (the origin) in the command line. Press **<Enter>**.

```
Command:
Command: _rectang
RECTANG Specify first corner point or [Chamfer Elevation Fillet Thickness Width]: 0,0
```

Now define the opposite corner of the rectangle by entering the second point as **420,297** in the command line. Press **<Enter>**. This is the size of an A3 sheet of paper in mm. Coordinates are entered in the order **X,Y**.

```
Command: _rectang
Specify first corner point or [Chamfer/Elevation/Fillet/Thickness/Width]: 0,0
RECTANG Specify other corner point or [Area Dimensions Rotation]: 420,297
```

Your drawing should now contain a large rectangle with one corner at the origin. You may need to zoom or scroll to see it. Zoom and move the drawing so that the rectangle fills most of the drawing area. For the rest of this chapter try and draw the examples inside this box. This will ensure that everyone using the book is zoomed in by roughly the same amount so that the suggested text sizes and other dimensions are not too large or small to be seen easily. These text sizes will also be compatible with the A3 sized template which we will create later.

Draw a rectangle by specifying dimensions

Select the **Rectangle** button again and click the screen to place the first corner point. Notice the command line asks how the second point will be located as shown.

```
Command: _rectang
Specify first corner point or [Chamfer/Elevation/Fillet/Thickness/Width]:
RECTANG Specify other corner point or [Area Dimensions Rotation]:
```

You could just ignore the command line and click to give the second point. Instead we will use the command line to specify dimensions. Type **d** and press **<Enter>** (you don't need to use capitals) to say you want to specify the opposite corner using dimensions. You will then be asked to specify the length.

```
Specify first corner point or [Chamfer/Elevation/Fillet/Thickness/Width]:
Specify other corner point or [Area/Dimensions/Rotation]: d
RECTANG Specify length for rectangles <10.0000>: 50
```

Type a value of **50** for the length (x axis dimension) and press **<Enter>**. Then specify the width (y axis dimension) as 30 by typing **30** and pressing **<Enter>** again.

```
Specify other corner point or [Area/Dimensions/Rotation]: d
Specify length for rectangles <10.0000>: 50
RECTANG Specify width for rectangles <10.0000>: 30
```

Your rectangle should appear on the screen. There are still 4 different ways a rectangle can be displayed while having the dimensions and starting point specified. Move the mouse around the starting point and you will see the four possible positions. Click the left mouse button to select one.

Most of the time you can use the cursor and ignore the command line but sometimes the command line is more powerful or faster. One example would be if you were producing a scale drawing and wanted your rectangles to be a precise size.

Polygons

Click the small arrow beside the **Rectangle** button. A menu appears giving you the option of polygons or rectangles.

Hover the mouse over **Polygon** and wait a few seconds. First a small window appears telling you what the button does. Wait another second or two and a little help window will appear as shown below explaining how the polygon button works. Move the mouse again and this help prompt disappears.

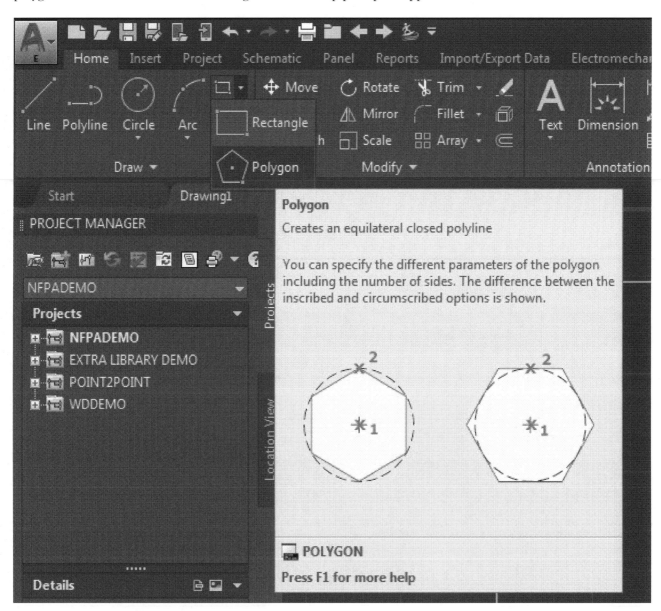

For a polygon you need to use the command line to specify the number of sides. The command will then draw an equal sided polygon either inside or outside an imaginary circle which you define with the mouse.

Drawing a hexagon:
Click the small arrow beside the **Rectangle** button to display the **Polygon** button described above. Click on the **Polygon** button. The command line will ask you how many sides. Type **6** and press **<Enter>** as shown below.

```
x  Command:
      POLYGON _polygon Enter number of sides <4>: 6
```

Note that the command line shown offers a default of **4**. If you just pressed **<Enter>** without typing a number you would get a square. These defaults remember your last action and can speed up your work when you become familiar with the software.

Now you are asked to define the centre of the polygon. Click the drawing area with the mouse. You could also press **E** and define the polygon position by its edge instead of its centre point.

```
x  Command: _polygon Enter number of sides <4>: 6
      POLYGON Specify center of polygon or [Edge]:
```

The polygon will be drawn within a circle which you are about to define. AutoCAD needs to know if you want it just inside or outside the circle. Press **<Enter>** to accept the default of '**I**' for Inscribed.

```
x  Specify center of polygon or [Edge]:
      POLYGON Enter an option [Inscribed in circle Circumscribed about circle] <I>:
```

Move the mouse away from the centre point you selected and a hexagon will appear. Moving the mouse will change its size and rotation. Click the left button to fix it in the position you want. You could also have set its size by typing the radius of the defining circle in the command line.

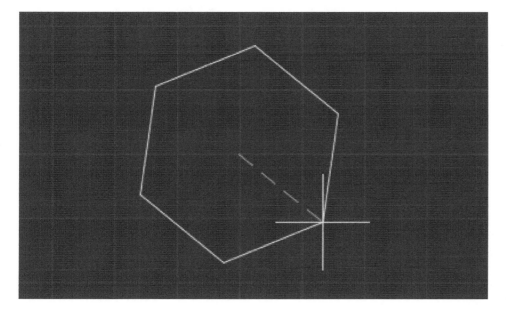

Look at the ribbon. You will see that the **Rectangle** button has changed to a **Polygon** button. If you now want to draw a rectangle you need to click the little arrow beside the button to get the **Rectangle** option back. Many buttons on the AutoCAD ribbon are stacked this way. AutoCAD remembers your most recent action with the rest hidden until you click the drop down arrow.

Lines and other shapes

Click the **Line** button. It is on the **Home** tab of the ribbon, near the **Rectangle** tool. Click in the drawing area to select the first point. Click again for the next point. If you click further points the line will be extended with a straight section to each new point you specify. When you have finished drawing your line press **<Enter>** to end the command.

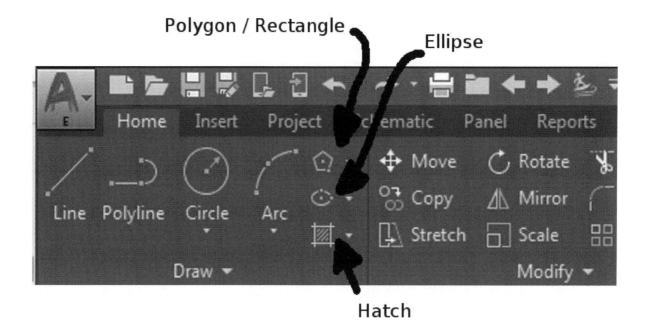

Polygon / Rectangle

Ellipse

Hatch

You can also try the **Polyline, Circle, Arc** and **Ellipse** buttons. **Hatch** is used to fill shapes - don't try that yet. It can be tricky to use so we will explain it later.

Selecting and manipulating shapes

Now you can draw simple shapes it is important to understand how to select and modify them. Don't jump ahead to the electrical schematics chapter! Learning to manipulate objects by experimenting with these simple shapes will save you hours later.

Draw a few lines and rectangles on the screen. Press **<Esc>** to be sure you have exited from any running commands.

Right click an empty part of the drawing. Click **Options** in the menu that appears.

In the **Options** dialogue box choose the **Selection** tab. Make sure the **"Allow press and drag for Lasso"** box is not ticked. If this box is ticked then you must click and release the mouse buttons to get the behaviour described below. Holding and dragging the mouse will provide an alternative method of selection using a lasso.

All examples in this book assume the Lasso function is unticked and not used. You may want to try it, however, and see if you like the different behaviour it produces.

Try selecting objects in three different ways (**Lasso** function assumed to be off) :

- First position the mouse over a line or the edge of a shape. When it is exactly over it the shape will be highlighted. Left click and the object will be selected. This is shown by small blue boxes at the corners and other critical points.
- The second method is to press the left mouse button and hold it down while dragging it **UP** and **LEFT** on the screen (**DOWN** and **LEFT** gives the same effect). A rectangle appears as you drag the mouse. Any shapes even partially inside this rectangle are selected when you release the mouse button.
- The third method is to press the left mouse button and drag the mouse to the RIGHT and DOWN the screen (**RIGHT** and **UP** gives the same effect). Unlike the second method, this will only select items completely enclosed in the rectangle.

Make sure you try all three methods. They sound trivial but using a combination of them makes it easy to modify crowded schematics. Selecting a number of objects within a rectangular area (window) by dragging the mouse is often referred to as **"windowing"** in AutoCAD help forums.

If you select new objects, those you have already selected stay selected. This is another useful feature and different to many other software packages.

To deselect all objects press the **<Esc>** key.
To deselect individual objects, hold down the **<Shift>** key while selecting them again.

Text

AutoCAD has a default text size which you can set. Although the size of text can easily be changed later, it is inconvenient if it initially appears too small to be visible or so large it is off the screen. Since we are drawing in a box 297mm high, we will set the default text height to a convenient 5mm.

In the command line type **textsize <Enter>**.
Then enter a value of **5** (and press **<Enter>**).

Now add some text. The button on the ribbon for this is shown below. Like the geometric shapes, it is in the **Home** tab. The drop down arrow below the **Text** button allows you to select multiline or single line text. The multiline option is most flexible. Select multiline text and click in the drawing area.

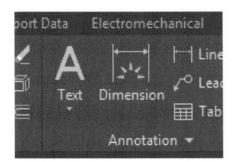

Move the mouse and click again. This defines the width of the box you will type your text in. If necessary you can click on the diamond at the top right of the text box and drag it left or right to change the width of the box. You can also drag the stripes in the bottom right corner of the text box to increase its height. The text will usually wrap automatically but sometimes the box itself can be too small and AutoCAD starts to split up the text into a second box if you do not increase its size.

Type some text in the box, pressing **<Enter>** to force a new line. When you have finished, click outside the box to exit the **Text** command.

Modifying object properties

Now you are able to draw a few shapes it is important to learn how to modify them.

Draw some rectangles, circles and at least two pieces of text in the drawing area. Select one of the pieces of text. Ensure nothing else is selected. Right click on the drawing background. Choose **Properties** from the menu that appears. The **Properties** window will open.

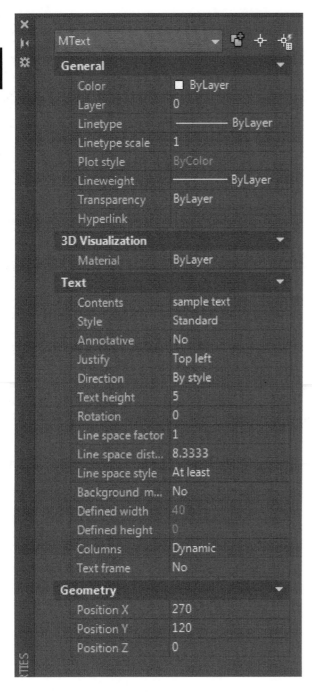

This window lists all the properties of the selected items. Change **Text height** to a larger value, for example from **5** to **7** and press **<Enter>**. The text will become bigger.

Now select both pieces of text (nothing else). Look at properties again and you will now see the **Text height** given as ***VARIES*** because the selected items are different. Click on ***VARIES*** and type **10**. Then press **<Enter>**. Both pieces of text will be increased to a height of **10**. Close the **Properties** window by clicking the **X** in the corner of the window. Press **<Esc>** to deselect the text.

Modifying lines and shapes

Select some lines and rectangles. They will be highlighted with small blue squares at their corners and other important points. Left click the mouse on one of these points then move it and click again. It is possible to move and distort the shapes.

Copying and moving

Select one or more shapes then right click on the drawing. You will see a menu. Hover over **Clipboard** in this menu to get more options as shown below.

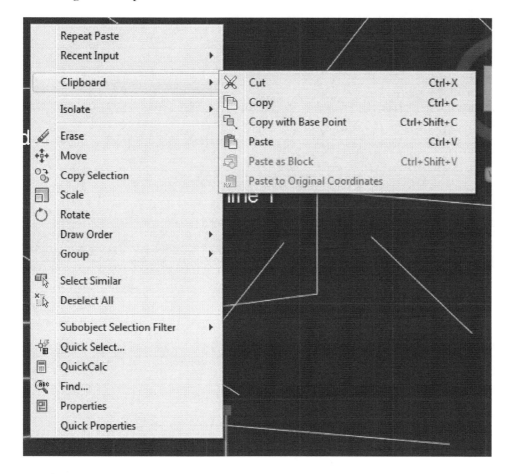

Erase and **Move** in the main part of the menu are self-explanatory and very useful.

The submenu under **Clipboard** allows you to **Cut**, **Copy** and **Paste**. These clipboard options are particularly useful for copying between separate drawings. Alternative methods often work only within the same drawing.

After using the **Copy** command, the **Paste** command is used to position the copied items.

Copy with Base Point allows you to mark a reference point by left clicking the mouse. This makes the copied objects easier to line up with other items when you come to paste them. Be sure to try it. You will use it a lot to paste items in an exact position relative to existing components and wires in your drawing.

CTRL+Z, CTRL+Y

Like many software packages, **CTRL+Z** undoes your last action. **CTRL+Y** does it again. Very occasionally, when moving or copying items, the original can disappear due to a bug. Use **CTRL+Z** to get back to where you were and try again.

Hatch

Often you might want to fill a shape with a colour or a pattern. The hatch command does this but can give strange effects if you do not use it correctly.

Draw three small rectangles close together. Then draw three more below them. Select the **Hatch** button from the **Home** tab of the ribbon. If it is not shown, click the drop down arrow beside its button to get it.

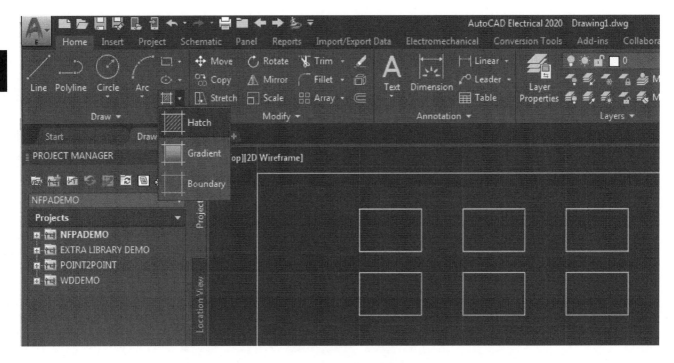

When you click **Hatch** the following menu will appear over the ribbon.

Select **SOLID** as shown. Then click the drop down menu for hatch colour. (In the screenshot above this is shown with the value **Use Current** in the centre of the menu.) Select a colour for the hatch area.

Click inside the first rectangle. It will be filled with solid colour. Press **<Enter>**.
Now fill the next two rectangles. For each one select **Hatch**, click inside the rectangle and press **<Enter>**.

Pressing **<Enter>** each time is necessary to make the filled areas separate shapes.

Left click in the centre of one of the filled areas to select it, then right click **in a blank part of the drawing** and select **Move** from the menu that appears. Left click on the drawing area to specify a start position then left click again for an end position. The one filled area you selected will move. The other areas will be unchanged.

For the second row of rectangles select **Hatch** and fill them by clicking each one. This time do not press **<Enter>** in between each fill. Instead press **<Enter>** once, after filling all three. This is less work because you do not keep reactivating the hatch command. Unfortunately the filled areas are classed as one unit. If you move the filled area from one, all three will move. This is useful to remember if you add filled shapes to your schematics later.

2.5   Layout tab and printing

So far we have drawn our objects in model space, an infinite canvas that allows you to produce a 1:1 scale drawing of any size. The **Layout** tabs allow you to select part or all of this model and arrange it on a sheet of paper for printing.

Suppose you had a large mechanical structure, for example a bridge. You could draw the whole thing in model space. The infinite canvas would allow you to produce a bridge hundreds of metres long yet zoom in for every nut and bolt.

To print this you would set up a number of layouts. One might be an overview of the whole structure. Another could be a close up of the bolt fixings on an individual joint. Each layout would be on a separate piece of paper.

It is possible to print directly from model view but it is better to use a layout. In this book we will split our electrical schematics into separate sheets with each page in its own drawing file. The drawings will exist in model space and be printed from layout space.

The next few pages explain how to do this. We will go over this again in more detail when we set up our drawing templates in Chapter 6.

Save your drawing. Then click the **Layout1** tab.

You should see your drawing on a white background. Unlike the **Model** tab this is not infinite since it represents a sheet of paper. Think of this as a print preview showing how your drawing will be transposed onto a printed page.

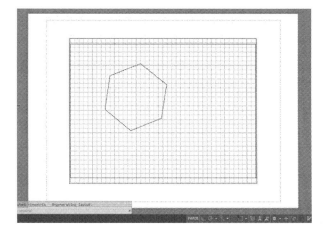

The first step is to set up the paper to match your printer. Click the **Application button**, hover the mouse over **Print** and select **Plot** from the submenu that appears.

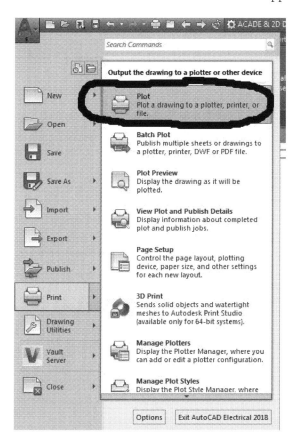

The **Plot** dialogue box will open.

2

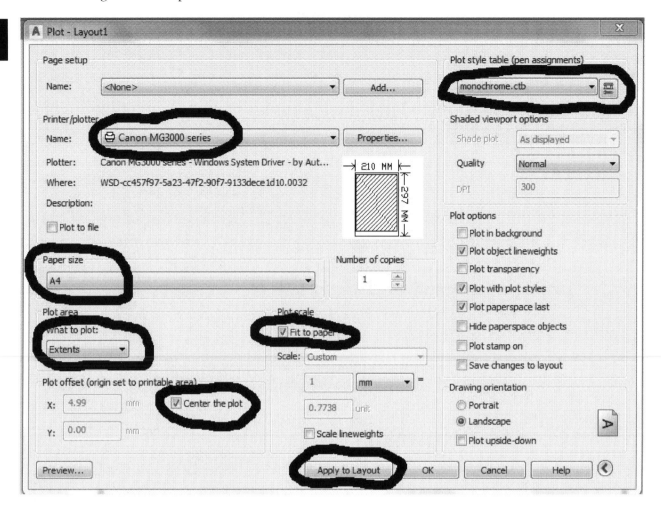

Select your printer and paper size.

For plot style select **monochrome.ctb** from the drop down menu. This will plot in greyscale (with a few exceptions which are covered in chapter 5 on page 85).

In the **Plot area** section, under **What to plot** select **Extents** from the drop down menu.

Tick **Center the plot** and **Fit to paper** as shown above. Click **Apply to Layout**. This will save these page settings but not print anything.

Finally, click **Cancel**, since we do not want to print the drawing yet. The view of the paper has probably changed now that you have the correct paper size.

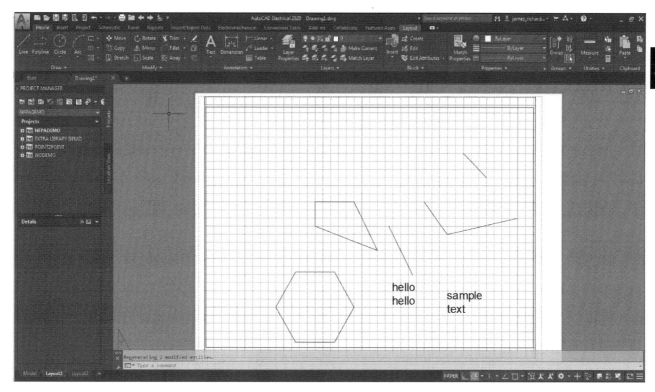

The dotted line around the edge shows the printable area of the paper. The solid line within this is the viewport - a window through which you can see part of your model drawing.

At the bottom right of the screen, next to the **Orthogonal** button, you should see the word **PAPER**. This means you are working on the sheet of paper, the viewport itself and on other objects that only exist in the **Layout** view. If instead you see the word **MODEL** (in capitals, next to the buttons) and the viewport is shown by a thick black line, then you are working on the model inside the viewport. In this view, which we will use later, you can manipulate the model position inside the viewport. For now we need **PAPER** view so if you drawing says **MODEL**, click this word and it will change to **PAPER**. Do not confuse this with the **Model / Layout** tabs which will have **Layout1** selected whether you are in **MODEL** or **PAPER** view.

We want the viewport to fill the available printable area on the paper. Left click the solid viewport line once to select it. You could also select it with the "windowing" technique described earlier. It will be highlighted in blue with small blue squares showing the corner points. Do not confuse it with the large rectangle on your drawing which cannot be selected in **PAPER** view.

Move the blue corner squares of the viewport to match the dotted line (the printable area of your printer) by left clicking on them and then left clicking on the corner of the dotted line. Press **<Esc>** when complete to deselect the viewport and get rid of the highlighting. Now your viewport should exactly match the printable area of your printer.

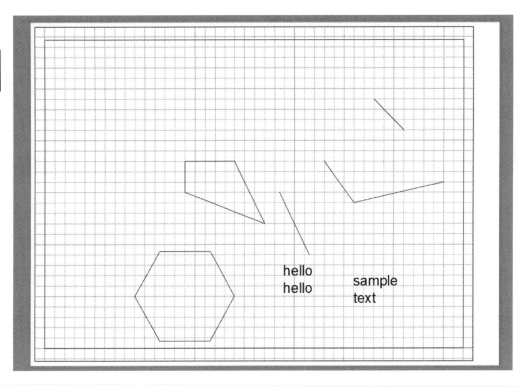

Next we will set up the viewport to look at the correct part of the model.

Double click the left mouse button in the centre of the drawing, inside the viewport window. The viewport border will change to a thick black line, indicating that you are editing the way the viewport looks at the model. You will see that the word **PAPER** changes to **MODEL**.

You could instead change to **MODEL** view by clicking on the word **PAPER** which has the same effect as double clicking inside the viewport.

First we will get rid of the blue grid lines. Press **F7** to toggle them off.

Next we will position the viewport over the model. Place the mouse inside the viewport and move it with the wheel held down to move the view around the model. Release the wheel and rotate it to scroll in and out. In a mechanical drawing this is how you would select different views of a structure.

Now double click the mouse wheel. The viewport will automatically scale and pan to fit the entire model into the viewport. For our electrical drawings this is what we want.

To exit the viewport editing mode, double click outside of the viewport. The bold border will return to normal. Any zooming or scrolling with the mouse will alter your view of the piece of paper but not affect the printed image. Leave it like this to avoid the risk of accidently changing the view. You can also leave **MODEL** view by clicking the word **MODEL** at the bottom of the screen so it changes to **PAPER**. This is particularly useful if you are zoomed in on the viewport and it is not practical to click outside of the viewport area.

Save your drawing. Now you can select **Print > Plot** from the **Application button** while in **Layout** view and print your drawing. Unfortunately you will find the rectangular edge of the viewport is plotted around your drawing which may be undesirable. To get rid of this we need to understand **Layers**.

2.6   AutoCAD layers

AutoCAD uses a system of layers when producing a drawing. The complete drawing consists of objects on different layers stacked on top of each other. This allows properties to be set for each layer, keeping the drawing consistent. It also makes it easy to turn off one layer. This is easiest to understand in a mechanical drawing. One layer might contain a building plan. Another layer on top of it could show pipework. Both could be viewed together. Alternatively you may want to view either the building plan or the pipes on their own.

For electrical drawings, this ability to hide layers is less used. The main use of layers is to represent wiring and other special objects. Each type of wire (for example black 2.5mm² wire) is given its own layer. AutoCAD relies on the wires being in these special layers when labelling and numbering wires.

You can see layers within the drawing directly by going to the **Layers** panel of the **Home** tab on the ribbon and clicking **Layer Properties**.

This opens the **Layer Properties Manager**

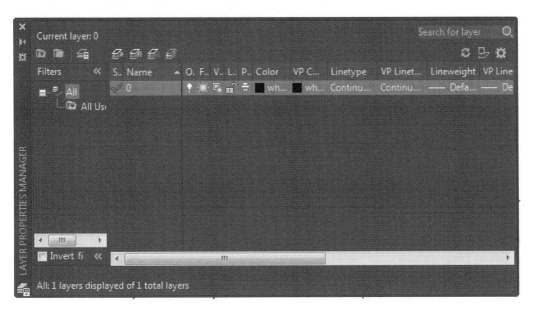

You will probably only have one layer, layer **0.** We are going to make a new layer and call it **Viewport**. We will tell AutoCAD that this layer is not to be plotted. We can then move the viewport frame to this layer so that it appears on screen but is never printed.

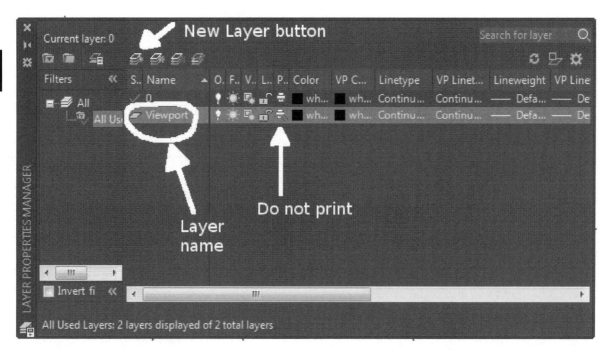

In the **Layer Properties Manager** dialogue box, click the **New Layer** button as shown above. A new layer will be created with the default name **Layer1**. Click on this name and type over it to give the layer the new name **"Viewport"**. Then click the printer symbol for this layer so that it changes to the "do not print" symbol, a printer with a red circle, as shown.

Close the **Layer Properties Manager**.

Now select the viewport window. It will be highlighted with blue squares at its corners. Right click and a menu will appear. Choose **Properties** from this menu. The **Properties** window will open.

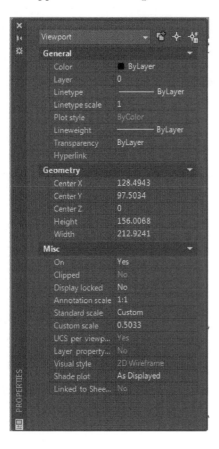

You will see that the viewport is currently on layer **0**. Click the box with the **0** and a small drop down arrow will appear.

Click this arrow to get a list of all the available layers. Choose **Viewport**, the new layer we created.

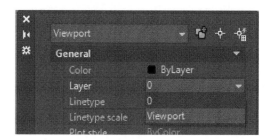

Close the **Properties** window. Press **<Esc>** to deselect the viewport. Save your drawing.

Now go to the **Application Button** and choose **Print > Plot**. You can also just click **Print** without going to the sub-menu since **Plot** is the default choice.

The **Plot** window will open again. Since you have already set the print details for your drawing, you just need to click **OK**. Your drawing should be printed correctly. On the print out you will see the large rectangle we drew as a border using the **rectangle** tool but there should no longer be a second rectangle for the viewport border.

2.7 Locking a viewport

After setting your viewport to show the correct part of your model you can lock it. This prevents you changing the scale, or the area of the model shown, by accident. Select the viewport and right click the drawing area to see a menu.

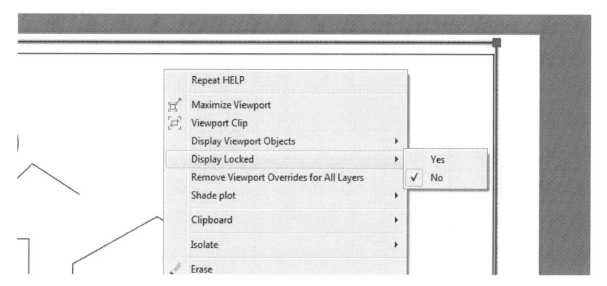

Place the cursor over **Display Locked** to see the **Yes / No** submenu above. Select **Yes** to lock the viewport and **No** to unlock it.

If you are ever unable to modify a viewport, you should check if it is locked.

2.8   File types

AutoCAD drawings are saved as **.dwg** files. These files allow someone to open a drawing in AutoCAD and use all the intelligence within it. If you just want someone to look at a drawing, without being able to alter it in AutoCAD, print or save the drawing as a **.pdf** file.

The file format **.dxf** is used if you want to exchange files between AutoCAD and non-AutoCAD software while keeping the detailed drawing information.

2.9   Summary so far

If you have followed this chapter you can now create a simple drawing using lines, shapes and text. You can scroll around the screen and select groups of items. You are able to copy, paste and erase these items and modify their properties. You can also configure the layout tab and use it to print your drawings.

While we are only starting to use the functionality of the AutoCAD software, this will let you produce a few simple drawings without resorting to a felt tip pen or the graphics features of your word processor. If some of the methods for scrolling and selecting objects seem alien don't worry. With practice they will soon become familiar and very fast.

In the next four chapters we will group drawings into projects, create a border to make the drawings look professional and set up template drawings and projects. These things are necessary before we can work effectively on electrical schematics.

3. Projects (45 minutes)

3.1   Introduction to the next four chapters

Before going further it is essential to understand AutoCAD projects and create a template for your drawings. The next four chapters are designed to get through this tedious stage as fast as possible. Do not skip them.

In this chapter we set up a new project which we will name **Setup1**. In chapter 4 we add a drawing to this project and draw a frame for your drawing template.

In chapter 5 we import this frame into a second drawing to create the template itself. We will look in more detail at how AutoCAD projects work and store your preferred drawing and project settings as defaults.

In chapter 6 we set up a new project ready for your first schematic drawings. We also cover other project features - drawing titles, sheet numbering and contents page setup. Finally we explain how to copy projects, giving you a fast way to create projects for your real work.

We return to drawing electrical schematics in Chapter 7, using our project and drawing templates to draw a simple motor starter system.

3.2   Why you need projects

So far our drawings have just been single sheets of paper. Most electrical drawings have multiple sheets within an overall package called a project. The sheets will share common properties. They also contain cross-references, for example wires that jump between sheets or a relay coil which operates child contacts on another page.

Projects don't just keep your drawings tidy. They make it easier to set up drawing properties and track relationships between components on different pages.

3.3   Choose a folder to store the files

By default the AutoCAD Electrical program will store your projects in the **Proj** folder found at:

   C:\Users*your windows username***\Documents\Acade 2020\AeData\Proj**

It is possible to store them elsewhere. In this chapter we will assume you have created a folder called **Learn AutoCAD** to store your drawings.

If you wish to do this, use Microsoft Windows Explorer to create a **Learn AutoCAD** folder now in a convenient place, such as on your desktop. Alternatively, you can keep the files in the **Proj** folder or another location of your choosing.

Note that when navigating to the **Proj** folder above, the **Documents** folder is sometimes displayed as **My Documents** rather than just **Documents**.

3.4   Make a new project

You are now going to create a project called **Setup1**. We will use this to hold our files as we create our template.

The AutoCAD software will not let you create a new project unless you have a drawing open. It will also not let you re-open the **Project Manager** window if it is closed. Many functions in AutoCAD are like this, requiring a drawing to be open, even one with no connection to the task in progress.

If you do not have a drawing open, either open one of your existing drawings or create a blank one. You do not need to save this blank drawing. Just discard it later when you close AutoCAD.

A fast way to open a new drawing, especially one you do not care about, is to click the **+** symbol next to the drawing tabs. This opens a drawing with whatever template file you used last.

If the **Project Manager** window is not already open then go to the **Project** tab on the ribbon and click the **Manager** button to open it.

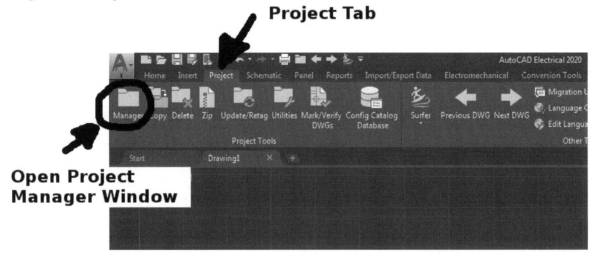

The **Project Manager** window will open. By default it is docked at the left of the screen.

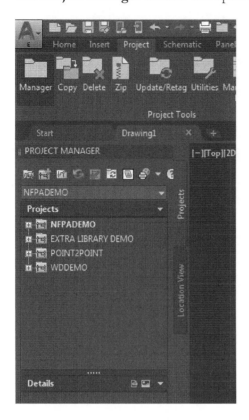

In the **Project Manager** window click on the **New Project** button. (This is greyed out unless you have an open drawing on the screen)

A dialogue box will appear. Type the name for your project which will be **Setup1**.

The location box allows you to select where your project is stored. By default AutoCAD will put it in the **proj** folder found at:

> **C:\Users** *your windows username* **\Documents\Acade 2020\AeData\Proj**

If you would like to store a project elsewhere, use the **Browse** button to choose a different location. For our example browse to the **Learn AutoCAD** folder you created earlier to store your new project there.

If the **Create Folder** box is ticked then AutoCAD will create a new folder named after your project. For our example leave it ticked so that a folder, **Setup1**, will be created.

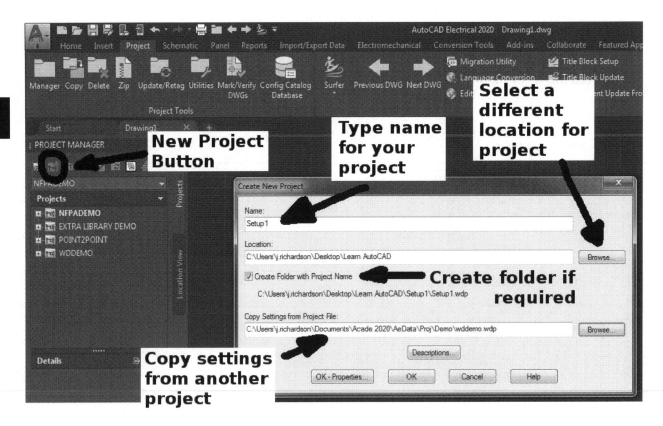

Copying settings from another project is compulsory and defaults to your last project. Since this is our first project we will copy our settings from **wddemo.wdp**. This is one of the demo files supplied with AutoCAD. You will find it by clicking **Browse** and looking in the folder:

C:\Users*your windows username***\Documents\Acade 2020\AeData\Proj\Demo**

Note that when browsing, the **Documents** folder may be shown as **My Documents**.

The **Descriptions** button allows you to enter data for your project - date, customer, drawn by, revision number, etc. We will cover this later so leave it for now.

The **OK-Properties** button creates the project then immediately opens a window to set the project properties. Again, we are going to leave these for later. Instead press **OK** and your project will be created without asking you to set its properties yet.

You will see that the **Project Manager** window now shows the **Setup1** project.

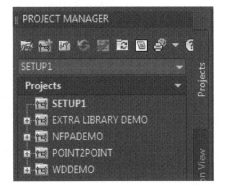

Use Microsoft Windows Explorer to look in the **Learn AutoCAD** folder you created earlier on your desktop. Inside you will find a new folder, **Setup1** containing the project files. There will be two files, **Setup1.aepx** and **Setup1.wdp**.

The **.wdp** file is the main file for your project. It contains various settings and links to your project's drawings. It is this file you would select to open a project.

The **.aepx** file is a file created by AutoCAD as part of its internal operations. Do not alter it.

3.5   Activating a project

Your new project should be at the top of the list of projects in the **Project Manager** window with its name in slightly bolder letters. This signifies that it is the active project. The **Project Manager** window can have a number of projects open but only one is active at any time.

When altering drawings in a project, always make sure it is active (at the top of the list). Altering a project which is not active can cause problems with cross-references, wire numbering and other functions that depend on data from multiple pages.

When a new project is created, AutoCAD makes it the active project. To activate a different project, right click on its name in the **Project Manager** window and select **Activate**. The project will become active and move to the top of the list.

3.6   Setting project properties

Before going further we will set up some basic project properties. We can refine these later when we create the template.

Right click on the **Setup1** project in the **Project Manager** window. As with most things in AutoCAD, you must have a drawing open for this to work. Select **Properties** from the menu that appears. The **Project Properties** window will open. This window contains a number of tabs which control different aspects of your project.

The first tab, **Project Settings**, controls which database tables the project uses. In particular it controls which symbol libraries are used. All drawings within a project have the same library settings, defined on this tab. Later we will see that individual drawings have a complementary tab, **Drawing Settings**, which covers settings unique to individual drawings, for example the drawing title and subtitle.

The other tabs: **Components**, **Wire Numbers**, **Cross-References**, **Styles** and **Drawing Format** are duplicated, existing at both project level and for individual drawings. Should values at the two levels ever be set differently, the settings for individual drawings override those set at project level. In this book we will try and keep them the same.

Despite existing at both project and drawing level, these duplicated tabs do contain a small number of settings that are only shown on the project level version of the tab.

Project settings

Select the **Project Settings** tab.

3

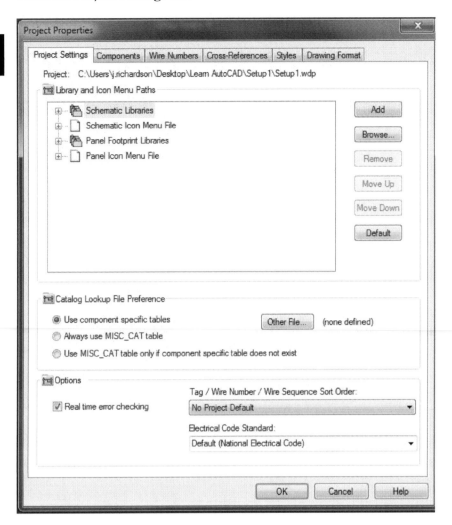

The **Project Settings** tab lets you choose which component libraries to use. Click the **+** beside **Schematic Libraries** to expand the list and see what libraries are used.

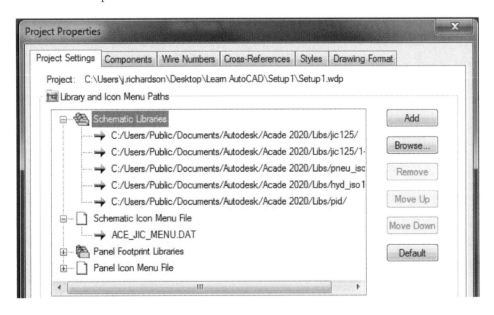

At this stage decide which schematic library you want to use and change if necessary. This book will use the **IEC4** library. This is based on the IEC60617 symbols and has 3.5mm high text.

There is also an **IEC2** library which has 2.5mm high text and the **IEC60617** library itself. The **IEC60617** library not only has different text sizes to the **IEC4** library, some of the symbols have different family codes, for example switches in the **IEC4** library are numbered S1, S2 etc whereas those in the **IEC60617** library are labelled SF1, SF2 etc.

3

To use the **IEC4** library click the heading **Schematic Libraries** to highlight it and then click the **Add** button. An extra arrow and a blank space will be added at the bottom of the list of libraries. Now click the **Browse** button. Navigate to the following location and select the **iec4** folder:

C:\Users\Public\Documents\Autodesk\Acade 2020\Libs\iec4

The **IEC4** library will be added at the bottom of the list of libraries. Click this library with the mouse to highlight it and use the **Move Up** / **Move Down** buttons to put it at the top of the list of libraries. Note that the folder **"Documents"** may appear as **"Public Documents"** when browsing for it.

You must also load an appropriate menu to match your symbol library. This is the picture menu you will choose from when inserting electrical symbols into your schematic.

The appropriate symbol menu for both the **IEC4** and **IEC2** libraries is **ACE_IEC_MENU.DAT**

To select this menu, click the library file currently listed under the **Schematic Icon Menu File** heading to highlight it then click **Browse**. Ensure you click the file, not the heading. It will probably have a name ending **_MENU.DAT**. You may need to click the **+** symbol beside the **"Schematic Icon Menu File"** heading to see it.

Navigate to the following location and select the **ACE_IEC_MENU.DAT** file which matches the **IEC2** and **IEC4** symbols. The **Browse** button will probably take you straight to the right folder since all of these menu files are in the same place. For different versions of AutoCAD the folder **R23.1** will have a different name.

C:\Users*your windows user name*\AppData\Roaming\Autodesk\AutoCAD Electrical 2020\R23.1\ enu\Support\ACE_IEC_MENU.DAT

The symbols in the IEC libraries are intended for metric drawings and will require you to choose **Metric - mm** as the scale factor of your drawing later in this chapter so they appear the correct size.

Instead of the **IEC4** or **IEC2** libraries you may decide to use the **IEC-60617** library. In this case you must use the appropriate symbol menu for the **IEC-60617** Library which is **ACE_IEC-60617_MENU.DAT**

If you prefer to use the **JIC** symbol library you will need to set your drawings to **Imperial - Inch** later in this chapter rather than **Metric - mm**. For this library you will need to use the **ACE_JIC_MENU.DAT** symbol menu file

While multiple libraries can be assigned to a project, AutoCAD searches them for symbols in order, starting with the top library. Suppose you choose to insert a relay from the **Icon Menu** (covered later in chapter 7). The picture you click to insert the relay comes from the **MENU.DAT** file. This tells AutoCAD which filename to use.

Each library will have identically named relay symbols with different appearances. The one you actually get in your drawing is the first one AutoCAD finds as it works through the list of assigned libraries in order. This lets you create your own custom library containing a small number of modified symbols. These will override the supplied ones provided you place it above them in the list. More on this in chapter 10.

When adding a library, AutoCAD requires the name of the folder containing the symbols. It ignores subfolders. For example, the **IEC4** library folder contains a subfolder called **"1-"** which has symbols for single line diagrams. If you wish to use these then you must add the **1-** folder as a separate library. Position it in the list below the main

IEC library. Since its symbol filenames will be different to those in the main **IEC4** library they will still be found by AutoCAD.

For the screenshots in this book, the pneumatic and hydraulic schematic libraries are not installed. This keeps the examples clear. You may however wish to install them. They are available in metric (names ending **_mm**) and imperial (names ending **_iso125**) versions. There is also a **pid** menu for piping and instrumentation diagrams.

Panel footprint libraries

Panel footprints are scale mechanical drawings of each component. They are used to create physical panel layouts. Click the **+** symbol next to **Panel Footprint Libraries** to see which panel footprint library is used.
This library should be set to **"panel"** if you intend to use English imperial measurements (inches). If your panel layout drawings will be metric (mm) then use the **Browse** button to replace this with the **"panel_mm"** library.

You will find the panel libraries in the same place as the symbol libraries:

C:\Users\Public\Documents\Autodesk\Acade 2020\Libs

Either select **panel** or **panel_mm**.

There is only one supplied icon menu for panel footprints. It is called **ACE_PANEL_MENU.DAT**. Ensure this is selected under **Panel Icon Menu File**.

If experimenting with libraries you may get confusing results when changing libraries mid-drawing. Drawings remember symbol blocks that have been used and keep a local copy, often ignoring changes made external to the drawing.

To get rid of these copies, all instances of a symbol on the drawing must have been deleted and then the **Purge** command used. Chapter 10, "Custom Symbols" covers this and explains in more detail how the symbol libraries work.

Component settings

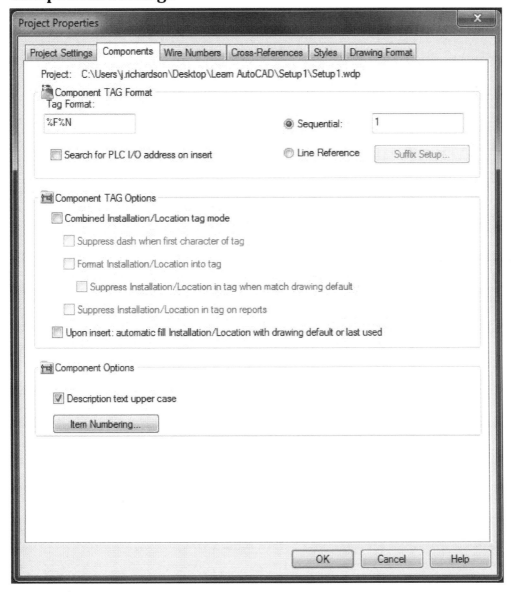

Open the **Components** tab. This tab controls the way components are labelled.

Leave **Tag Format** as its default of **%F%N**. This means that components are labelled by default with a family code (**%F**) followed by a number (**%N**). For example the switch symbol in the IEC4 library is set up to have a family code of 'S' with switches on the drawing being labelled **S1, S2** etc.

Ensure the **sequential** button is selected and has a value of **1**. This means AutoCAD will assign numbers to components automatically as you insert them, starting at **1**. This is useful, particularly as AutoCAD will check which numbers are already used, choosing the lowest value not already assigned to a symbol of that type. Should you delete switch **S3** on a drawing with many switches, AutoCAD will suggest '**3**' as the next number when you insert another switch.

You can override both family code and number on a component by component basis if required. In this case AutoCAD will warn you if you try to create two components with identical tags.

If the **Description text upper case** box is ticked then all descriptions you enter for your components will be automatically converted into capital letters.

Wire number settings

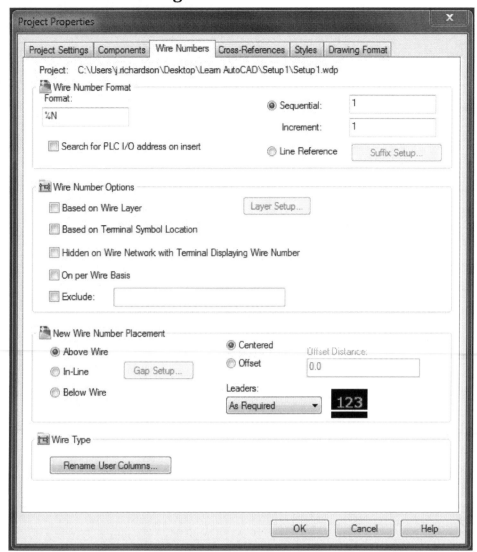

Next select the **Wire Numbers** tab. This tab controls the way wire numbers are assigned and displayed. We will be using sequential numbers for our wires. Leave **Format** as **%N** and ensure **Sequential** is selected and set to a value of **1**.

New Wire Number Placement covers cosmetic items. Leaders are small lines connecting wire numbers and the wires they refer to. AutoCAD uses them if the drawing is too cluttered to put the wire number beside the wire. Leave the settings for this with the default values shown above.

Cross-Reference settings

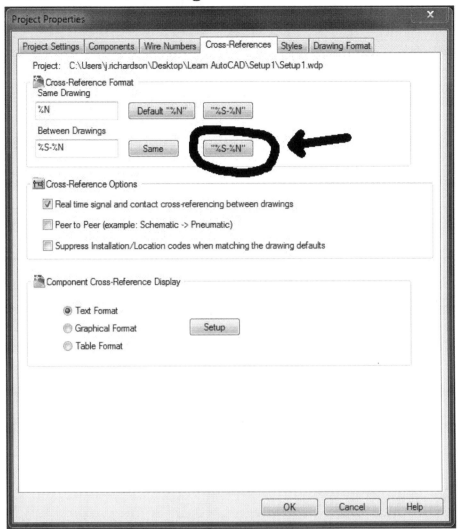

Open the **Cross-References** tab.

In this book we are going to set up an X-Y grid around our schematic drawings with letters along the x axis and numbers along the y axis. This grid reference identifies where a component will be found. For example, a wire continued on another page will be labelled with the sheet number and grid reference of the page where it is continued.

The **Cross-References** tab controls this automatic labelling.

Within a drawing the default of **%N** is adequate - a wire or component is referred to by its position on the page but its sheet number is not given, indicating that it is elsewhere on the same sheet.

Between drawings you should change the default to **%S-%N** so that references include the sheet number. Select this option under **Between Drawings** by clicking the **%S-%N** button.

Style settings

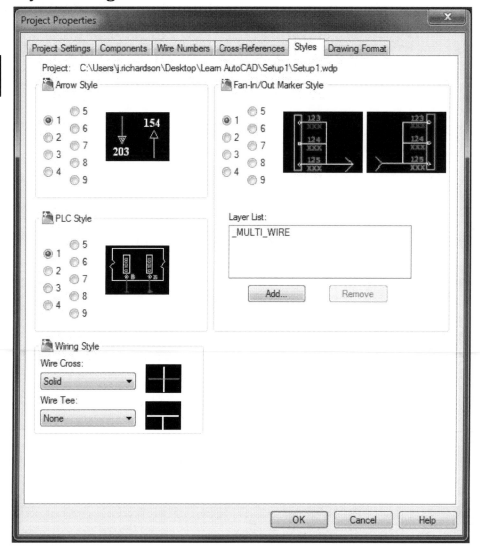

Now open the **Styles** tab.

The **Styles** tab includes **Wiring Style.** This determines how wires crossing and joining are depicted. Set this to suit your own preference. I always have wires crossing without a loop and joining without a dot.

The other settings are for PLC ladder drawings and the appearance of wires when they join to form cables. Leave these set to their defaults and change later if you need them to look different.

Drawing Format settings

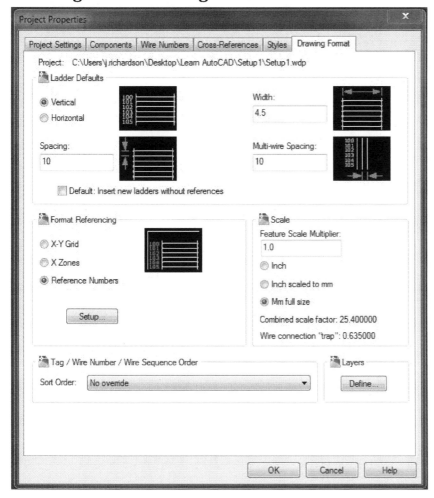

Finally, open the **Drawing Format** tab. This tab contains many critical items that affect the appearance of your drawings. We will cover each in turn:

Drawing Format - Ladder spacing

The top section, **Ladder defaults** is mainly for drawing PLC ladders. You can choose to have your rungs vertical or horizontal and set the spacing between rungs. Changing the value of width adjusts the length of the rungs.

The value **Spacing** at the left is important even if you are not drawing PLC ladders. It not only affects PLC ladders but also controls the spacing of multi-pole components, for example a 3 pole circuit breaker.

For the **IEC4** library set this to **10**. The drawing below shows the problem you will see if it is set incorrectly for the size of the components in your library.

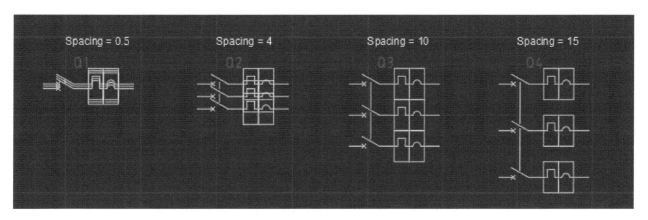

The value **Multi-wire Spacing** sets the gap between wires if you draw multiple phases at once, for example to draw a 3 phase circuit. Set this to be the same as **Multi-wire Spacing**. For our examples using the **IEC4** library this would be **10**.

If you are using an imperial scaled library then set the **Spacing** and **Multi-wire Spacing** to **0.5** so that your symbols are 0.5 inches apart.

Drawing Format - Format Referencing

The **Format Referencing** section defines the system that cross-reference labels use to refer to parts of the page.

Selecting **X-Y grid** divides the drawing into a horizontal and vertical grid. Wires or components can then be referred to by their position in this grid. **X zones** is a similar system but divides the page into vertical strips rather than a grid. The **Reference Numbers** option is used for PLC drawings (see chapter 18) where the circuit is drawn as a ladder with a series of numbered horizontal rungs.

In this book we will mostly use the **X-Y grid** option. Since the exact dimensions of the grid need to match our drawing frame we will set it up in chapter 4. Therefore leave the **Format Referencing** section alone for now.

Drawing Format - Scale

The **Scale** section controls the scaling of the drawing. If this is wrong your schematic symbols may be very small or very large.

For a symbol library based on metric measurements (For example all of the IEC libraries) choose **Mm full size**. If you use an imperial based library (For example the JIC library) choose **Inch**.

When AutoCAD draws electrical symbols these are actually mechanical shapes of a certain size. In the IEC4 library the circuit breaker shown in the spacing example above is a 10 unit wide square. If you use it in an **Mm full size** drawing it will appear as 10mm wide on your paper (possibly 5mm, etc if you scale your drawing to different paper sizes). If you accidently scale your drawing as imperial you will get a giant 10 inch high symbol. Likewise, using a 0.5 inch symbol from an imperial library will give you a tiny 0.5mm high symbol in a metric drawing.

Leave **Feature Scale Multiplier** at **1**. You will not normally need to adjust it if you select **Imperial/Metric** correctly for the symbols you are using.

Wire connection "trap" defines how close a wire must be to a component terminal for AutoCAD to automatically attach it. Too big and you will find wires jumping to components when you don't want them to. Too small and it will be fiddly to get your wires and components to link up. If your other scaling factors are set correctly you should not need to adjust this.

3.7   Saving your settings

Once you have set all the items in the **Project Properties** tabs as you want them, click **OK** to save the settings and close the **Project Properties** window.

4. Creating a drawing frame (1½ hours)

Schematic drawings usually have a border around them. This makes the drawings look neat and carries important information about both the project and the individual sheets. When using the AutoCAD Electrical software, it is best to set up a template containing both the details of this border and the default drawing settings to be used by all the drawings you produce.

In this chapter we will make the border for our template by doing the following:

- Open a blank drawing with the correct scaling
- Draw a border around the drawing with space for text items like project name and drawing number
- Add fixed text, for example "Drawn by" and "Commercial in confidence"
- Add text items that change between projects but are the same on each drawing within the project, for example the project title. These are called **project attributes**.
- Add text items that change between drawings within a project, for example the sheet number. These are called **drawing attributes**.
- Learn how to add a logo - either as a separate file or imported into the drawing.
- Create a file for the **project attribute** labels. This gives users of the template meaningful prompts when entering information, ie. **"Project Title"** rather than **"LINE1"**. Such a file is not needed for the **drawing attributes** which are predefined by AutoCAD.

This chapter is really a precursor to setting up a drawing template. I have split out drawing the frame as a separate task to make creating a template seem a less monstrous process.

4.1   What to include in your template

While the philosophy of this book is to get drawing quickly, this chapter and the next are points where it is worth slowing down. Think about the drawings you will produce and consult others in your organisation.

Things to consider:
- What size paper will your drawings be printed on?
- Will they be portrait or landscape?
- What text items are needed on the drawings?
- Do you have a logo that needs to be included?
- Is there an existing drawing frame that must be copied?

The more frame and text you have, the less space there is for the actual drawing so consider if all the items on your frame are really necessary.

4.2   Choose your project and drawing attributes

Before going further, choose the project and drawing attributes which will be displayed on your drawing frame. The **project attributes** will be the same on every drawing in the project. The **drawing attributes** will change on each sheet. You may wish to copy the example frame described in this chapter exactly or tweak it to suit your own requirements. The example frame is shown on the next page.

4

Example frame which will be created in this chapter

Rev	Description	Date	By	Chkd	App
A1	First draft	08/01/2020	AB	EF	GH
B1	For tender	06/02/2020	AB	EF	GH
B2	Pump removed	08/02/2020	CD	EF	GH

COMMERCIAL IN CONFIDENCE

Wiring Company Ltd
Tel: 0123 456 789

Quarry Project
Water Treatment Plant

Motor Starter
Power Wiring

SQP 000132

08/02/2020

B2

Sheet 3 of 3

Fixed text and logo (does not change between projects)

Rev	Description	Date	By	Chkd	App

COMMERCIAL IN CONFIDENCE

Wiring Company Ltd
Tel: 0123 456 789

Sheet of

Project attributes (Change between projects but do not change between sheets within a project)

Rev	Description	Date	By	Chkd	App
A1	First draft	08/01/2020	AB	EF	GH
B1	For tender	06/02/2020	AB	EF	GH
B2	Pump removed	08/02/2020	CD	EF	GH

Quarry Project
Water Treatment Plant

SQP 000132

08/02/2020

B2

Drawing attributes (Change between sheets within the same project)

Motor Starter
Power Wiring

3
3

4.3   Plan your own frame

Decide now what you wish to use for your own frame and fill in a table like that below. Having a completed table as a reference will speed up later steps so don't skip this. You will notice the revision history section requires a big chunk of the effort and it is hard to fit much into this area without wasting drawing space.

I usually keep the same drawing number and revision history for the whole project rather than having different sheets with different revision numbers. Minor changes are added electronically during assembly and commissioning as they arise (rather than saving them up for a big update). The revision number is only changed when drawings are issued to an external party or a similar milestone takes place. The exact method you choose will depend on your company and the type of work you are doing.

In this book we will produce the frame shown opposite using the following project description attributes.

Tag	Prompt	Purpose	Example content
Title	Project Title	Title of Project	Quarry Project
Subtitle	Project Subtitle	Subtitle of Project	Water Treatment Plant
DrawingNo	Drawing No.	Drawing number	SQP 000132
Revision	Revision Number	Revision Number	B2
Date	Date	Date of latest change	08/02/2020
Rev1	Rev 1 Revision No.	Revision History	A1
Des1	Rev 1 Description	Revision History	First Draft
Date1	Rev 1 Date	Revision History	08/01/2020
By1	Rev 1 Drawn by	Revision History	AB
Chk1	Rev 1 Checked by	Revision History	EF
App1	Rev 1 Approved by	Revision History	GH
Rev2	Rev 2 Revision No.	Revision History	B1
Des2	Rev 2 Description	Revision History	For Tender
Date2	Rev 2 Date	Revision History	06/02/2020
By2	Rev 2 Drawn by	Revision History	AB
Chk2	Rev 2 Checked by	Revision History	EF
App2	Rev 2 Approved by	Revision History	GH
Rev3	Rev 3 Revision No.	Revision History	B2
Des3	Rev 3 Description	Revision History	Pump Removed
Date3	Rev 3 Date	Revision History	08/02/2020
By3	Rev 3 Drawn by	Revision History	CD
Chk3	Rev 3 Checked by	Revision History	EF
App3	Rev 3 Approved by	Revision History	GH

4.4   Create a project attribute custom labels file

By default, AutoCAD refers to the project descriptions as LINE1, LINE2, LINE3 etc. This is confusing and you will end up referring to a piece of paper to remind yourself that, for example, LINE3 is the attribute for the drawing number.

To avoid this create a custom labels file. In a plain text editor (for example Microsoft Notepad) type the following, modified if you are using different project attributes to the example. The capitalisation and spaces are not critical.

```
LINE1 = Project Title
LINE2 = Project Subtitle
LINE3 = Drawing No.
LINE4 = Revision No.
LINE5 = Date

LINE6 = Rev1 Revision No.
LINE7 = Rev1 Description
LINE8 = Rev1 Date
LINE9 = Rev1 Drawn by
LINE10 = Rev1 Checked by
LINE11 = Rev1 Approved by

LINE12 = Rev2 Revision No.
LINE13 = Rev2 Description
LINE14 = Rev2 Date
LINE15 = Rev2 Drawn by
LINE16 = Rev2 Checked by
LINE17 = Rev2 Approved by

LINE18 = Rev3 Revision No.
LINE19 = Rev3 Description
LINE20 = Rev3 Date
LINE21 = Rev3 Drawn by
LINE22 = Rev3 Checked by
LINE23 = Rev3 Approved by
```

Save the file as **default_wdtitle.wdl** and place it in the **setup1** project folder. Take care to ensure it has the **.wdl** extension to its filename, not **.txt**

Note that by using this filename, the file can be used for any project. You can also replace the word **"default"** with the project name, for example **setup1_wdtitle.wdl**, and have different custom label files for each of your projects.

4.5 Drawing attributes

Unlike project attributes, drawing attributes are already set up with meaningful names so do not require you to set up a custom labels file. Many of these are also automated. For example, filename, sheet number and total number of sheets can be updated automatically.

In our example drawing frame we will use:

- **Drawing Description 1**
- **Drawing Description 2**
- **Sheet** (the page number of an individual drawing)
- **Sheet Maximum** (the total number of sheets in the project)

4.6 Creating a drawing for your frame

Open a new drawing from the **Application Button**. Use the **acadiso.dwt** template.

Your new drawing will be created. The tab at the top of the drawing will show its name which, until you save it as something else, will be a default value of **Drawing1**, **Drawing2**, etc.

Save the drawing by clicking the **Application Button** and selecting **Save As**. Browse to the **Learn AutoCAD** directory (or alternative location) where you created **Setup1**.

Browse inside the **Setup1** folder. Save the drawing as **titleblock1.dwg** inside the **Setup1** folder.

You can use Microsoft Windows Explorer to confirm the file is in the correct place. The tab at the top of the drawing in AutoCAD should now give its new name, **titleblock1**. These tabs are a useful way to flick between drawings when multiple drawings are open.

4.7   Adding the drawing into your project

Right click the **Setup1** project in the **Project Manager** window.
Click **Add Active drawing** in the menu that appears.

You will be asked if you want to apply project defaults to the drawing settings.
Click **Yes** so that the changes we made to the **project properties** in chapter 3 are applied to this drawing.

There will now be a small '**+**' next to the **Setup1** project in the **Project Manager** window. If it is not visible, click the **Setup1** project name in the **Project Manager** window to refresh it. Click the '**+**' to expand the list of drawings in the project. You will see **titleblock1** listed as one of its drawings.

Click on **Drawing Properties** in the **Schematic** tab of the ribbon.

This will open the **Drawing Properties** dialogue box. This contains a set of tabs similar to those we saw in chapter 3 when we looked at the **Project Properties**. The difference is that these settings refer to this individual drawing, not the whole project. The project settings we made in chapter 3 should have been copied to drawing level since we accepted the project defaults when we created the drawing.

One difference from the **Project Properties** is that instead of the **Project Settings** tab there is a **Drawing Settings** tab. This tab allows you to enter drawing titles and other information that changes between individual drawings within a project.

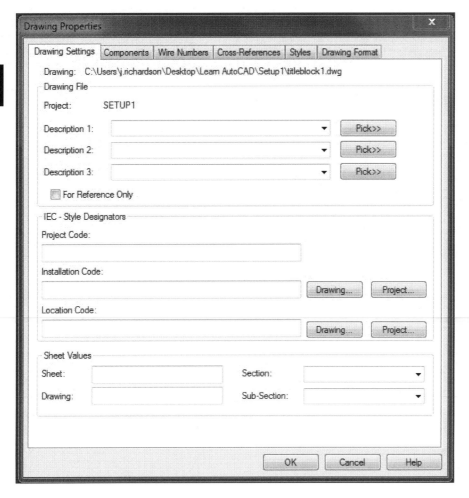

There is no need to change anything now so click **OK** to exit the **Drawing Properties** dialogue box. Note that an alternative method to open the **Drawing Properties** is to right click the individual drawing name in the **Project Manager** window and choose **Properties** followed by **Drawing Properties** from the menu that appears.

4.8   Drawing the frame

We will design our frame to print at full scale on A3 paper. It will still print well on A4 which is half the size but has the same length/width ratio. A3 paper is 420mm x 297mm but we do not want to print to the very edge. We also need space around the outside for grid labels so will make our drawing frame slightly smaller.

We will start by drawing a rectangle 400 wide and 270 high. This will form the outer edge of our new drawing frame. Since the drawing is set up as metric these numbers are actually mm.

We will leave a 10mm margin between it and the edge of the paper so the bottom left corner of the frame should be 10mm from the origin. Rather than the mouse, we will use the command line. (Press **CTRL + 9** if it is not visible.)

On the **Home** tab click the **Rectangle** button (You can also type **RECTANG** at the command line)

4

The command line will ask you for the first corner point. Type **10,10 <Enter>**

Now the command line will ask for the opposite corner. We want a rectangle 400mm wide and 270mm high. This will fit nicely onto a sheet of A3 paper while leaving enough margin for us to add grid reference labels later.

Since we started at **10,10** the opposite corner will be **410,280**. (The X coordinate is typed first)

```
×  Specify first corner point or [Chamfer/Elevation/Fillet/Thickness/Width]: 10,10
×  ▾ RECTANG Specify other corner point or [Area Dimensions Rotation]: 410,280
```

This will draw a large rectangle which will be the outer boundary of your drawing frame. You may need to zoom in or out to see it.

4.9   Add the fixed parts of your frame

Next we are going to add lines and text which will not change from project to project. For example the lines forming the frame and the words **"Drawn by"** and **"Date"**. We will leave space for the varying information (the project and drawing attributes) which we will add later.

To maximise space for your drawing, resist the temptation to have a big, complicated frame.

You could draw the frame by clicking on the screen but it is faster and more accurate to use the command line. Here is a list of rectangles that will give you a nice frame in five minutes by entering them at the command line. For example, to enter the first line, type the following:

rectang   **<Enter>**
10,15   **<Enter>**
130,25   **<Enter>**

This will draw a rectangle from point x=10, y=15 to point x=130, y=25
You can just type **rect** and AutoCAD will autocomplete to **rectang**.

Revision history frame
rectang   10,15   130,25
rectang   10,20   130,30
rectang   10,10   20,30
rectang   60,10   85,30
rectang   100,10   115,30

Spaces for text and Logo
rectang   130,10   185,30
rectang   185,10   235,30

<u>Project and drawing titles</u>

rectang 235,10 330,20
rectang 235,20 330,30

<u>Date, drawing number, revision number and sheet numbers</u>

rectang 330,10 390,20
rectang 330,20 410,30
rectang 390,15 410,30

4

You should now have a large rectangle for your drawing with empty boxes at the bottom as shown below.

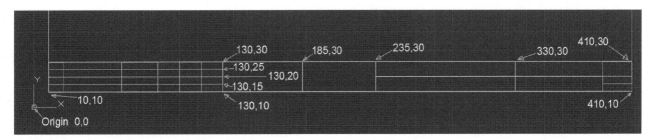

4.10   Add fixed text

Now we will add the fixed text which will not change between projects, for example, the word **"Date"**.

First set the default text size to 2.5mm height by typing the following at the command line:

textsize **<Enter>**
2.5   **<Enter>**

Use the text tool to add each piece of text. It is easiest to type all the pieces of text in a blank area of the drawing and then select each item and move it into position. They should be separate objects so re-open the text tool for each one. If required, you can select a piece of text and use the **Properties** window to centre justify it or make other changes to font, size, etc.

For the example title frame there are nine separate pieces of fixed text. They are as follows:

- Rev, Description, Date, By, Chkd, App
- COMMERCIAL IN CONFIDENCE
- Sheet, of

Note that if you open the **Properties** window when the **Project Manager** is open, the two boxes will share the space at the left of the screen. This means many properties are not visible. Either use the very small (and hard to see) dark grey scroll bar at the left of the **Properties** dialogue box or temporarily close the **Project Manager** window to give you more space.

4.11   Add a logo

You may want to include a company logo in your border. There are two ways to do this. You can either include the image within the drawing or reference a separate file.

If you include the image in your drawing it is much harder to change it later so it is better to reference a separate image file.

To add a logo as a separate file

Place your image in the project folder **Setup1** by moving it manually using Microsoft Windows Explorer.

Go to the **Insert** tab on the ribbon. (See the **Ribbon** section on page 9 if you need to add this tab.)

Select the **Attach** button. This is shaped like a document and is in the **Reference** panel of the **Insert** tab. On older versions of AutoCAD take care not to confuse it with a different **Attach** button shaped like a cloud.

In the dialogue box that appears, browse for your image. After you open it the following window is displayed.

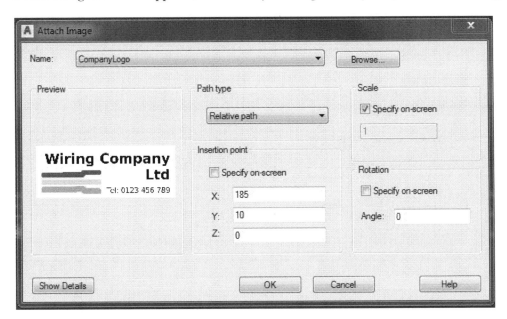

Path type is set to **Relative path** by default. This means AutoCAD will look for the image in the same place relative to the drawing file. In our example we have put them together so it will always expect the image in the same folder as the drawings.

You can specify **Insertion point** and **Scale** on screen. Alternatively you can specify the insertion point manually.

The **Insertion point** is the place where the bottom left of the image should be placed. For our border this is point **185,10**. Untick **Specify on-screen** and enter these values as shown in the above image.

If you leave **Specify on-screen** ticked for **Scale** then you can set the image size by clicking with the mouse. This function is hard to use. Moving the mouse changes the image size rather than allowing you to select the opposite point on the drawing. Try it but you will find it difficult.

Alternatively you can calculate a scale factor and enter it manually. If you click the **Show Details** button, the dialogue box expands to give you information about the size of your image, allowing you to calculate the correct scale.

4

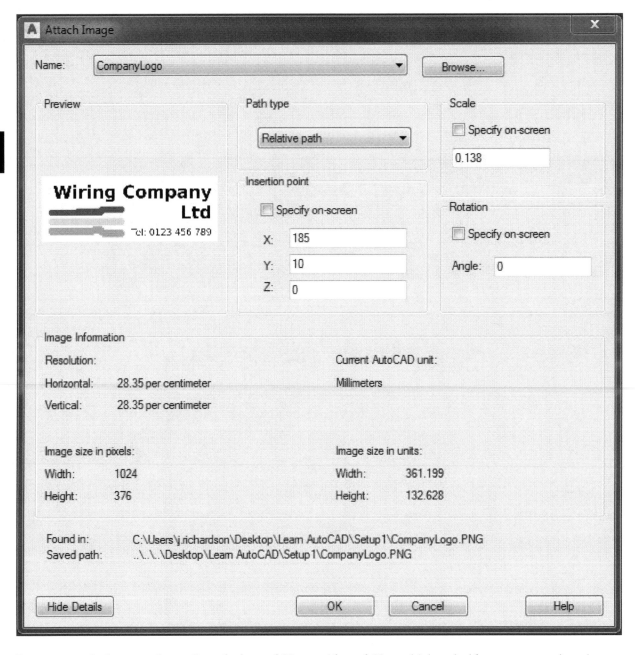

In our example frame we have allowed a box of 50mm wide and 20mm high to hold our company logo image.

The value **Image size in units** tells us how big the image will be if drawn with a scale factor of **1**. In this case it will be 361.199mm wide and 132.628mm high. To make it fit in our box we need to enter a scale factor of 50/361.199 which is **0.138**. You will need to calculate this value for the size of your image.

Press **OK** to insert the image. In our example there is a small gap above the image since the scaled height is smaller than the height of the box, even though the width fits perfectly.

Once the image is inserted you can move and resize it. To select it click on its edge or drag the mouse to select it inside a rectangular window. Clicking in the middle of the image does not work. Once the image is selected, click on a corner and drag. This is might be easier than scaling the image as you insert it, provided the image is not so big or small that it is hard to see in the drawing window.

To add a logo within the drawing

Generally it is better to attach an image as a separate file in case it changes. You will only need one copy for multiple sheets. If you prefer to embed the image within your drawings then you should paste it from the Microsoft Windows clipboard rather than using the AutoCAD attach button.

First open the image in another software package that allows you to copy an image, for example Microsoft Word. Select the image and copy to clipboard - in Microsoft Word this can be done by right clicking the image and choosing **copy** from the menu that appears. Or select the image and press **CTRL+C**.

Go to AutoCAD and select **Paste.** This is at the far right of the **Home** tab on the ribbon. Alternatively, you can right click on your drawing and press **CTRL+V**. Below the **Paste** button you can choose **Paste Special** which gives more control on the data format of the copied image.

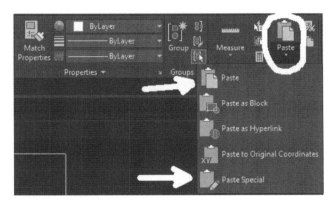

You can resize the image but be careful to move it by the corner rather than the edge so you do not distort its aspect ratio.

4.12   Drawing and project attributes (non-fixed information)

The text items in the border that change for different drawings and projects are called attributes. Those attributes which are identical for all drawings within a project, for example, the project title, are called **project attributes**.

Each attribute is given a name, called a tag. The **project attributes** display pieces of information from the project description settings. You can have as many of these as you want and they are text labels with no special properties. Each has a name defined in the custom labels file, **default_wdtitle.wdl** that you set up on page 51. If you do not define names using this file they are called **LINE1, LINE2**, etc.

Drawing attributes are similar to **project attributes** but change between different drawing sheets in a project. Unlike the **project attributes**, whose purpose must be set up by you, the **drawing attributes** are pre-configured. Some of the **drawing attributes** are linked to automated functions, for example the sheet number or the filename of the drawing. Others are linked to descriptions you enter in the **Drawing Properties** box for your drawing.

The following **drawing attributes** are available. You do not need to use all of them.

- Filename and path
- Descriptions entered in the **Drawing Properties** for the drawing
- IEC project, installation and location codes entered in the **Drawing Properties** for the drawing
- Sheet value, total number of sheets in the project, number of next sheet and previous sheet
- Time / date of plotting

4.13   Add project and drawing attributes (ATTDEF command)

You now need to position each attribute on the drawing using the **ATTDEF** command.

You can use the following list of attribute tags, which match the example on pages 50 and 51. Alternatively, modify the list to suit your needs.

Project Attribute Tags

ProjectTitle	**Rev1**	**Rev2**	**Rev3**
ProjectSubtitle	**Des1**	**Des2**	**Des3**
DrawingNo	**Date1**	**Date2**	**Date3**
Revision	**By1**	**By2**	**By3**
Date	**Chk1**	**Chk2**	**Chk3**
	App1	**App2**	**App3**

Drawing Attribute Tags

DrawingTitle	**SheetNo**
DrawingSubtitle	**TotalSheets**

To add the tags type **ATTDEF** at the command prompt. The **Attribute Definition** dialogue box appears:

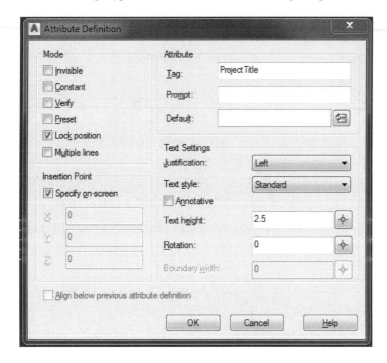

Type the tag name for the first attribute you wish to insert in the **Tag** box. If you are copying our example drawing frame, this would be **ProjectTitle**.

You can leave the **Prompt** and **Default** boxes blank. The **Default** value is an optional piece of text which will appear on drawings if that attribute has not yet been assigned a value. For example, you might make the default revision value "**A**" or display "**--**" for values that have not been specified.

Ensure text height is correct (2.5mm is a reasonable size for our example template). You can also change justification to **center** if required. For **Insertion Point** tick **Specify on screen.**

Click **OK** and then click on the point in the drawing frame where you want the attribute to appear. The tag name for the attribute will be placed on the drawing.

Now type **ATTDEF** again and repeat for the tag name of the next attribute until all project and drawing attributes are placed.

This may seem a tedious process. If you are using the example list of tags you will need to type **ATTDEF** and place a tag 26 times. However, it is very fast if you have your tags listed. For each one you are just typing **ATTDEF**, entering the tag name and choosing a location on the template. You do not need to click on the command line before entering **ATTDEF**, just type immediately after placing the previous attribute.

Remember to visualise what the frame will look like when the tag name is replaced by real text in a drawing. For example, **SheetNo** will be replaced by a one or two digit number and **ProjectTitle** could be a long name. Do not worry that the **SheetNo** tag name overlaps the border.

If you use left justification place the tag name to the left of the box in your frame, rather than the centre, so that there is space for the text to expand to the right. For most attributes, centre justified looks neatest. For some attributes, for example revision number, you might choose a larger text size.

If attributes are not in the right position you can click on them and drag to a different place. You can also select them and then right click and choose **Properties** from the menu that appears. This will let you change the text size or justification.

The end result should look like this:

REV1	DES1	DATE1	BY1	CHK1	APP1
REV2	DES2	DATE2	BY2	CHK2	APP2
REV3	DES3	DATE3	BY3	CHK3	APP3
Rev	Description	Date	By	Chkd	App

PROJECTTITLE PROJECTSUBTITLE	DRAWINGNO	REVISION
DRAWINGTITLE DRAWINGSUBTITLE	DATE	Sheet SHEETNO of TOTALSHEETS

Save your drawing.

4.14 Linking attributes to drawing and project properties using a WDT file

Now that the attributes are placed, you must tell AutoCAD what values they represent. You can either use a separate WDT file to do this or embed the information in the drawing. We will use the WDT file method which is more flexible but does require a having a separate WDT file as part of your project.

Click **Title Block Setup** in the **Project** tab of the ribbon.

The following dialogue box appears.

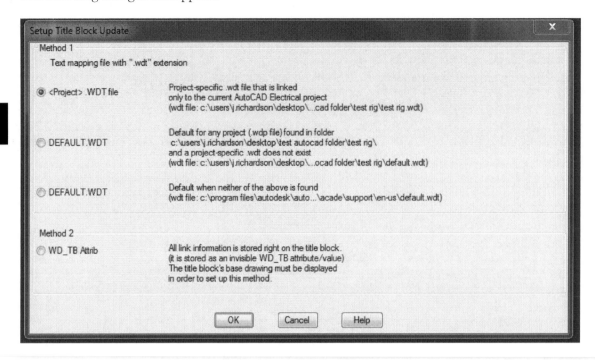

Select the first option, **<Project> .WDT file**, then click **OK**. You are now asked to name the title block you are creating.

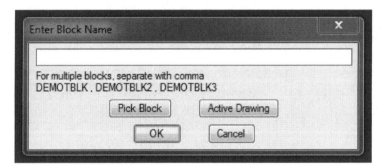

Click the **Active Drawing** button and the name box will be automatically filled with the name of your drawing, **titleblock1**. Then click **OK**.

The following box appears. It allows you to select which of the attributes placed on your drawing (the **Attribute** column) should display the value of each project description item (the **Project Value** column).

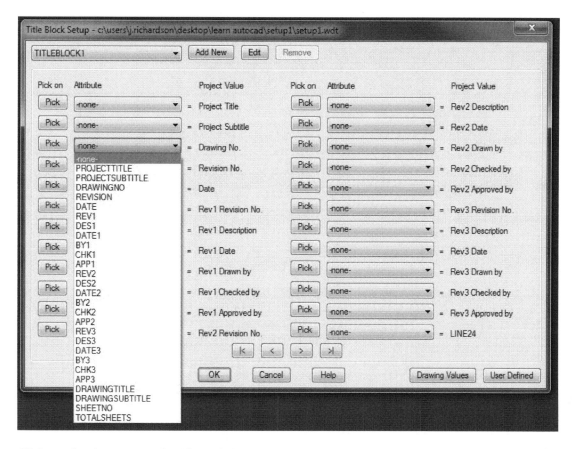

Click on the down arrow beside each line to get a list of the attributes which you placed on your drawing frame when you used the **ATTDEF** command.

The names in the **Project Value** column are taken from the descriptions you assigned in your **default_wdtitle.wdl** custom labels file on page 51. If you did not create this file, the project values will say LINE1, LINE2, etc. You can see an example of this with LINE24 (which we are not using) at the bottom right of the above screenshot.

For each line in the **Project Value** column, select the matching attribute from the drop down menu in the **Attribute** column.

If you did not create the **default_wdtitle.wdl** file you will have to assign them arbitrarily to LINE1, LINE2, etc. and note down which line number you used for reference when you use your template. This is inconvenient and not recommended.

The completed dialogue box for our example looks like this:

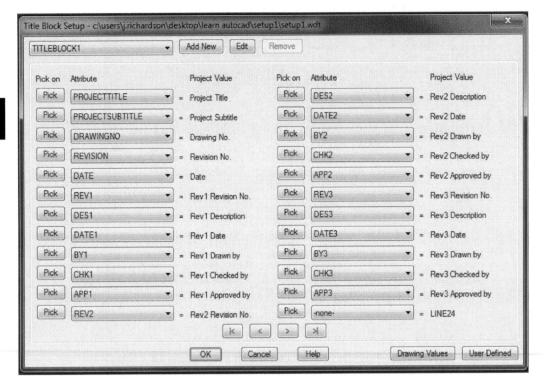

Now that you have assigned all of your **Project Value** tags, click the **Drawing Values** button at the bottom right. This displays the following page to set up the tags assigned to **Drawing Values**.

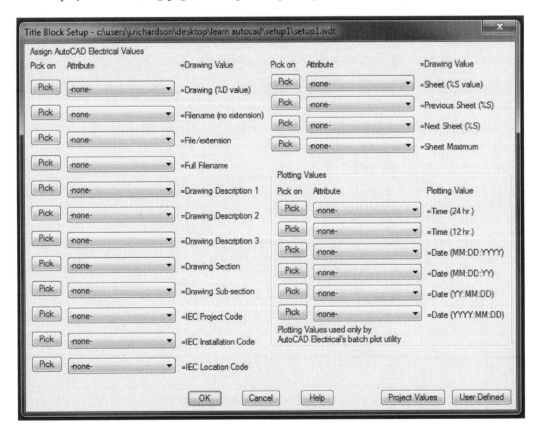

For each **Drawing Value** that you wish to assign to an attribute tag, select the attribute tag name from the drop down list in the **Attribute** column. For the tags in our example drawing, these would be:

TAG	Drawing Value	Explanation
SHEETNO	= Sheet (%S value)	AutoCAD can automatically assign a sequential number to each of the sheets within a project
TOTALSHEETS	= Sheet Maximum	The total number of sheets in the project
DRAWINGTITLE	= Drawing Description 1	Text values that can be assigned to each drawing in the **Drawing Properties** dialogue box.
DRAWINGSUBTITLE	= Drawing Description 2	

The completed form looks like this:

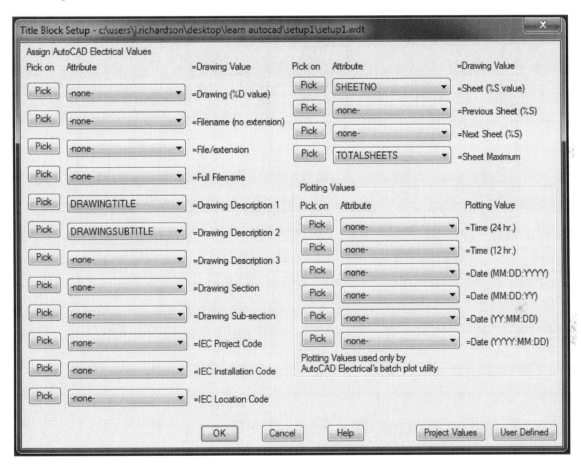

Click **OK** to save the values and exit the dialogue box. Then save your drawing.

4.15 Text height

In a moment we will set up a cross-reference grid and place grid reference labels around the border. The size of these labels is determined by the default text size.

Type **TEXTSIZE <Enter>** on the command line and then enter a value of **5 <Enter>** (a good value for an A3 metric template).

This will make the labels in the next section a sensible size.

4.16 Set up XY cross-referencing

Now we will set up a reference grid around the border. This is used when cross-referencing child components, such as relay contacts, or for labelling wires which continue on another sheet.

First we must go to **Drawing Properties** to set up the XY grid. Then we will use the **XY grid Setup** tool on the ribbon to label the grid. Although these two grid setup tools look similar they contain slightly different options so you must use both and in this order.

Click **Drawing Properties** on the ribbon at the right hand side of the **Schematic** tab. On the dialogue box that opens choose the **Drawing Format** tab.

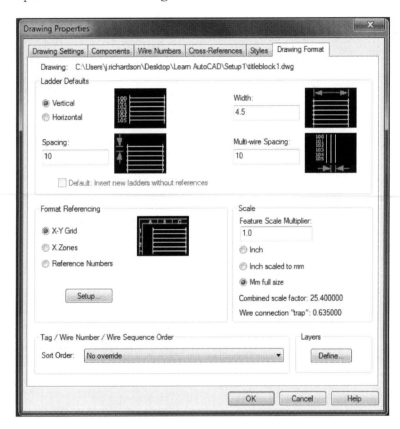

Under **Format Referencing** select the **X-Y Grid** option as shown above. Then click the **Setup...** button. The following box will open.

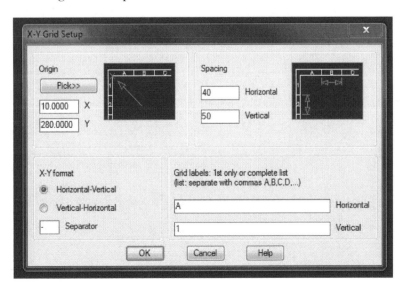

First set the X and Y coordinates of the origin to be the top left corner of the rectangle forming your drawing frame. By clicking the **Pick>>** button you can select this point on screen and the values will be filled in for you. Alternatively you can calculate it from the size of your frame. If you are using the example frame design in this book then this point will be X=10, Y=280.

Next enter the horizontal and vertical spacing for the grid. The example frame is 400mm wide so I have selected 40mm spacing to divide it into ten columns. The frame is 270mm high but the bottom 20mm consists of drawing border. To only cover the 250mm of actual drawing space with the grid, set the Y spacing to 50mm, dividing the drawing into five rows.

Under **X-Y format**, at the bottom of the dialogue box, select **Horizontal-Vertical**. This will allow you to enter the labels for the axis. Enter **A** for horizontal and **1** for vertical as shown. Delete the '-' symbol in the **Separator** box if you prefer grid references to be displayed in the format **"A1"** rather than **"A-1"**.

Click **OK** and the grid reference system will be set up. Click **OK** again to exit from the **Drawing Properties** dialogue box.

Although the grid has been set up, the grid labels around the border still need to be added. To do this go to the **Schematics** tab on the ribbon. Click the drop down arrow beside the **Insert Ladder** button and select the **XY Grid Setup** tool.

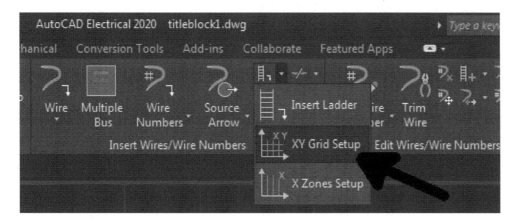

Clicking this will open the **XY Grid Setup** dialogue box as follows:

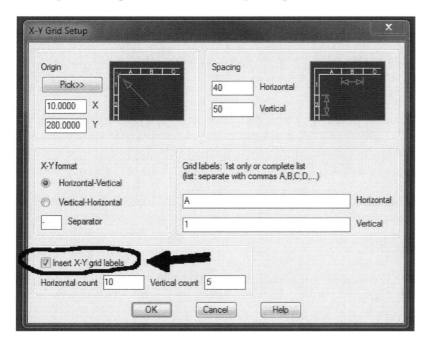

Most of the values will already be filled in for you from your entries in the **Drawing Properties** dialogue box.

Tick the **Insert X-Y grid labels** box then enter **10** for horizontal count and **5** for vertical count. This is the number of divisions on each axis that you need to label.

Click **OK** and grid labels will be added to your frame:

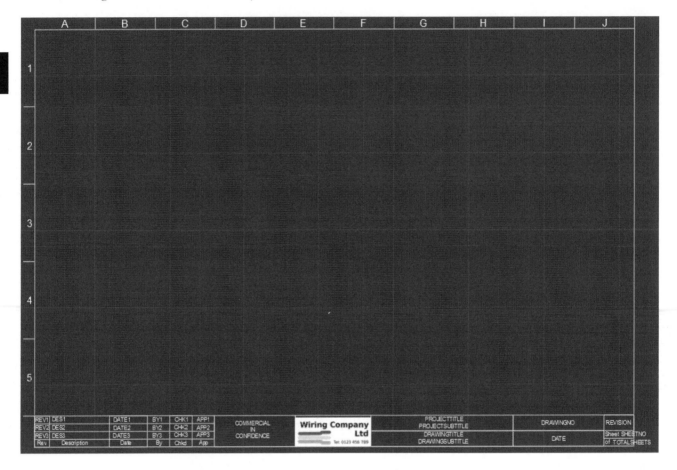

If the labels and grid are not as you would like, press **CTRL+Z** to undo the label insertion. Change the grid settings then use the **XY Grid Setup** tool on the ribbon to re-insert the labels.

Save your drawing.

4.17   Compare project and drawing properties

Earlier we saw that many settings can be defined for either a whole project or for individual drawings. If they are different then the settings for the individual drawing take precedence. We also saw that when adding a drawing to a project you are given the option to apply the project settings to that individual drawing.

In this chapter we have made settings at drawing level. To avoid the risk of these being over-written we will now copy them to the project level settings.

From the **Schematics** tab select **Settings Compare** from the drop down menu under **Drawing Properties**. It is also possible to get this function by right clicking on a drawing in the **Project Manager** window and selecting **Properties > Settings Compare...**

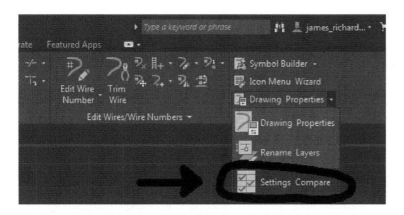

The **Compare Drawing and Project Settings** window opens. Ensure that the **Show Differences** button is selected. This shows any discrepancies between the project and drawing settings.

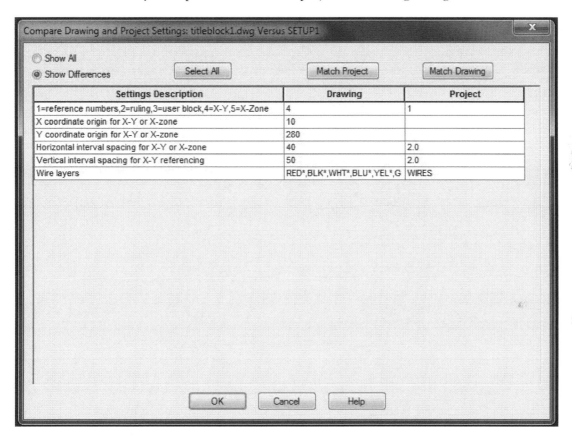

In this case we see the X-Y cross-referencing we have just set up only exists at drawing level.

Another difference is wire layers. The project only contains a single layer called **WIRES**. The drawing contains a few sample wire layers that came from the **acadiso.dwt** template. We do not need these so click the **Wire Layers** box to select it. Click the **Match Project** button. Both drawing and project will now only contain the **WIRES** wire layer.

The remaining differences are the X-Y grid settings. We need to copy these to the project.
Click the **Select All** button to highlight every item. Then click **Match Drawing.**

The drawing settings will be copied to the **Setup1** project properties.

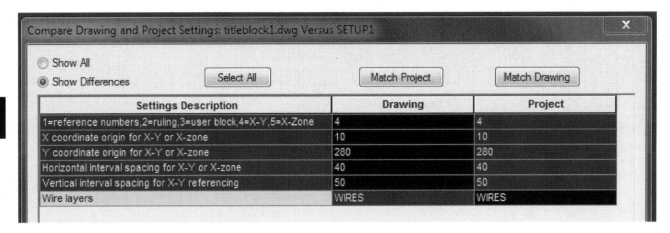

Click **OK** to exit **Settings Compare**.

Save your drawing.

You now have a completed drawing frame. In the next chapter we will insert this drawing as a block into another drawing to produce a drawing template.

5. Making a template (1 hour)

In this chapter we create a drawing template which will form the basis of your future drawings. It will include the frame drawn in the last chapter and the settings you prefer for your drawings. We will also create layers for wire types you expect to use.

Topics covered:

- Opening a new document
- Importing the drawing frame from chapter 4 as a block
- Setting up line types
- Setting up wire layers
- Copying wire layer definitions between drawings
- Setting up the template to print correctly
- Saving the drawing as a template for future drawings

5.1   Create a new drawing which will become the template

Open a new drawing. When asked which template to use, select the **acadiso.dwt** template. Now save this drawing in the **Setup1** directory as **templatedrawing1.dwg**

Add **templatedrawing1.dwg** to your **Setup1** project by using the **Project Manager** to add the active drawing. When prompted, apply the project defaults to the drawing to copy the project settings made earlier into the drawing.

Although it is possible to create a new drawing by right clicking the project name and selecting **New Drawing...** from the menu that appears, it is not recommended to do this here. This option adds the new drawing to the project automatically and runs a **Title Block Update** which will give an error message because we have not set up the project attributes yet.

At this stage **templatedrawing1.dwg** is not a template. It is just an ordinary drawing. We are going to import the frame made in the last chapter, set up wire layers and other details and then configure the print layout. Once all these things are complete we will save a copy as a template file.

5.2   Import a frame into the drawing

First we will import the title block frame drawn in chapter 4. By importing it in this way the attributes we set up for the frame become linked to the project and drawing properties of the new drawing.

Ensure you have **templatedrawing1.dwg** open and are working in it. Type **INSERT** in the **Command Line**. If you are using AutoCAD Electrical 2020 the **BLOCKS** window will open. (We will cover older versions of AutoCAD in a moment on page 73)

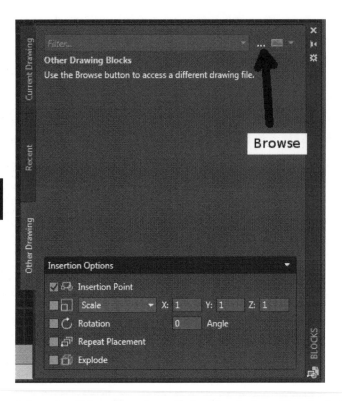

Select the **Other Drawing** tab in this window. Use the '**...**' button to browse for your **titleblock1.dwg** drawing. Select this as the block to insert. A small image of the **titleblock1.dwg** file will appear in the window as shown below.

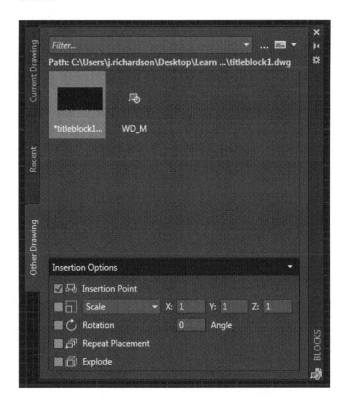

There should be a tick beside **Insertion Point**.
Scale should be **1**.
Explode should not be ticked.

Click the **titleblock1.dwg** image to select it. Do not hold the mouse button down. Move the mouse over the drawing area. You will see a representation of the block at the cursor. In the **Command Line** you will be asked for the insertion point.

Type **0,0 <Enter>** and the block will be inserted at the origin of your drawing.

Press **<Esc>** to ensure the command is finished and close the **BLOCKS** window by clicking the **X** at the top right corner.

If you are using an older version of the AutoCAD Electrical software you will not see this **BLOCKS** window. Instead you will get the **Insert** dialogue box when you type **INSERT** which asks for the same information. The following screenshot from AutoCAD Electrical 2018 shows this dialogue box.

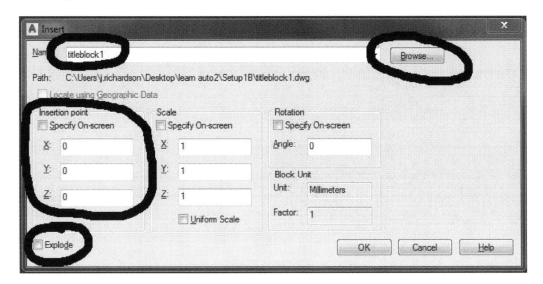

In this case, click the **Browse** button. Navigate to the **titleblock1.dwg** file in your **Setup1** project folder and select it. Ensure **Explode** is not checked. Specify **Insertion Point** as **0,0,0**. Click **OK** to insert the block.

If you are asked for attribute values leave them blank.

Whichever version of AutoCAD Electrical you are using, the frame you drew in the last chapter should now be inserted into the drawing at the origin. You may have to zoom in or out with the mouse wheel to get the right scale to see it.

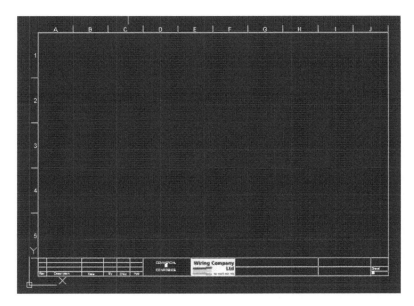

If you assigned any default values to the attributes, these values will be visible now. If not the attributes will be invisible and only the fixed text and frame lines shown.

Save the drawing.

5.3   Compare project settings

Run the **Settings Compare** tool from the **Schematic** tab of the ribbon as you did in the last chapter. The only difference between **templatedrawing1.dwg** and the **Setup1** project should be the wire layers. Select this item and click **Match Project** so that the drawing only contains the layer **WIRES**.

5.4   Drawing properties

Open the **Drawing Properties** dialogue by clicking on **Drawing Properties** in the **Other Tools** panel on the **Schematic** tab of the ribbon. Since you have just used **Settings Compare**, this button will be hidden so you need to click the small triangle beside **Settings Compare** to see it.

The **WD_M block** is a hidden block within the drawing that makes the AutoCAD Electrical commands work. If your drawing does not contain it you are prompted to add it the first time you use an AutoCAD Electrical function. Agree to this if asked although your drawing will already contain this block if you have worked through previous chapters.

The **Drawing Properties** dialogue box has a number of tabs. The first tab, **Drawing Settings**, shows information unique to drawings which is not covered by the project settings, for example descriptions for each individual drawing. It is these descriptions that feed into the **drawing attributes**. Since we are just producing a template we do not need to enter them now.

Press **OK** without changing anything.

5.5   Set up linetypes

AutoCAD has a selection of dotted and dashed lines. These can be used directly by you to modify the shapes you draw. They are also used by some of the automated AutoCAD features. By default only a few line types are loaded. This reduces your choice and may result in things AutoCAD is meant to display with dotted lines being drawn solid. We will correct this now in your template by loading more linetypes.

In the **Properties** panel of the **Home** tab click the **Linetype Manager** drop down menu shown below.

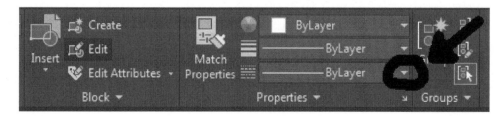

A menu of all the installed linetypes will appear.

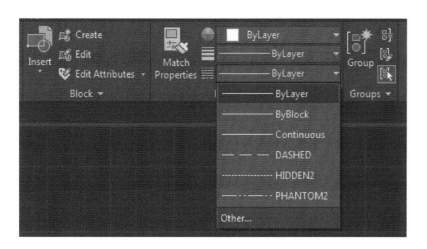

In the above example the only patterns available are **Continuous, DASHED, HIDDEN2** and **PHANTOM2**. Depending on your version of AutoCAD you may have even less.

To add more click **Other...** at the bottom of the list. The **Linetype Manager** dialogue box will appear.

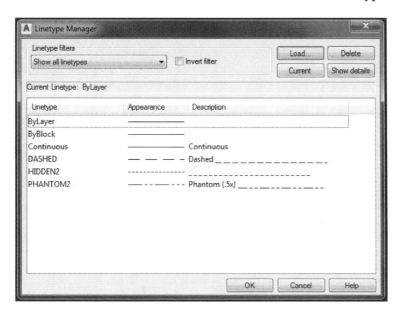

Now click **Load...** The **Load or Reload Linetypes** window appears:

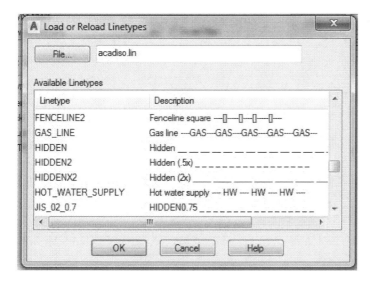

In this window click a **linetype** you want to add. You can press **<CTRL>** while clicking to select more than one. I recommend you right click the list and choose **Select All** from the menu that appears. This will import all of the linetypes.

You can also change the linetype file to match the scaling (metric or imperial) of your drawing. If this is wrong the dashes will be too long or too short. Do this by clicking the **File...** button. You can choose between:

- **acad.lin**
- **acade.lin**
- **acadiso.lin**

For a metric drawing choose **acadiso.lin**
For an electrical drawing using imperial measurements choose **acade.lin**

After selecting the linetypes you want to insert, press **OK**. You will now have access to these extra styles in your drawings. If you chose **Select All,** any linetypes which were already present will be loaded again. If prompted you should agree to this.

5.6   Layers

We saw in chapter 2 that AutoCAD electrical uses a system of layers. Each electrical wire type, for example 2.5mm² black wire, is on its own layer. Wires that are not assigned to a particular wire type are placed on the default **WIRES** layer. It is being on these wire layers that allows AutoCAD Electrical to process wires properly when adding wire numbers, components, etc.

In the **Layers** panel of the **Home** tab click the **Layer Properties** button.

This opens the **Layer Properties Manager.**

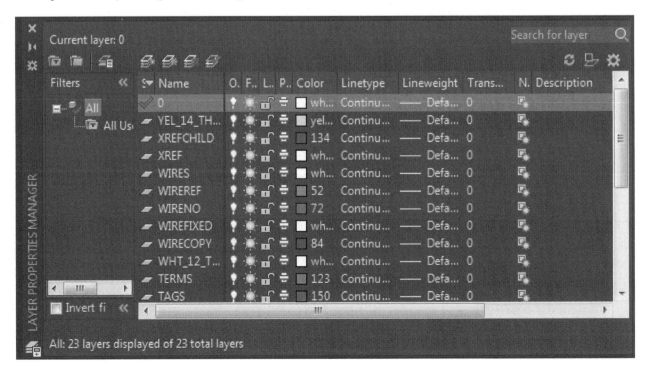

The **Layer Properties Manager** allows you to view and modify layers directly. We will not be using it just yet so close the it for now by clicking the **X** in the corner. If an **X** is not visible it will appear when you hover the mouse over the window.

5.7   Set up wire layers

It is useful to set up a list of the common wire sizes and colours that you will be using. It will not be practical to predict every future wire type but please take a few moments to consider what will be needed for your first few drawings. Later on you can add individual wire types as required or import them from other drawings.

Go to **Create/Edit Wire Type** in the **Schematics** tab. It shares a drop down menu with the **Change/Convert Wire Type** button which may be on top.

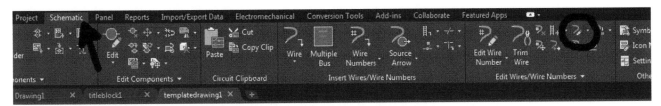

The following dialogue box will appear.

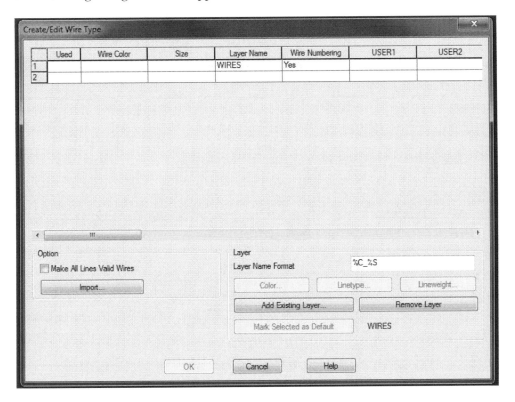

To add a new wire, click on the blank line at the bottom of the list (line 2 in the above screenshot) in the **Wire Color** column. Type **RD** (as an abreviation for "red"). Then click in the **Size** column and type **2.5mm**. Click on another box so that AutoCAD accepts the **2.5mm** value.

The **Layer Name** and **Wire Numbering** columns will be filled in automatically and a new blank line added as below:

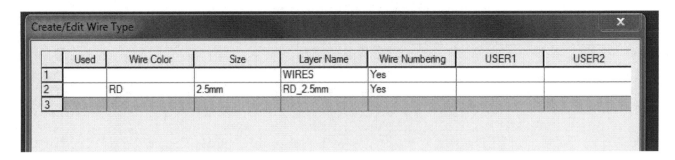

5

By default, wires in your schematics are able to accept wire numbers. If you need to create a wire type that will never be numbered, you can click on the box in the **Wire Numbering** column (containing the word **"Yes"**) and select **"No"** from the drop down menu that appears.

After entering the wire layers you can set the colours used to display the wires on your drawing. Click on a line to highlight it. Then click the button **Color** in the lower part of the dialogue box. Select one of the index colours from the **Select Color** box that appears and click **OK**. Avoid using the non-index true colours unless you have a good reason. The index colours convert to monochrome properly if you use the monochrome print function. The true colours do not.

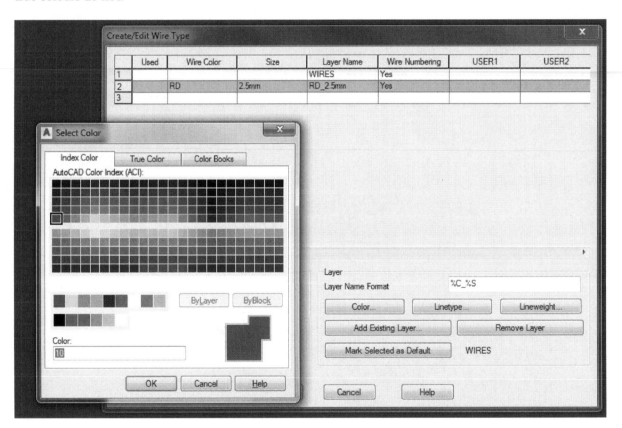

After entering your wires and setting their display colours click **OK** to leave the **Create/Edit Wire Type** dialogue box. The **OK** button will be greyed out if you have clicked on the last line and AutoCAD is expecting further text to be entered. If this happens click on one of the completed wire layer lines and the **OK** button will become available.

If you are entering many wire types you can select a number of lines at once to change them all to a particular colour at the same time. You can also use a limited amount of cutting and pasting by right clicking the table.

The fastest way to enter many wire types is to make a two column table in Microsoft Excel for **Wire color** and **size** as follows:

	A	B	C
1	BU	0.25mm	
2	BU	0.33mm	
3	BU	0.5mm	
4	BU	0.75mm	
5	BU	1mm	
6	BU	1.5mm	
7	BU	2.5mm	
8	BU	4mm	
9	BU	6mm	
10	BU	10mm	
11	BU	16mm	
12	BN	0.25mm	
13	BN	0.33mm	
14	BN	0.5mm	

You can then copy this in Microsoft Excel and paste it into the **Wire Color** box on the blank line in AutoCAD.

Before pasting be sure you will not be creating duplicate layers with the same name. Also save your drawings before pasting. The AutoCAD Electrical software can sometimes crash during this operation, especially if you paste something it doesn't like. If you do paste duplicate layers you will need to delete these lines before you can click **OK** to close the **Create/Edit Wire Type** dialogue box.

Note that the symbols **< > / \ " : ; * , = '** are not allowed. If you type one by mistake you will need to click in the **Layer Name** column and type something else to get rid of the error message and continue using AutoCAD. If you import a large number of wires from Microsoft Excel with forbidden characters then you may have to close the software to get out of it.

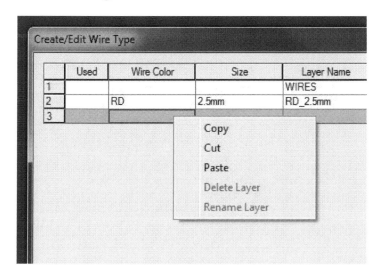

The lines for the extra layers will be created, with the Microsoft Excel data going in the **Color** and **Size** columns. The other columns will be filled in automatically.

Ideally you should enter the wires you expect to use in your future drawings now although it will not be practical to predict them all. You may wish to use the following list of wires.

Wire colour	size
BU	0.25
BU	0.33
BU	0.5
BU	0.75
BU	1
BU	1.5
BU	2.5
BU	4
BU	6
BU	10
BU	16

Wire colour	size
BN	0.25
BN	0.33
BN	0.5
BN	0.75
BN	1
BN	1.5
BN	2.5
BN	4
BN	6
BN	10
BN	16

Wire colour	size
GY	0.25
GY	0.33
GY	0.5
GY	0.75
GY	1
GY	1.5
GY	2.5
GY	4
GY	6
GY	10
GY	16

Wire colour	size
GN-YE	0.25
GN-YE	0.33
GN-YE	0.5
GN-YE	0.75
GN-YE	1
GN-YE	1.5
GN-YE	2.5
GN-YE	4
GN-YE	6
GN-YE	10
GN-YE	16

Wire colour	size
BK	0.25
BK	0.33
BK	0.5
BK	0.75
BK	1
BK	1.5
BK	2.5
BK	4
BK	6
BK	10
BK	16
BK	25
BK	35
BK	50
BK	70
BK	95

Wire colour	size
RD	0.25
RD	0.33
RD	0.5
RD	0.75
RD	1
RD	1.5
RD	2.5
RD	4
RD	6
RD	10
RD	16

Wire colour	size
OR	0.25
OR	0.33
OR	0.5
OR	0.75
OR	1
YE	0.25
YE	0.33
YE	0.5
YE	0.75
YE	1
GN	0.25
GN	0.33
GN	0.5
GN	0.75
GN	1

Wire colour	size
VT	0.25
VT	0.33
VT	0.5
VT	0.75
VT	1
WH	0.25
WH	0.33
WH	0.5
WH	0.75
WH	1

After entering your wire layers save your drawing.

Line weights

As well as colours, you can also set line weights for your wire types. If you do this you will find that the wires do not change, either in model or layout view, even though the extra thick lines print correctly. By default AutoCAD hides this increased line thickness on screen. If you would like to use increased line thicknesses you can force AutoCAD to display them on screen by typing the following at the command line.

LWDISPLAY   **\<Enter\>**
ON   **\<Enter\>**

5.8   Compare project and drawing properties

As in the last chapter, we now want to copy our drawing level changes to the project settings. This keeps everything in step.

From the **Schematics** tab select **Settings Compare** from the drop down menu under **Drawing Properties**. Alternatively, click on the **templatedrawing1** drawing in the **Project Manager** window and select **Properties > Settings Compare...**

The **Compare Drawing and Project Settings** window opens. Ensure that the **Show Differences** button is selected.

In this case we see the wire layers we have just set only exist in the drawing. Click the **Select All** button to highlight every item. Then click **Match Drawing** followed by **OK** to copy the drawing settings to the **Setup1** project properties.

5.9 Transferring wire layers between drawings

You have now set up enough wire layers for your first few drawings. For the simple examples in this book you should have few problems. Before moving on, however, it is worth explaining a little more about wire layers. This will help you when manipulating wire layers in your own projects. Once you start copying wire layers between projects you may find AutoCAD Electrical does not behave as you expect.

We have seen that each wire type is defined as a layer. You can look at these layers directly by clicking the **Layer Properties** button in the **Home** tab of the ribbon to open the **Layer Properties Manager**. Normally you should alter these wire layers indirectly, by clicking the **Create/Edit Wire Type** button in the **Schematic** tab of the ribbon to open the **Create/Edit Wire Type** window.

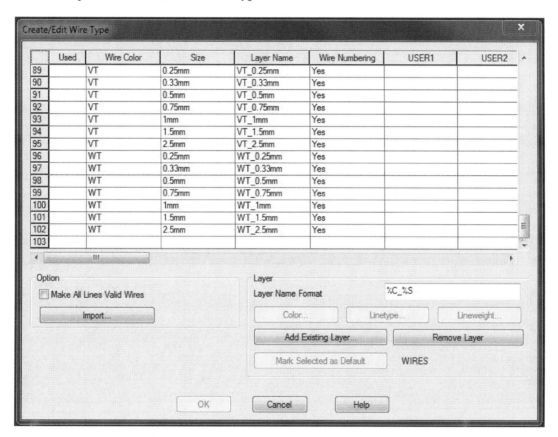

If you type in the **Wire Color** and **Size** columns on the blank line at the bottom of this table, AutoCAD Electrical will create a new layer for this wire type. AutoCAD will also register the new layer as being a special layer representing a wire. This final step allows the AutoCAD Electrical tools to process the wire properly.

Deleting wire types

Should you wish to remove a wire layer, you can right click a line in the **Create/Edit Wire Type** window. A menu appears and you can select **Delete Layer** from it. This will remove the wire layer completely, both from the **Create/Edit Wire Types** list and from the **Layer Properties Manager**.

There is a **Remove Layer** button but its operation is more confusing. If you select a wire layer to delete you will probably find the **Remove Layer** button is greyed out. You can only use it to delete all of the wires of one colour together. In the above image you could select all the wires (using **CTRL + Click** or **SHIFT + Click**) with layer names beginning **WT_**. Only after all seven are selected will the **Remove Layer** button become active.

Unlike the **Delete Layer** option mentioned above, **Remove Layer** will only delete the layers in the **Create/Edit Wire Layers** box. They are still in the drawing and are still visible in the **Layers Properties Manager**, AutoCAD just no longer treats them as wires.

Transferring wire layers between drawings

If you wish to transfer wire layers between drawings there are two tasks which you need to get right. First, you need to copy the layers themselves. Second, you need to copy the information which recognises the layers as wires and displays them in the **Create/Edit Wire Types** window.

Unfortunately the **Compare Drawing and Project Settings** tool only does the second of these two things. If you were to use the **Remove Layer** button in the **Create/Edit Wire Types** window to remove all the wire layers beginning **WT_** as discussed above, the actual layers themselves would still remain. In this case the **Compare Drawing and Project Settings** tool could be used to put them back into the **Create/Edit Wire Types** window and recognise them as wire layers again. As a stand-alone tool to copy wire layers between drawings, the **Compare Drawing and Project Settings** tool is insufficient since it does not create the underlying layers.

One alternative is to type all of your wire layers in a spreadsheet as described earlier. This provides a fast way to enter multiple wire definitions.

Another way is to use the **Import...** button in the **Create/Edit Wire Types** window. This button allows you to choose another drawing and select which of the wire layers in that drawing you wish to copy. You will need to do this for each drawing into which you need to import wire layers. This method will create the underlying wire layers, including any assigned ink colours. The only strange feature is that the **Size** and **Color** columns in the **Create/Edit Wire Types** window are left blank. The **Layer Name** column is filled in though, which is the part needed to make AutoCAD electrical work.

If you have many drawings then using the **Import...** button in the **Create/Edit Wire Types** window could be tedious. A project wide method is to use the **Project-Wide Utilities** tool. This can be activated by clicking the **Utilities** button in the **Project Tools** panel on the **Project** tab of the ribbon.

This will open the **Project-Wide Utilities** dialogue box.

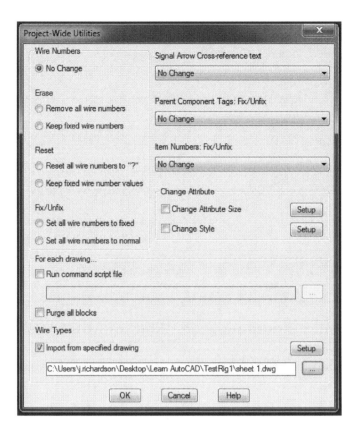

This box contains a number of project wide tools. Ensure you have **No Change** selected in the **Wire Numbers** section at the top left.

At the bottom click the box labelled **Import from specified drawing** under the heading **Wire Types**.

The '**...**' button at the bottom right will then become active. Click this button and browse through the file structure to find the drawing from which you want to copy the wire types.

You can now click the **Setup** button at the bottom right to open the **Import Wire Types** screen.

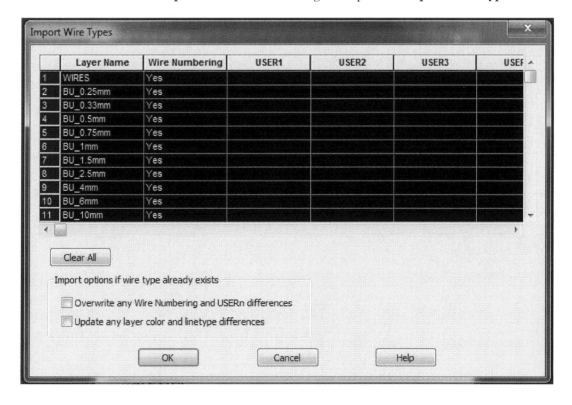

In this window you can select which wire types to import. They will be imported into all drawings of your project. The tick boxes determine whether the pen colour and numbered/not numbered selections are overwritten if any of the line types already exist.

As with the **Import...** function in the **Create/Edit Wire Types** dialogue box, the **Layer Name** and other important properties are copied but the **Color** and **Size** columns which create the layer name are left blank.

When we add wires to our drawings in later chapters, you will see a small **X** in the **Create/Edit Wire Types** dialogue box next to each wire type that is used for a wire in the drawing.

If you import wire types then the imported wire types all have a **X** beside them in the **Create/Edit Wire Types** window, incorrectly indicating they are used for wires in the drawing, even if they are not.

5.10   Set up print layouts.

Now we will set up a print layout for our template, just as we did in chapter 2. This ensures your future drawings will be set up for your printer as soon as you create them.

Click on the **Layout1** tab at the bottom left of the screen.

If these tabs are not visible turn them on by right clicking the screen, selecting **Options...** and ensuring **Display Layout and Model Tabs** is ticked in the **Display** tab of the **Options** screen. See page 13 for more details.

On clicking **Layout1** you will be taken to a print layout as shown below.

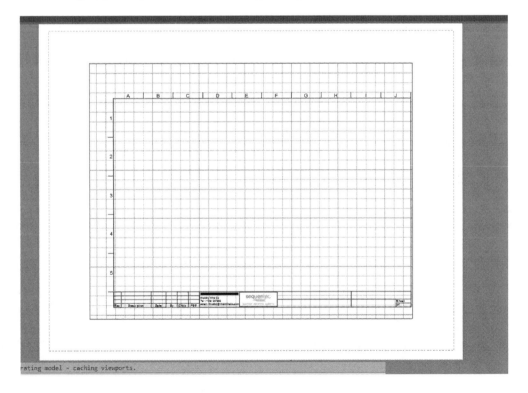

First select your printer and paper size. This will change the size and shape of the printable area so must be done before we can set the layout to fit this. To do this go to the **Application Button** and choose **Print**. You will see the following dialogue box.

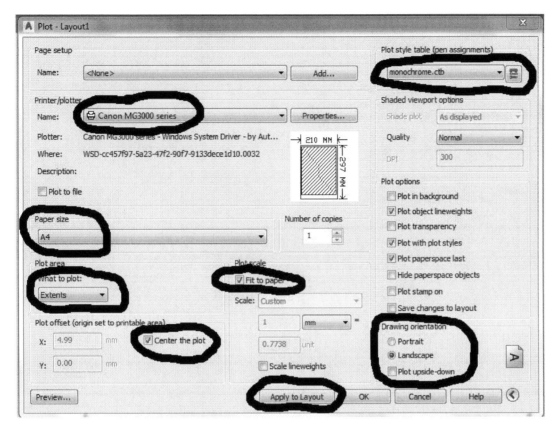

Choose your printer and paper size. You can select A4 or A3, depending on your printer. Even though we have created our drawing in model space as A3 it will be scaled to match other paper sizes. For the example drawing frame and most schematics you would choose **Landscape** rather than **Portrait** orientation.

Select **monochrome.ctb** as the **Plot Style**. This will print your drawings mostly in greyscale. Any objects or wires are converted to shades of grey, provided you used the **Index Colours**. Anything drawn in **True Colours** as well as imported logos or other images will still be shown in colour.

An alternative to monochrome is the **acad.ctb** plot style which will print everything in full colour.

Under **Plot Area** select **Extents**.

Tick the boxes for **Center the plot** and **Fit to paper**. Click the **Apply to Layout** button which saves these settings but does not actually start printing.

Click **Cancel** to go back to the **Layout** view without printing.

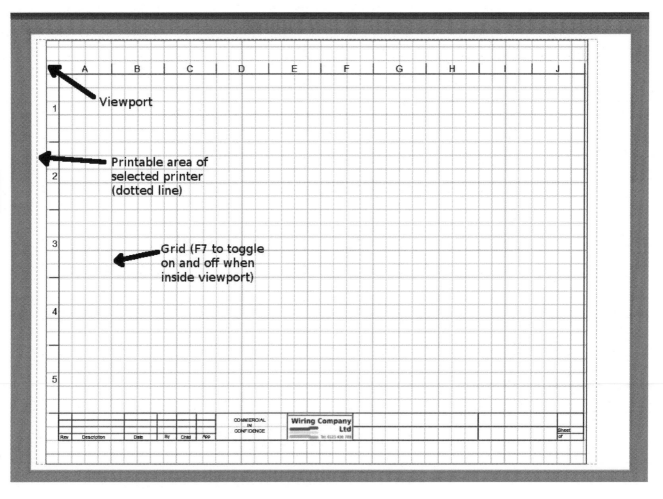

5

We now need to set up the layout viewport ready for printing our title block. This will ensure every drawing produced with your template is print-ready with minimum set up. We first looked at this in chapter 2 but we will work through it again for our template drawing and point out some extra tips.

The layout view shows a white sheet of paper of finite size, unlike the infinite model space. The dotted line around the edge shows the printable area of the paper. The solid black line is the **viewport**, a viewing window which shows the area of model space which will be printed.

There may be blue grid over the viewport area. To get rid of this, double click inside the viewport to select this area. The outline of the viewport will become thicker. Press **F7** to turn the grid off. Now double click on the paper outside of the viewport. The outline will go back to normal thickness.

If the viewport is normal thickness and you zoom in and out with the wheel of the mouse the view of the sheet of paper will shrink or be enlarged. This can make it easier to view on screen but the printed output will not change.

If you have double clicked inside the viewport to get double thickness lines, zooming and scrolling of the mouse will change the area of the model space seen through the viewport and its scale. In this way we can change what will be printed on the paper.

As in chapter 2, we will make the viewport fill the printable area of the paper and then scale the layout to make our drawing frame exactly fill this viewport.

To match the viewport to the printable area, move the mouse to be exactly over the edge of the viewport border. Click on it ONCE. The border will be highlighted.

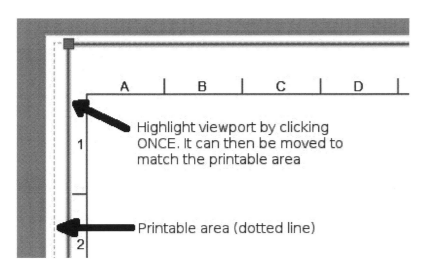

Click on the square at the bottom left hand corner of the highlighted viewport and click ONCE. Now move the mouse and this corner will move with it. Move to the bottom left hand corner of the dotted rectangle and click the left button of the mouse ONCE to place the corner of the frame there. Repeat this with the top right corner of the viewport. By rotating the mouse wheel you can zoom in for accurate placement.

The viewport will now exactly match the printable area of the paper. Press **<Esc>** to deselect the viewport.

Next, double click inside the viewport. The viewport will be drawn in thick black lines. Place the mouse inside the viewport. Double click the mouse wheel. AutoCAD will automatically zoom so that everything in model space exactly fills the viewport.

Double click outside of the viewport again to get rid of the bold lines.

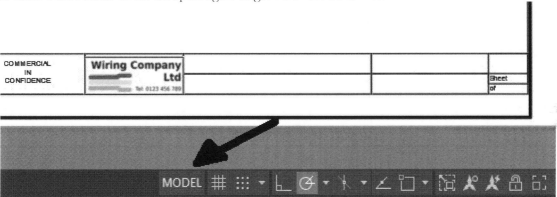

Sometimes you might double click inside the viewport and then be zoomed in so that there is nowhere on screen that allows you to click outside the viewport. In this case you can click on the word **MODEL** at the bottom of the screen to get back into paper space. When you are not inside the viewport, this button says **PAPER**. Clicking on **PAPER** has the same effect as double clicking inside the viewport.

Do not confuse this button with the tabs that say **Model**, **Layout1** and **Layout2**.

If you double click the border of your viewport, AutoCAD takes you into **Model** space. If you use a black background in model space the screen will change to that colour background. This can be confusing if you do it by accident. To exit back to layout view click the **MODEL** button shown above.

In this book we will not lock the viewport in our template. You could choose this option to prevent viewport settings being altered by accident. See page 33.

Make the viewport frame non-printing

We do not want the viewport frame to be printed as a rectangular box around our drawing. As in chapter 2 we will create a non-printing layer for viewports and move the viewport to this layer.

In the **Home** tab of the ribbon, click on the **Layer Properties** button.

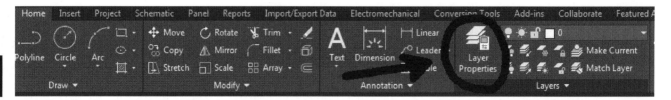

The **Layer Properties Manager** will open.

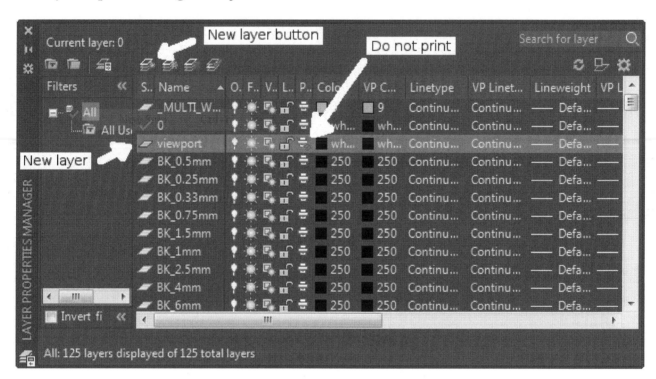

Click the **New Layer** button. A new layer called **Layer1** will be created. Type over this name to change it to **viewport**.

For the **viewport** layer click the printer icon to change it to the **do not print** symbol with the red circle as shown above.

You will see a green tick next to layer **0**. This is the current layer. Should you draw, for example, a rectangle, it will be placed on this layer. You can double click on a layer in the **Layer Properties Manager** window to make it the current layer. If you do this by accident, double click on layer **0** to put the tick there. It will cause much confusion if you accidently start drawing your shapes on the non-printable **viewport** layer since they will appear on screen but not print.

Selecting a default layer other than layer **0** can also stop the wire tool (chapters 7 and 8) from drawing wires in the correct default wire layer.

Close the **Layer Properties Manager** window.

Click once on the edge of the viewport to highlight it. Then right click on the drawing to bring up a menu. Select **Properties** from this menu to see the properties of the viewport.

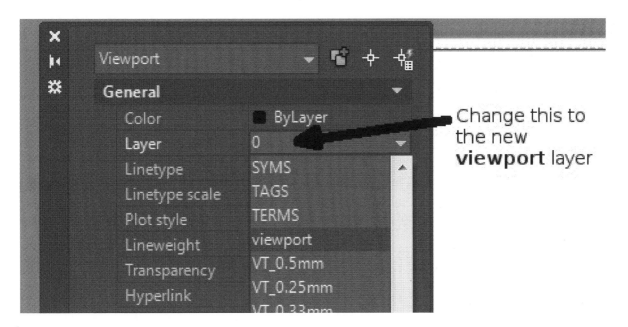

You will see that it is on **Layer 0**. Click the **0** value and a drop down arrow will appear next to it. Select the new **viewport** layer from the drop down menu. You may need to scroll down past many other layers.

Close the **Properties** window and press **<Esc>** to deselect the viewport. Save your drawing.

5.11 Test printing

Now go to the **Application Button** and print the layout to your printer. Ensure it prints correctly with the frame filling the page.

If your printing is not successful check your paper size and margins are set correctly. If you change the paper size the dotted printable area will change requiring you to repeat the last section.

5.12 Final settings

When you are happy with the print settings, click the **Model** tab at the bottom left of the screen (next to the **Layout1** and **Layout2** tabs). This is so your template will open in model view, rather than layout view, after you have saved it.

Use the **Textsize** command to set the text height to a sensible setting. For a metric drawing I recommend **5**.

Turn on **Display drawing grid** and **Snap to drawing grid** using the buttons at the bottom of the screen. Turn off **Restrict cursor orthogonally**.

Set the grid and snap settings to convenient values. For a metric drawing I recommend a **Grid spacing** value of **10** and a **Snap spacing** value of **2.5**.

When you save your template these settings will be stored with it and become the default starting point each time you create a new drawing.

5.13 Save your template

Now save your drawing in the normal way. Keep this drawing (**templatedrawing1.dwg**) and the **titleblock1.dwg** drawing. Keeping copies of these files allows you to easily repeat parts of the last few chapters if you need minor changes to the title block. This can be easier than altering your template directly.

Finally hover over **Save As** in the **Application Button** menu and select save as **Drawing Template** from the sub-menu that appears.

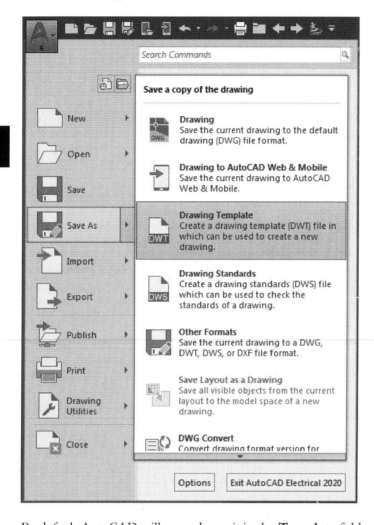

By default AutoCAD will try and save it in the **Template** folder.

C: /Users/*Your username*/AppData/Local/Autodesk/AutoCAD Electrical 2020/R23.1/enu/Template

This is the place AutoCAD looks for templates by default and it is easiest to leave your templates here. I recommend you do this but you can put them elsewhere if you want.

Enter a file name for the template. It should have the **.dwt** extension. For this book we will use the name **first_template.dwt**

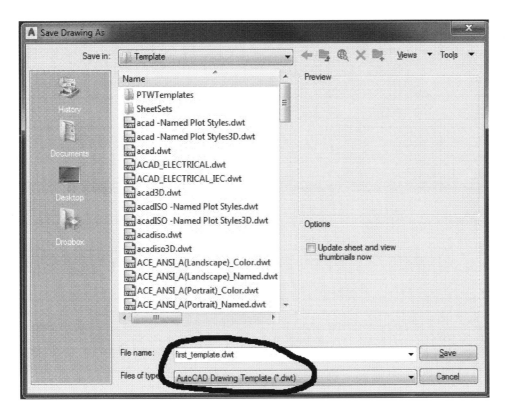

Click **Save**. The template options box appears.

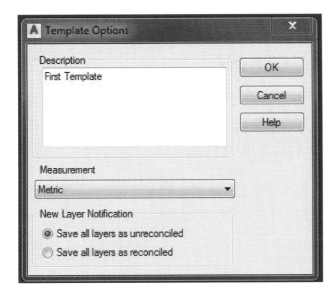

Type a brief description for your template in the **Description** box. Select measurement as **Metric** (or **English** if you used imperial measurements). Click **OK**.

Your drawing template is now created.

6. Working with projects (1 hour)

This chapter explains how to create your first real project ready for drawing schematics.

We will produce a project called **SampleProject1** containing all the settings we made in the **Setup1** project. The drawings within it will be based on our new drawing template.

When you need a project in future, you can either follow the steps in this chapter or just make a copy of the **SampleProject1** project.

Topics covered:

- Creating a new project using our drawing template
- Adding title block information
- Saving and printing multiple drawings
- Adding a table of contents
- Copying projects
- Changing the title block in an existing set of drawings

6.1   Create a project

In the **Project Manager** window select **New Project**. (Remember that a drawing must be open for this button to work.) Call your new project **SampleProject1**.

In the **Location** box, browse to the folder where you want to keep your new project, either in the AutoCAD **proj** directory or anywhere else. For the examples in this book we will save it in the **Learn AutoCAD** folder we created in chapter 3. Leave the **Create Folder with Project Name** box ticked.

In the **Copy Settings from Project File** box, browse to the **Setup1** project we created earlier so the new project can inherit its settings. Select the **Setup1.wdp** file.

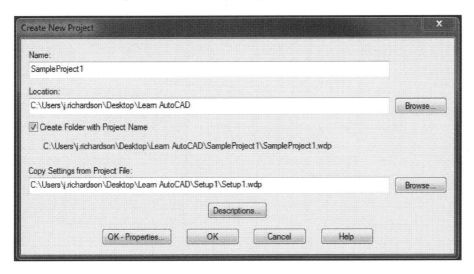

Click **OK.** (Do not click **OK-Properties...**)

The new project, **SampleProject1** will be created. It will become the active project, shown at the top of the list in the **Project Manager** window.

Use Windows Explorer to manually copy the file **default_wdtitle.wdl** we created in the **Setup1** project directory in chapter 4 to the **SampleProject1** directory. This file is necessary so that the **project attributes** have their correct names rather than LINE1, LINE2, etc.

Also copy the **Setup1.wdt** file from the **Setup1** project directory into the **SampleProject1** directory and rename this copy **SampleProject1.wdt**. Ensure any capitalisation matches your project name. This **.wdt** file (do not confuse it with the **.wdp** one) links the drawing and project attributes to the title block and is necessary for the **Title Block Update** command (covered later) to work with our drawing frame.

If you have included a company logo or other image in your frame as a separate file, rather than embedding it in the template, then you should place a copy of this in the **SampleProject1** directory as well.

Your **SampleProject1** project folder should now look like this:

Do not be discouraged if this seems a rather manual process. We will use some automated tools later but for now it is good to understand what is happening to the project files.

6.2   Create some sheets

Create a new drawing using the **first_template.dwt** file we created in chapter 5 as the template.

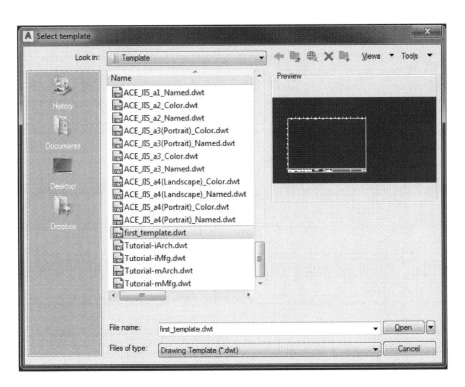

From the **Application Button** select **Save As > drawing** and save your drawing in the **SampleProject1** directory as **sheet 1.dwg**

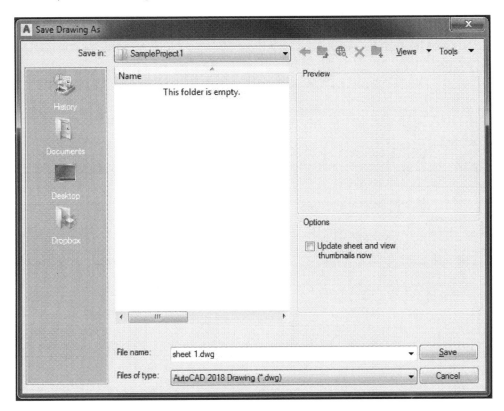

Notice that the drawing is saved as an AutoCAD 2018 drawing. Although a new version of the AutoCAD Electrical software is issued every year, the drawing format only changes every three or four years so 2018 is the most recent. Occasionally you might complete work using the current version of AutoCAD then re-save drawings as, for example, AutoCAD 2013 format to give to someone with an old version of AutoCAD.

Now add the **sheet 1.dwg** drawing to the **SampleProject1** project. To do this right click the **SampleProject1** project in the **Project Manager** and select **Add Active Drawing**.

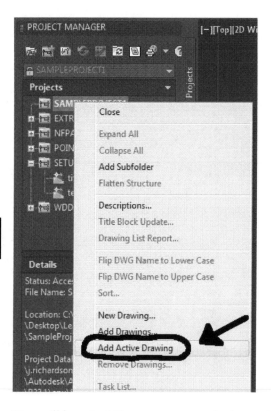

6

You will be asked if you want to apply the project defaults to the drawing settings. It does not matter whether you do as the settings should be the same. You can verify this by clicking **No** and then using the **Settings Compare** tool.

Click the **+** beside the **SampleProject1** project name and you can see your new drawing in the **Project Manager** window. If the **+** is not visible, click the **SampleProject1** project name to refresh the list.

Now create two further drawings using your template and add them to the project. Call them **sheet 2.dwg** and **sheet 3.dwg**. A fast way to do this is to right click the project name in **Project Manager** and select **New Drawing...** from the menu that appears.

You will see the **Create New Drawing** dialogue box:

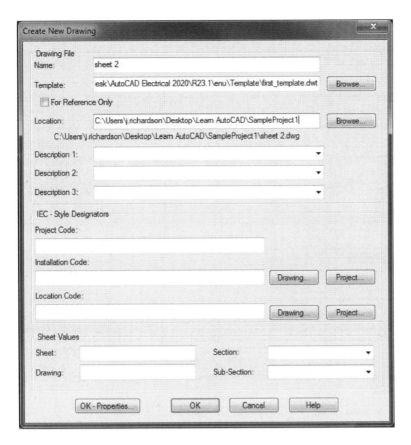

Type the drawing name, **sheet 2**. AutoCAD will remember the last details you used so **Template** should already be filled in with the **first_template.dwt** file and **Location** with the **SampleProject1** directory path. Leave the other items blank and click **OK**.

Repeat to create **sheet 3**.

While I did not recommend this method of adding a new drawing in chapter 5 there is no problem with it now. The attributes in our drawing border are matched with a **.wdt** file in the project directory so AutoCAD does not create an error message.

All the sheets will now be listed in the **Project Manager** window under the **SampleProject1** project. If they are not visible then click the small **+** next to the project name to expand the list. When working on a project you can open sheets quickly by double clicking on them in this list. Switch between open drawings by clicking on the tabs at the top of the screen.

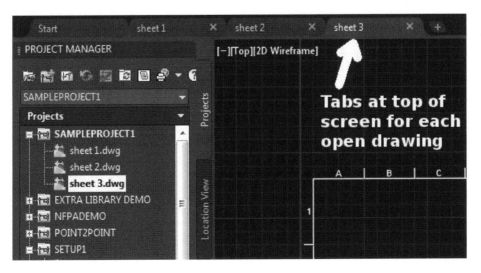

The drawings are listed in order. This matters because we will be using the **Title Block Update** function to automatically apply sheet numbers. To change the order, place the mouse over the drawing you wish to move, press and hold down the left mouse button and drag the drawing to the point in the list of drawings where you want it to go.

Right clicking on a drawing name gives you a menu which includes the option to rename. This rename function changes the filename of the drawing as well as the entry in the AutoCAD **Project Manager** window. You cannot rename a drawing if you have it open. Also you must have at least one (unconnected) drawing open for the rename function to work.

I normally name my drawings **sheet 1**, **sheet 2** etc, but you may prefer descriptive names, for example **Motor Starter.dwg**

6.3   Saving multiple drawings

When working on a complex project with dozens of sheets it is tedious to save each one.

If a drawing has been modified (even zooming in is counted as a change) a small asterisk (*****) appears next to the drawing name in the drawing tab at the top of the screen. In the example below, **sheet 2** has unsaved changes.

An easy way to save multiple drawings is to right click on one of the drawing tabs. A menu appears which includes the option **Save All**. There is also a **Close All** option which can be useful.

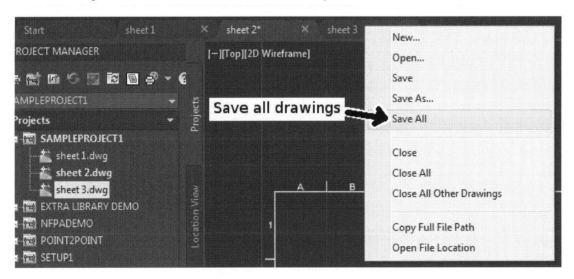

6.4   Converting multiple sheets to an older version of AutoCAD Electrical

Sometimes you might need to send a project with many drawings to someone who has an old version of AutoCAD Electrical. Saving each one as, for example, AutoCAD 2013 format would be time consuming. Instead you can use the **DWG Convert** tool to change the format of multiple sheets. There is no need to do this now but if you need this function in the future the operation is as follows:

Click the **Application button** and expand the **Save As...** option.

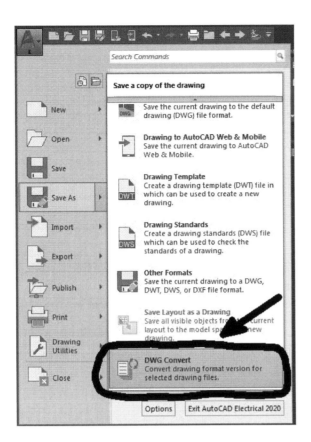

Click **DWG Convert**. The **DWG Convert** tool will open.

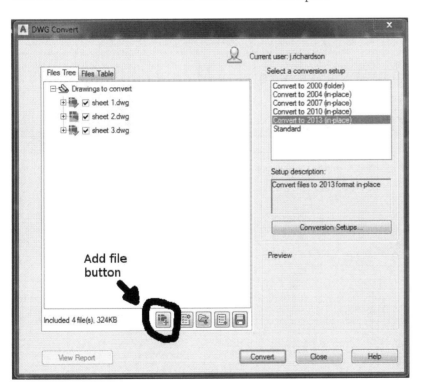

Use the **Add file** button to select the files you wish to convert. They will then be listed in the **Files Tree** window. Choose the AutoCAD version you wish to convert them to in the **Select a Conversion Setup** box and then click the **Convert** button.

The files you selected will be replaced with modified versions which can be opened by older versions of AutoCAD. Since the original files are replaced you should use this function on copies of your project files. You can then send these copies to other people while keeping the original copies in the latest AutoCAD format.

6.5   Set up descriptions

Right click the project title (**SampleProject1**) in the **Project Manager** window.
Select **Descriptions...** from the menu that appears.

The following window will open. Enter the text for the **Project Descriptions**. These are the **project attributes** we saw in chapter 4 which have the same value for every drawing in the project.

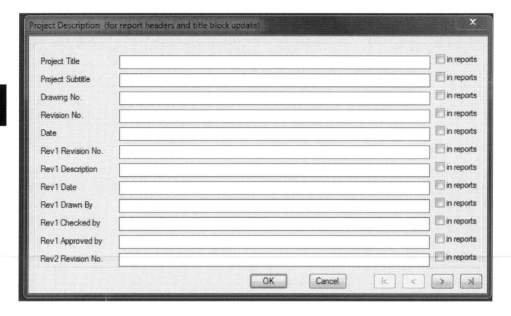

Provided you have the **default.wdtitle.wdl** file in your project directory, the items will have meaningful names. Items you have not defined (either because you are not using them or because the **default.wdtitle.wdl** file is missing) will be called **LINE1**, **LINE2** etc.

Enter some information so that we can see the AutoCAD tools in action. You could use the following:

Prompt	Example content
Project Title	Quarry Project
Project Subtitle	Water Treatment Plant
Drawing No.	SQP 000132
Revision No.	B2
Date	08/02/2020
Rev 1 Revision No.	A1
Rev 1 Description	First draft
Rev 1 Date	08/01/2020
Rev 1 Drawn by	AB
Rev 1 Checked by	EF
Rev 1 Approved by	GH
Rev 2 Revision No.	B1
Rev 2 Description	For tender
Rev 2 Date	06/02/2020
Rev 2 Drawn by	AB
Rev 2 Checked by	EF
Rev 2 Approved by	GH
Rev 3 Revision No.	B2
Rev 3 Description	Pump removed
Rev 3 Date	08/02/2020

Rev 3 Drawn by	CD
Rev 3 Checked by	EF
Rev 3 Approved by	GH

Note that you can click the **>** button to see more values if there are too many to be displayed in the dialogue box at once. When you have entered the **Project Descriptions** click **OK.**

Next we will enter properties specific to individual drawings.

Right click on **sheet 1** in the **Project Manager** window. Select **Properties > Drawing Properties** from the menu that appears.

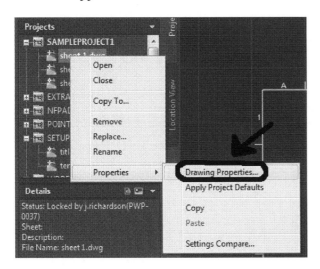

The **Drawing Properties** window will open. This controls values specific to each sheet. For now we are only going to change the drawing description text.

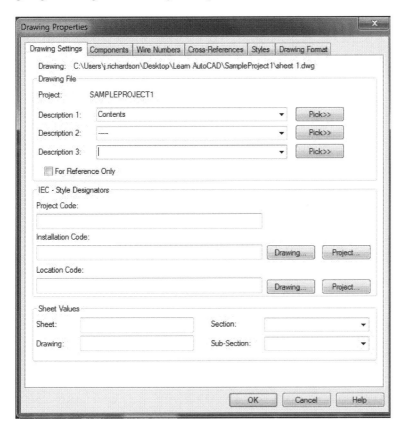

Enter values for **Description1** and **Description 2** in the **Drawing Settings** tab then click **OK**. Repeat for **sheet 2** and **sheet 3** and then save your drawings. The following table gives the descriptions to use for each sheet:

Drawing	Description 1 value	Description 2 value
Sheet 1	Contents	----
Sheet 2	Motor Starter	Control Wiring
Sheet 3	Motor Starter	Power Wiring

6.6   Title Block Update tool

Now that you have assigned descriptions to your drawings and project it is time to use the **Title Block Update** function. This will fill in your drawing frame with the text entered in the **Project Descriptions** and **Drawing Properties** boxes. It will also calculate the sheet numbers and total number of sheets.

Right click on the **SampleProject1** project in the **Project Manager** window. Select **Title Block Update** from the menu.

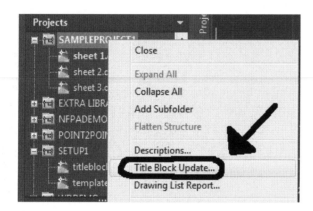

The **Title Block Update** dialogue box will appear. Tick boxes let you choose which items to update.

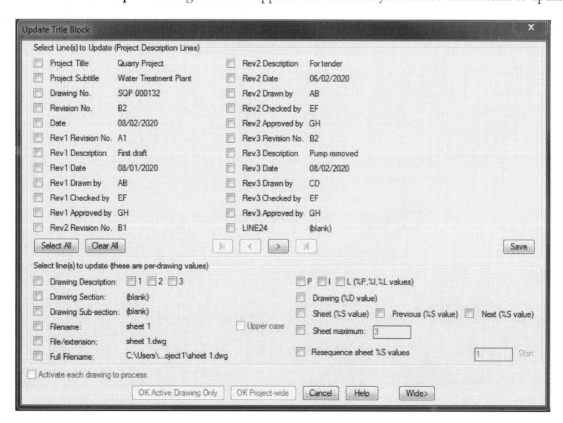

In the top section tick all of the **Project Descriptions** used in your frame to update them. The **>** button lets you see a second screen if there are too many to fit on one page. An easy way to update them all is to click **Select All**.

In the lower section click **Drawing Description** and the numbers **1** and **2** next to it. Click **Sheet (%S value)** and **Sheet maximum**. Also tick **Resequence sheet %S values**. This re-numbers the sheets if you have changed the order of the drawings in the **Project Manager** window.

If you used other items from the drawing values section, you would tick those too. For example, it is possible for each drawing to include the sheet number of the next drawing.

Click **OK Project-wide**. The following dialogue box asks which drawings to update.

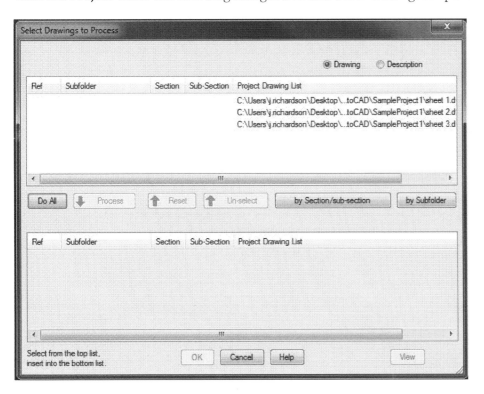

Click **Do All** then press **OK**.

The description and sheet information for all of your drawings will be updated. You will find the frames of your drawings have been automatically filled with the information.

If you were to change the descriptions or add more drawings you would run the **Title Block Update** function again to update the drawing frames.

6.7   Contents page

To give your drawings a professional look it is nice to add a table of contents.

Although we are doing this before we start our schematic, you could easily add it later, after completing a project. In that case you would add in an extra drawing, move it to the start and then re-run **Title Block Update** to re-sequence your sheet numbers.

The contents page is generated automatically from the **Drawing Properties** attributes in the title block.

Note that the automated report takes information from attributes in the drawing title blocks themselves, not the **Drawing Properties** settings that feed into them. Ensure the title blocks on the drawing sheets contain these attributes and that they have been updated (with **Title Block Update**) before creating or updating the contents page.

To create a table of contents open the **sheet 1** drawing. Right click on the project name, **SampleProject1**, in the **Project Manager** window. Select **Drawing list report**.

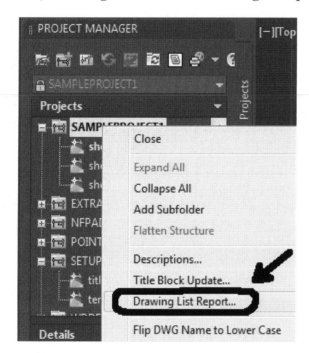

The **Drawing List Report** dialogue appears.

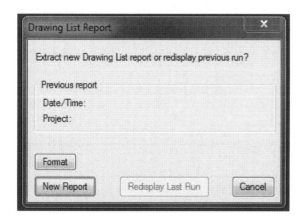

Select **New Report**. You will be asked which drawings to include.

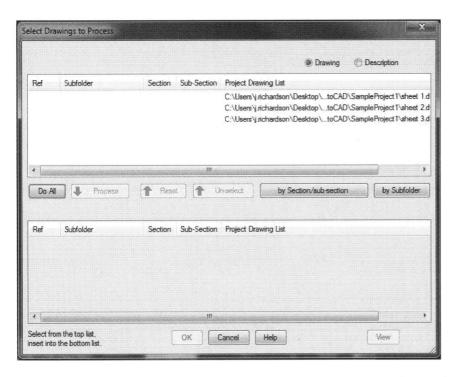

Click **Do All** then click **OK**. The **Report Generator** window will be displayed.

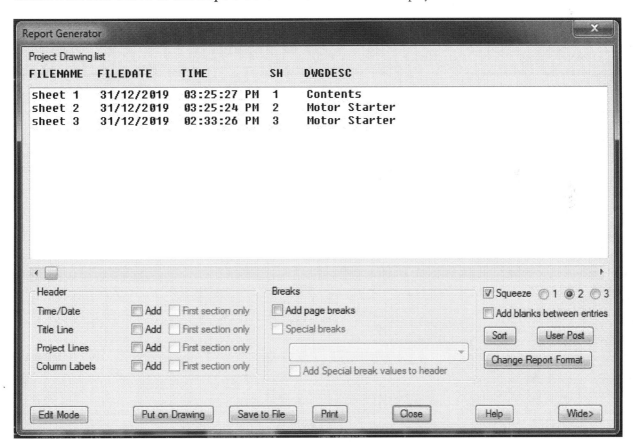

This window gives a preview of the items that will be displayed in your table of contents. By clicking the **Change Report Format** button you can alter the fields listed and the way the table is presented.

We will look at this in a moment but for now just press **Put on Drawing**. The **Table Generation Setup** box will be displayed.

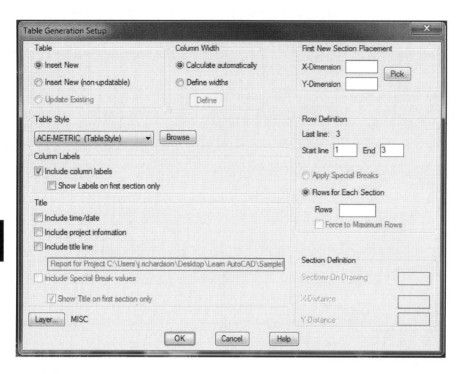

Be sure to set **Table Style** to **ACE-METRIC (TableStyle)** if you have a metric drawing or **ACE-INCH (TableStyle)** if you are using imperial measurements, otherwise your table will be very large or very small. You can leave the other formatting items alone for now and press **OK**.

A box representing the size of the contents table will appear at the cursor for you to place on the drawing by left clicking the mouse. Position the table. The contents table will be placed on the drawing. Confusingly, the **Report Generator** dialogue box will then reappear.

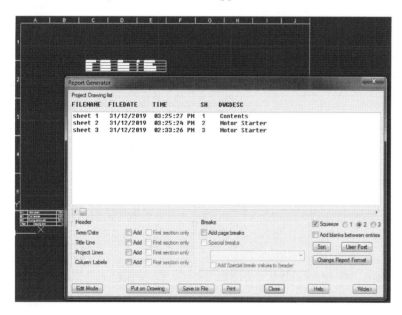

Click **Close**. If you now look at your drawing you will see a contents table as below.

FILENAME	FILEDATE	TIME	SH	DWGDESC
sheet 1	31/12/2019	03:25:27 PM	1	Contents
sheet 2	31/12/2019	03:25:24 PM	2	Motor Starter
sheet 3	31/12/2019	02:33:26 PM	3	Motor Starter

Any time you want to update the contents page, go to the sheet with the contents table and repeat the above steps. You will not be asked to position the contents table again. Instead, when you click **Put on Drawing**, the new contents table replaces the old one.

Remember that if you have changed drawing and project descriptions you must update the information by clicking on the project in the **Project Manager** window and doing a **Title Block Update** first. The contents list takes its information from the attributes displayed on your drawing, not direct from the values entered in drawing and project properties.

The fields shown are not the most useful so we will change them. Leave the **sheet 1** drawing open. Right click on **SampleProject1** in the **Project Manager** window and re-run **Drawing List Report**.

When prompted click **New Report**. Then select **Do All** and click **OK**. The **Report Generator** window opens and shows a sample report:

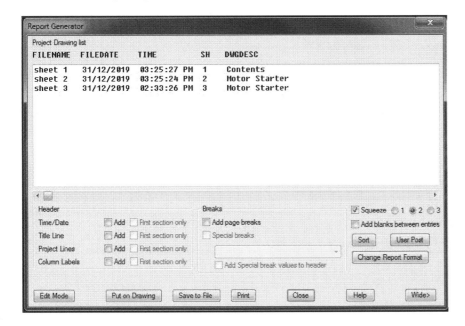

Click **Change Report Format**. The **Drawing List Data Fields to Display** box will open showing available fields for the report.

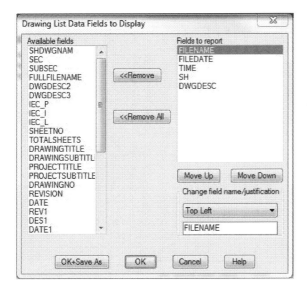

The list, **Fields to report**, on the right shows the items that appear in the contents table. Clicking on an available field on the left list moves it into the report. To remove fields, highlight them and click the **Remove button**.

Use this box to remove **FILEDATE** and **TIME**. Add the second line of the drawing description **DWGDESC2**. Rearrange the order with the **Move Up** and **Move Down** buttons as required. The box should now look like this:

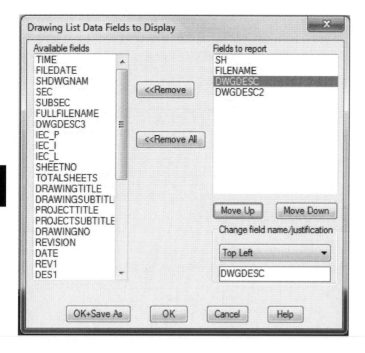

Now change the titles for the columns to something more meaningful. Click on each of the **Fields to report** in the top right of the box. The name of that field will be displayed in the box at the bottom right. Click on this box and type a more meaningful name as shown below. Change the field names **SH**, **FILENAME**, **DWGDESC** and **DWGDEC2** to **Sheet**, **File**, **Title** and **Subtitle**.

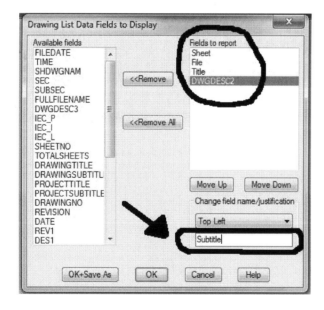

Click **OK** and you will see the revised preview.

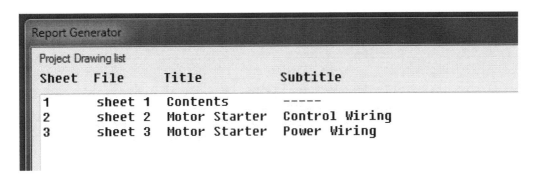

Click **Put on Drawing**. Then click **OK** to place the report. Click **Close**. You will see the finished contents list.

Sheet	File	Title	Subtitle
1	sheet 1	Contents	-----
2	sheet 2	Motor Starter	Control Wiring
3	sheet 3	Motor Starter	Power Wiring

Save your **sheet 1** drawing.

6.8   Printing multiple sheets

Once you have a number of sheets it becomes tedious to print each one separately. To print multiple sheets click the **Publish / Plot** button at the top of the **Project Manager** window. A menu appears.

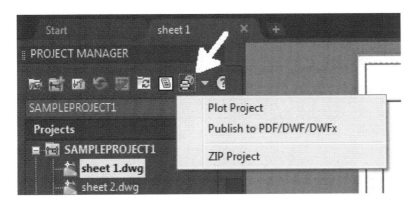

You can select **Plot Project** to print multiple drawings directly to your printer or **Publish to PDF/DWF/DWFx** to print to one of those file formats. In this book we will give an example of printing to a PDF file which you can then print or email as you choose.

Select **Publish to PDF/DWF/DWFx**. A dialogue box asks which sheets to plot.

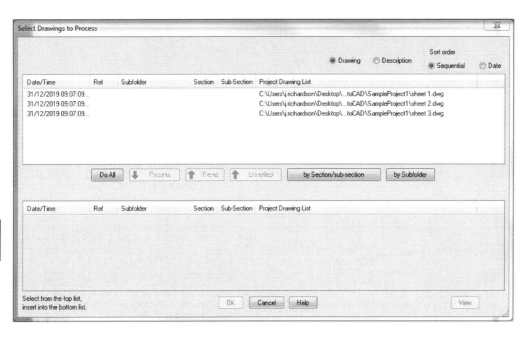

6

Select the sheets you want to print and click **Process**. Alternatively, click **Do All** if you want to print everything. Click **OK**. You are asked for some settings.

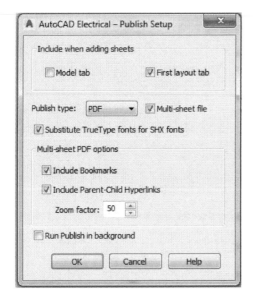

We wish to print using the print arrangement we set up earlier on the **Layout1** tab of our drawings. Untick **Model tab** as we don't want to print from that and tick **First layout tab** so that the unused **Layout2** tab is also ignored.

If you are only printing a few sheets, untick **Run Publish in background** so the printing happens immediately. If you are printing an enormous project and intend to do something else while it is printing then tick this box.

We will make a **PDF** document but you could also choose **DWF** or **DWFx**. These are formats developed by Autodesk to allow designs to be shared for review. Like PDF documents they can be opened by people who do not have an AutoCAD licence.

Multi-sheet file will put all our sheets into a single PDF document, which is usually what we want.

Substitute TrueType fonts for SHX fonts uses vector representation of fonts rather than bitmap in the PDF file. Ticking this box will allow people to search for text in your PDF file. This is useful if they wish to find, for example, a particular wire number or component within the drawings.

Press **OK**. You will see the list of files ready to print.

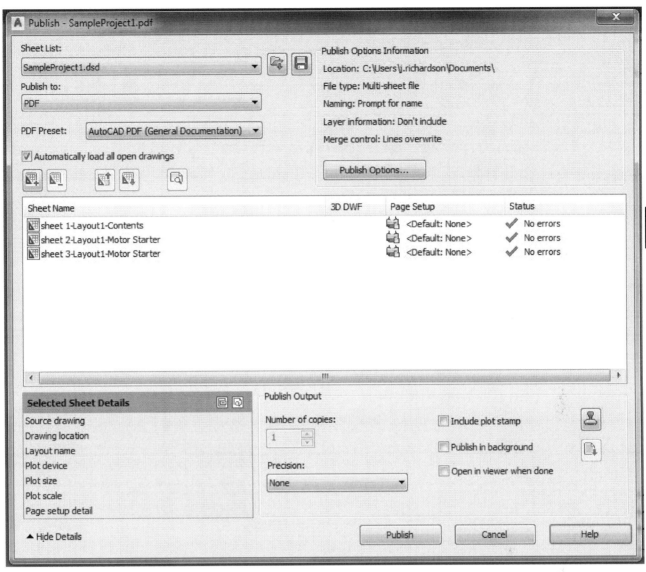

Click **Publish**. You are asked to specify a folder and filename for the **.pdf** file you are making.

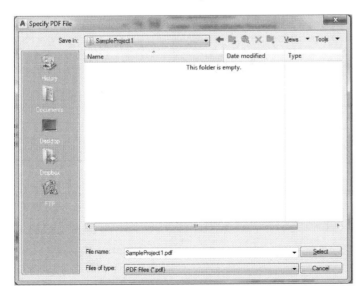

Navigate to your desired folder. Type a filename or accept the default and click **Select**.

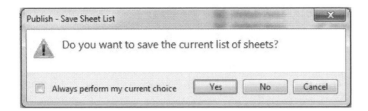

You have the option to save the list of sheets as a **.DSD** file. Click **No** unless you have a complicated list you wish to use again using the **Load Sheet list...** button in the **Publish** dialogue box.

Your **.pdf** file should now be created in the folder you specified.

Alternative method

6

The method described above is recommended since it is an integral part of AutoCAD Electrical. An alternative method is to select **Print > Batch Plot** from the **Application button**. This resembles the **Publish / Plot** method and uses a similar **Publish** screen.

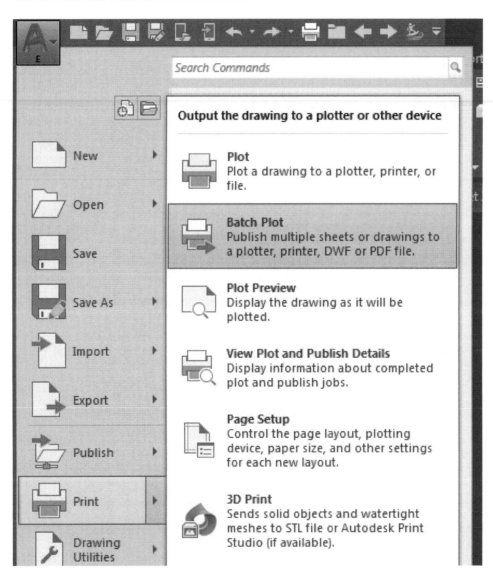

Batch Plot moves straight to the **Publish** dialogue box.

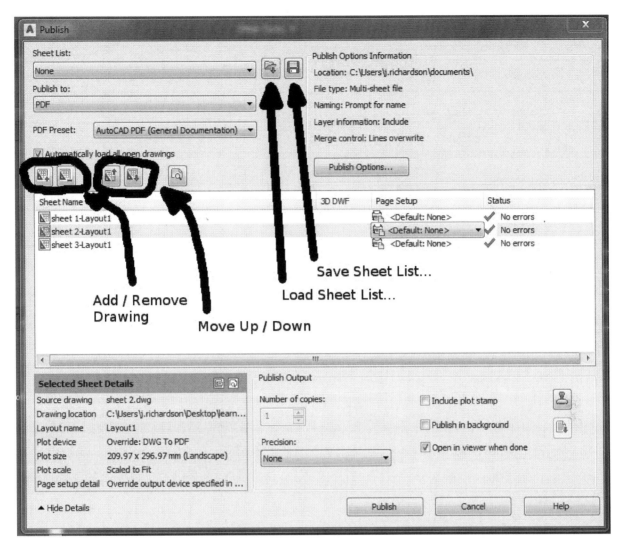

You can tick a box on this page to **Automatically load all open drawings** in future batch plots.

If you right click the selected sheets a menu appears. In this you can tick an option to open layout tabs in future batch plots and untick an option to avoid opening model tabs. Unlike the previous **Publish / Plot** method, you cannot choose to open the first layout only. If your drawings contain **Layout1** and **Layout2** (as in our example template) you must either delete **Layout2** in your drawings or manually deselect it.

You can change the print order by dragging drawings up or down in the list with the mouse or by using the **Move Up** and **Move Down** buttons.

Since you will need considerable work to create your desired list of layouts to print, it may be worth saving the sheet list as a **.DSD** sheet set file. You will get an error if you create a sheet set from drawings with unsaved changes so use the **Save All** command immediately before using **Batch Plot** to create a sheet set.

When making changes you usually need to complete the printing operation for the new settings to be stored.

Error messages

Both **Batch Plot** from the **Application Button** and the **Publish / Plot** tool that runs from the button in the **Project Manager** window have a **Publish Options...** button which bring up the settings screen shown below:

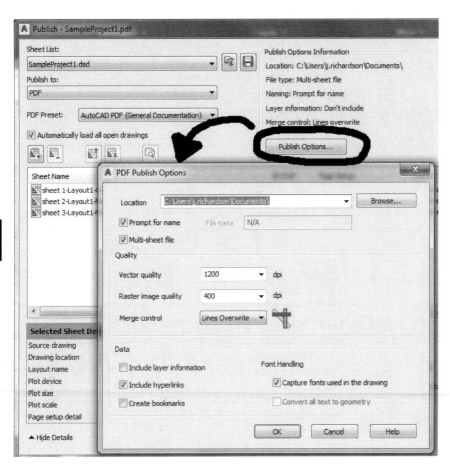

If the options set in the **Publish Options...** screens for the two tools are different you will get the following error message when using **Plot / Publish** from the **Project Manager**.

This error will not affect your publishing but is annoying. To get rid of it look at the **Publish Options...** screen in the **Plot/Publish tool** (run from the **Project Manager** window) and either note the settings or take a screen shot. Then print something with **Batch Plot** (run from the **Application button**) and change the settings in the **Publish Options...** screen for that tool to match those in the **Plot/Publish tool**. Complete the **Batch Plot** successfully to ensure the settings are saved.

It is best to match the options this way as they do not stay saved when changing them in the **Plot / Publish** tool. Despite the wording of the error message, it does not matter whether you are using a .**DSD** sheet list or not.

6.9 Copying a project

Congratulations if you have made it this far. We are nearly ready to start drawing schematics. In the next chapter we will draw a simple motor starter within a project we will call **TestRig1**.

To make this **TestRig1** project (and any future projects you need for your job) you have two options. The first is to repeat the steps in this chapter. That might seem a lot but once you know what you are doing it won't take so long.

An easier method is to copy the sample project we made then modify it as required. This is also a good method if you want to get other people using AutoCAD Electrical since they can dive straight into drawing schematics without learning to set up a project.

Copying a project manually

You can copy a project manually in Microsoft Windows Explorer. To do this you would copy the project folder and change certain filenames to the new project name. It is good to understand this so read through the following example. There is no need to try it as we are going to use the AutoCAD copy project function to achieve the same effect from within AutoCAD.

If AutoCAD is open you may see some temporary files so it is best to close it before doing this operation.

In Microsoft Windows navigate to your **SampleProject1** folder. Copy this folder and its contents.

Name	Date modified	Type	Size
SampleProject1	02/01/2020 08:41	File folder	
SampleProject1 - Copy	02/01/2020 08:47	File folder	
Setup1	02/01/2020 08:48	File folder	

Rename the new folder **TestRig1**.

Name	Date modified	Type	Size
SampleProject1	02/01/2020 08:41	File folder	
TestRig1	02/01/2020 08:47	File folder	
Setup1	02/01/2020 08:48	File folder	

Open the **TestRig1** folder and you will see the following files:

Name	Date modified	Type	Size
CompanyLogo.PNG	18/08/2019 12:18	PNG Image	28 KB
default_wdtitle.wdl	30/12/2019 12:00	WDL File	1 KB
plot.log	01/01/2020 16:11	Text Document	5 KB
SampleProject1.aepx	31/12/2019 14:27	AEPX File	1 KB
SampleProject1.wdp	31/12/2019 15:27	WDP File	2 KB
SampleProject1.wdt	30/12/2019 15:06	WDT File	4 KB
sheet 1.bak	31/12/2019 21:07	BAK File	76 KB
sheet 1.dwg	01/01/2020 16:10	AutoCAD Drawing	77 KB
sheet 2.bak	31/12/2019 20:45	BAK File	66 KB
sheet 2.dwg	31/12/2019 21:07	AutoCAD Drawing	66 KB
sheet 3.bak	31/12/2019 21:05	BAK File	67 KB
sheet 3.dwg	31/12/2019 21:07	AutoCAD Drawing	65 KB

Rename the files with names starting **"SampleProject1"** to start **"TestRig1"**. The **.dwg** files are your drawings.

The **.bak** files are back up copies of each drawing. Whenever you save a drawing, AutoCAD keeps the previous version and changes its name to end with the extension **.bak**. When copying drawings between projects you can ignore them. **Plot.log** is a text file produced as a report when AutoCAD prints something. You can delete it if you want.

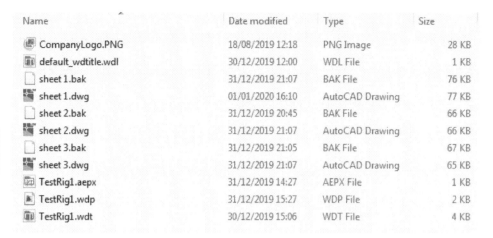

Name	Date modified	Type	Size
CompanyLogo.PNG	18/08/2019 12:18	PNG Image	28 KB
default_wdtitle.wdl	30/12/2019 12:00	WDL File	1 KB
sheet 1.bak	31/12/2019 21:07	BAK File	76 KB
sheet 1.dwg	01/01/2020 16:10	AutoCAD Drawing	77 KB
sheet 2.bak	31/12/2019 20:45	BAK File	66 KB
sheet 2.dwg	31/12/2019 21:07	AutoCAD Drawing	66 KB
sheet 3.bak	31/12/2019 21:05	BAK File	67 KB
sheet 3.dwg	31/12/2019 21:07	AutoCAD Drawing	65 KB
TestRig1.aepx	31/12/2019 14:27	AEPX File	1 KB
TestRig1.wdp	31/12/2019 15:27	WDP File	2 KB
TestRig1.wdt	30/12/2019 15:06	WDT File	4 KB

Now open AutoCAD. In the **Project Manager** window select **Open Project**.

Navigate to the **TestRig1** folder in the dialogue box that opens and select the **TestRig1.wdp** file.

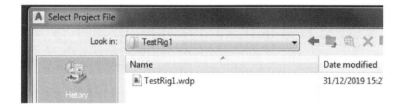

The **TestRig1** project will now be opened and shown as the active project. **SampleProject1** is no longer the active project and is moved down the list.

If you were to copy a project like this in future, you would now change the drawing and project descriptions from within AutoCAD and, if necessary, add or remove drawings. Then you would run a **Title Block Update** to refresh the information on the title blocks and redo the table of contents page.

For extra sheets you could copy an existing **.dwg** file in Microsoft Windows Explorer, rename it, open it in AutoCAD and add it to the active project. Alternatively you could create a new drawing using our **first_template.dwt** drawing template, save it in your new project folder and add it to your project using the **Project Manager** window..

For our example, however, our sample project was already filled with the correct information for our motor starter so we do not need to do this.

Copying a project using AutoCAD

Understanding the manual process to copy a project is useful. It will help you debug problems with your files and enable you to manually move files between projects if you need to.

In practice it is easier to duplicate a project with the AutoCAD **Copy** command. Work through the following steps to create the **TestRig1** project ready for the next chapter.

To use the **Copy** button you must have at least one (unrelated) drawing open but all of the drawings you wish to copy must be closed.

Ensure **SampleProject1** is the active project and that the drawings in it are closed. Ideally ensure they were last saved with **Model** view, rather than **Layout1** open so that your copied project will open on the **Model** view screen.

Since you need a drawing open, click the **+** symbol next to the drawing tabs to open a temporary drawing which you can discard later.

Click the **Copy** button in the **Project** tab of the ribbon.

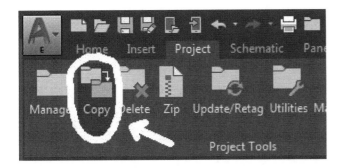

The **Copy Project Step 1** dialogue appears.

If the project you wish to copy is currently the active project then you can click the **Copy Active Project** button to fill in the project details automatically. If not, click the **Browse** button and navigate to the **.wdp** file of the project to be copied.

You cannot just type the name of an existing project, for example **"SampleProject1"**, you must enter a path to the **.wdp** file of that project. This screen also warns that you cannot copy open drawings.

Click **Copy Active Project** to copy **SampleProject1** and press **OK**.

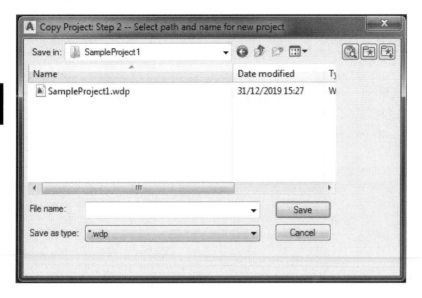

You are now asked where the copied files should go. By default AutoCAD suggests putting them in the project directory of the project you are copying. Instead navigate up a level, out of the **Sampleproject1** directory using the 🔼 button. Create a new folder **TestRig1** for our new project using the 🗂 button. Then open this folder as the place to save the files in.

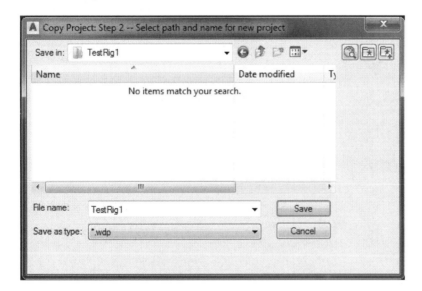

In the box **File name**, enter the name **TestRig1** for your new project files. Click **Save**.

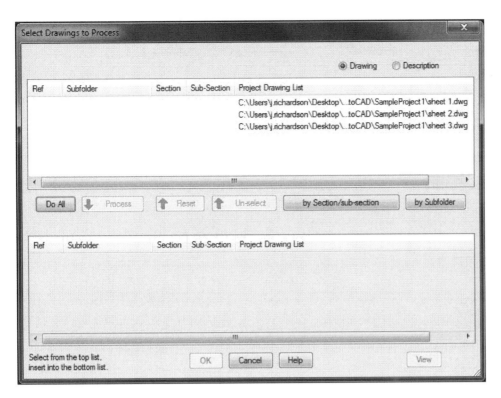

You are now asked which drawings you want to copy to the new project. You can select individual drawings and click the ↓**Process** button to move them into the lower part of the dialogue box for copying. For our example click **Do All** to copy everything. Then click **OK**.

A summary of the planned copy process is displayed.

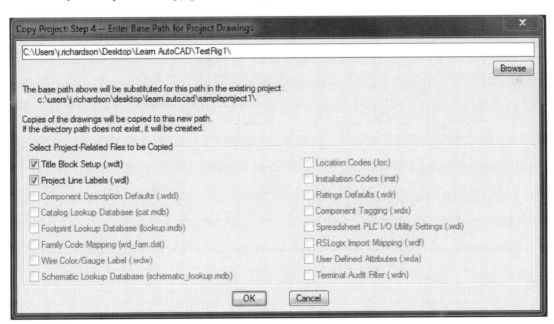

This screen shows where the new project will be created. You can see that it also copies the **.wdt** and **.wdl** files into the new project. In the manual example we had to duplicate these ourselves.

Click **OK**. You are now given the option to change the names of any copied drawings.

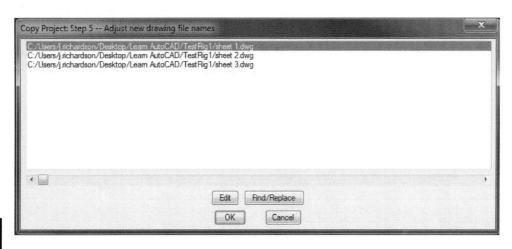

6

To change a drawing name, highlight it and click **Edit**. For our example we will leave the names unchanged so just click **OK**. The new project is created and made the active project in the **Project Manager** window.

If you used a company logo image as a reference in your title block then you must manually place this image in the new project folder using Microsoft Windows Explorer. If AutoCAD gives an error because it cannot find the reference file for a logo image then you can clear this error by closing the drawing and re-opening after putting the correct file in the new project folder.

6.10 How to create projects in the future

The **TestRig1** project we created will hold the files we produce in the rest of this book. When it is time for you to make a real project for your work you can copy **SampleProject1** again.

For extra drawings you can copy the **.dwg** files, give them new names, and add them to your project. Alternatively create blank drawings using the **first_template.dwt** drawing template we made in chapter 5.

With the templates and sample project set up this will be a quick, reliable process. There will be no need to repeat chapters 2 to 6.

You may, however, wish to improve your sample project, drawing frame and template once you are more familiar with AutoCAD. For this reason it is good to keep the **titleblock1.dwg** drawing file. It is much simpler to tweak this and re-insert as a block into the template than to alter the template itself.

6.11 Change a drawing frame with the Swap/Update Block tool

As you experiment with the AutoCAD Electrical software, you may refine your template. After a few projects you will probably settle down to a convenient template and use this for your new projects.

What happens if you need to change your title block in an existing project after you have populated it with dozens of drawings?

If only your company logo has changed then, provided it is included as an external reference, you just need to change the file.

If you need to alter the title block itself then you could cut and paste your drawings into new blank drawings with the correct title block. Alternatively, by double clicking on the drawing frame, you can edit the title block in situ. Neither of these is ideal, especially if you have many drawings. Instead it is far better to use the **Swap / Update Block** function. We will explain this now although there is no need for you to try it on our example project.

First create a copy of your **titleblock1.dwg** drawing. Modify it to produce the new title block design and save it. You will remember that we imported this drawing as a block into another file when we created our template. This time we will import it as a block directly into our project in place of the existing block using the **Swap / Update Block** tool.

In the following screenshots we assume the new border is in a file called **titleblock1.dwg** but this is not compulsory. You can use a different filename to the original for the replacement border and the **Swap / Update Block** function will still work.

In the project whose title block you wish to modify open any drawing, for example **sheet 2** of our **TestRig1** project.

In the **Schematic** tab of the ribbon click the **Swap / Update Block** button.

The **Swap Block / Update Block / Library Swap** dialogue box will open.

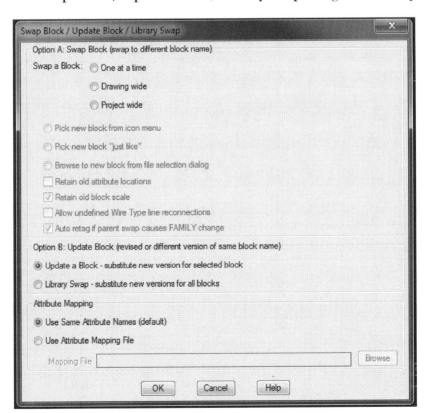

Select **Update a Block** under **Option B** as shown. Click **OK**.

You will be returned to your drawing with the cursor as a small hollow square. Use this to click on the border you wish to change. The **Update Block - New block's path\filename** box will appear.

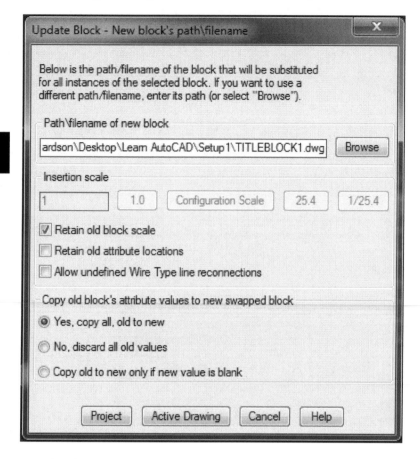

Use the **Browse** button to select the drawing file defining your new border. In our example this would be **titleblock1.dwg**, not the template or drawings we imported it into later.

Under **Insertion scale** choose **Retain old block scale**. If you have changed the size of the border to suit a mechanical scale drawing, as described in chapters 16 and 17, then this will preserve your changes.

Under **Copy old blocks's attribute values to new swapped block** choose **Yes, copy all, old to new**.

Then click the **Project** button to apply this change to every drawing in your project.

When asked which drawings to process choose **Do All** and click **OK**.

AutoCAD will then open each drawing of your project in turn and update your title block. Any attributes from the old block will be transferred to matching ones in the new block.

7. Electrical schematics (1 hour)

Now that we have set up our templates and created an empty project, we get to the good bit - drawing some schematics. We are not going to add component catalogue information at first. Instead we will learn to produce a basic schematic that you can give to people. The refinements will be in later chapters.

Topics covered:

- Drawing components, terminals and wires
- Moving and aligning components
- Modifying attribute text
- Adding child components
- Linking contacts with a dashed line
- Updating component cross-references

If you have followed the previous chapters you should have a project called **TestRig1** with three sheets. **Sheet 1** will be the table of contents. On **sheet 2** we are going to draw a simple motor starter control circuit with some switches operating a relay. **Sheet 3** will show the power circuit with the motor. The finished product will look like this:

Sheet 2:

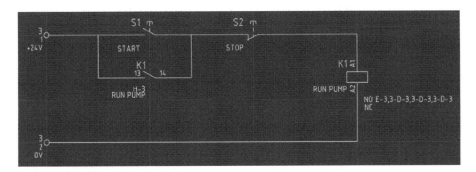

Sheet 3:

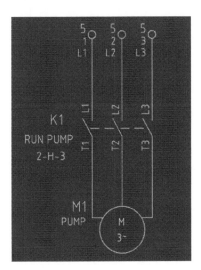

7.1 Draw the control circuit

Ensure that **TestRig1** is the active project.
Double click **sheet 2** in the **Project Manager** window to open it.
Ensure that display grid and snap to grid are on and that you are in model space.

Insert a push button

Go to the **Schematic** tab. Click **Icon Menu.**

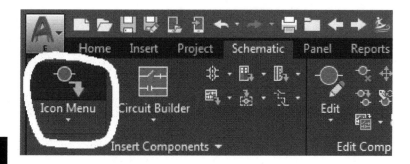

The **Insert Component** dialogue box will appear. If you have created a new drawing that does not contain a **WD_M block** then the AutoCAD Electrical program will ask your permission to insert one. Click **OK** to agree to this if asked. AutoCAD requires this hidden **WD_M block** on electrical drawings to make the electrical features work. If you have followed the earlier chapters, your drawing will already contain this block.

Click on the **Push Buttons** symbol to see the menu of available push button symbols. Alternatively you can use the menu list at the left of the dialogue box to expand the menus.

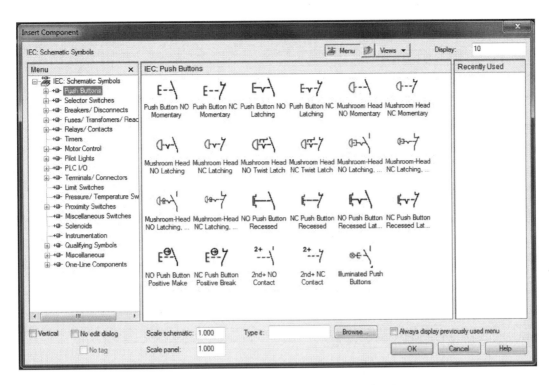

Ensure the **Vertical** box is not ticked. Click on **Pushbutton NO Momentary**.

The AutoCAD Electrical software will now return to your drawing with an outline of the pushbutton symbol around the cursor. Move the cursor to the position where you want to place the button and left-click the mouse to place the symbol. The **Insert / Edit Component** dialogue box will appear, allowing you to enter details of your newly inserted component.

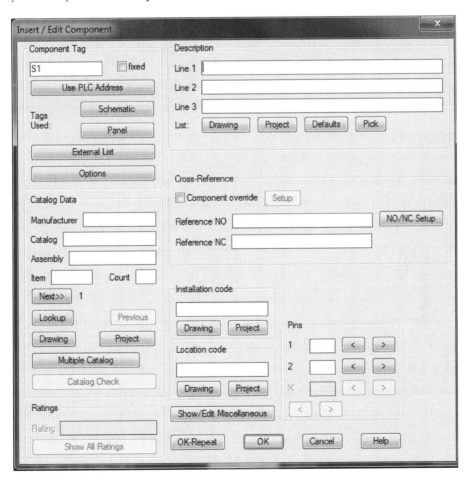

The **Component Tag** box should suggest the tag **S1** for your new switch. If it says **S?** then you need to select sequential numbering for your components in the **Project Properties** and **Drawing Properties**. You can change that for this drawing but see page 43 and set it up in your template.

Using the **Component Tag** box you can change the tag name of components to anything you like. For this example keep it as **S1**.

In **Description, Line 1** type **start** as a label for the pushbutton. Leave the other items blank and click **OK**. The switch will be inserted into the drawing.

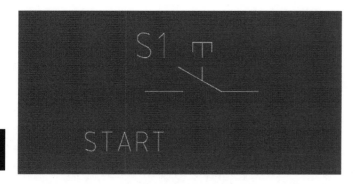

Repeat this process and add a **Pushbutton, NC, momentary** to the right of the first button. AutoCAD should suggest a tag of **S2** for this automatically. In **Description, Line 1** type **stop** as its label.

Notice that recently used symbols are shown at the right of the **Insert Component** dialogue box for fast access if you need them again.

Relay

Now we will enter a relay coil which will be controlled by our buttons.

Click the **Icon Menu** button in the **Schematic** tab again. In the **Insert Component** dialogue box tick the **Vertical** box. Then select the **Relays/Contacts** menu followed by **Relay Coil**.

7

Ticking the **Vertical** box rotates the symbol by 90 degrees. Place the relay coil on the drawing to the right and slightly below the switches as shown.

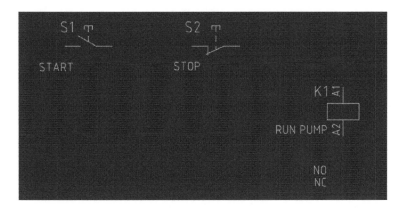

AutoCAD will suggest a **Component Tag** of **K1** for the relay coil. In **Description, Line 1**, type **Run Pump**. The pins on relay coils are often labelled as A1 and A2 by the manufacturer. Let us assume our relay is marked in this way and we want this information on our drawing.

At the bottom right of the **Insert / Edit Component** dialogue box, enter **A1** and **A2** for the pin labels as shown below. If you wanted numerical labels, the < and > arrow buttons beside these boxes are a fast way to label pins with 1, 2 ,3, etc. without typing.

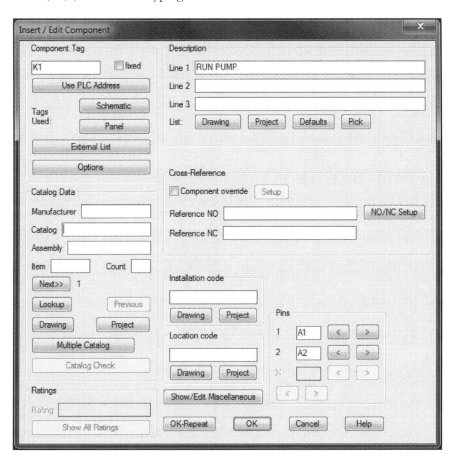

Press **OK** and the relay coil will be inserted, in the orientation shown below, and with the coil pins labelled. The labels **NO** and **NC** are for contact details. Ignore them for now.

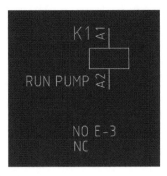

Relay contact

Now we will add a contact driven by relay coil **K1**. This will be in parallel to the start button, latching the relay on, as in a common motor starter circuit.

Click on **Icon Menu** in the **Schematic** tab of the ribbon to bring up the **Insert Component** dialogue box again. Be sure **Vertical** is not ticked and select **Relays/Contacts > Relay NO contact**. Click to insert the contact below the start button.

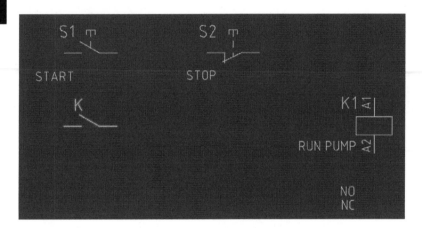

The **Insert / Edit Child Component** dialogue box will open.

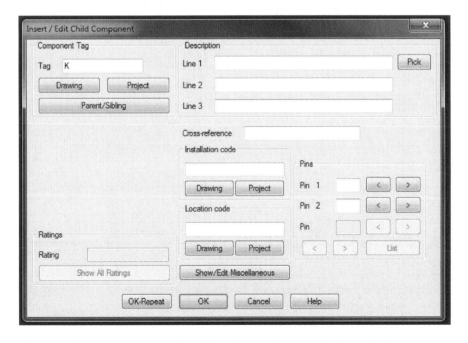

Click the **Drawing** button. The follow box will appear. It lists all relays in this drawing.

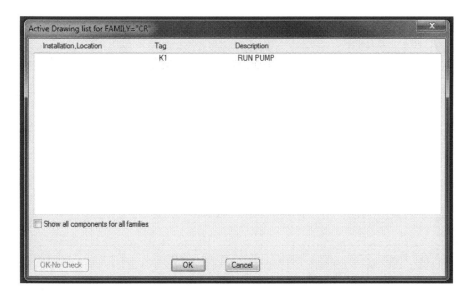

Click on the line **K1   RUN PUMP** to highlight it and click **OK.** AutoCAD returns to the **Insert / Edit Child Component** dialogue. The **Component Tag** and **Description** have now been completed automatically. Let us assume the relay we are using has its normally open contacts labelled as pins **13** and **14**. Enter these pin labels as shown below.

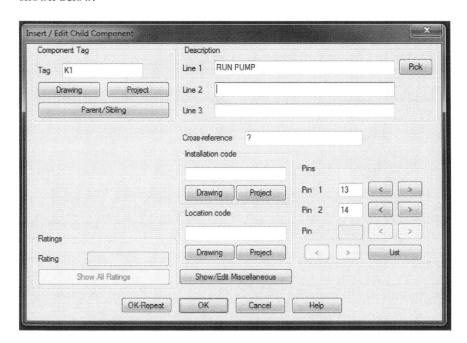

Click **OK** and the symbol will be inserted:

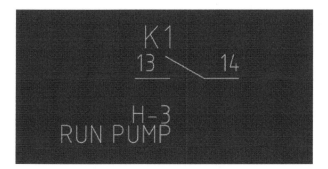

The contact has been labelled with the grid reference of the coil. In this screenshot this is **H-3** but the exact location in your drawing may be different. Beside the coil you will see the grid reference of the contact:

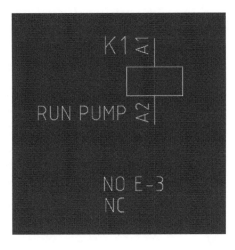

In this case it shows the coil has a normally open (**NO**) contact at position **E-3** on the sheet.

Now you see why it was so important to set up our reference grid.

7.2 Terminals

Next we will add a couple of terminals for external wires taking a 24V supply to the circuit.

From the **Icon Menu** select **Terminals/Connectors**. If you hover the mouse over the symbols in this menu their full name is displayed. Choose **Round with Terminal Number block:HT0002**.

This assumes you are using the **IEC4** library and **ACE_IEC_MENU.DAT** menu file. If you have a different schematic library and menu file assigned to your project you will see different symbols.

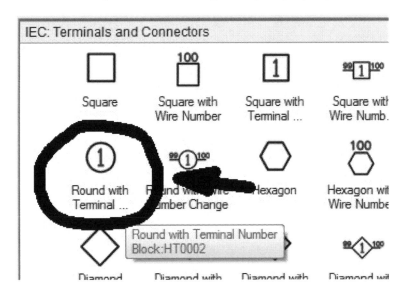

Place the terminal to the left of your schematic drawing, level with switch **S1,** as in the following image.

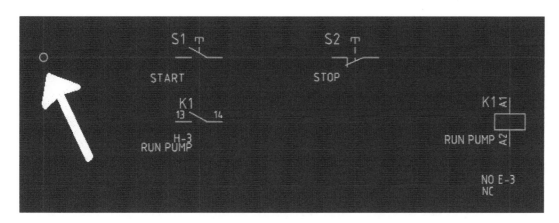

The **Insert/Edit Terminal Symbol** dialogue box will open. We are going to give our terminal a description of **+24V**. We will make it part of tag strip (block of terminals) number **3**. It will be terminal **1** within that block of terminals. Fill in the dialogue box with this information as shown below.

If the bottom part of this box is missing click the **Details >>** button at the bottom of the box to display it.

Click **OK** and the terminal will be inserted.

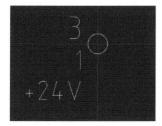

Repeat this process to insert a second terminal. In the **Insert Component** dialogue box you can select it from **Recently Used** symbols at the right, rather than having to click **Terminals/Connectors** again.

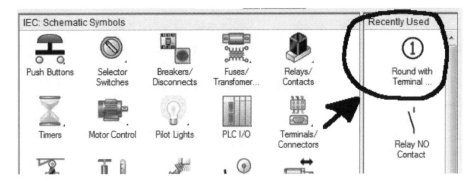

Place the terminal below the first as shown below. Give it a description of **0V** and label it as tag strip **3**, terminal **2**.

You will find AutoCAD automatically fills in its label as tag strip **3**, terminal **2**, since this is the next terminal number. You just need to type the **0V**.

You should now have a drawing as shown below.

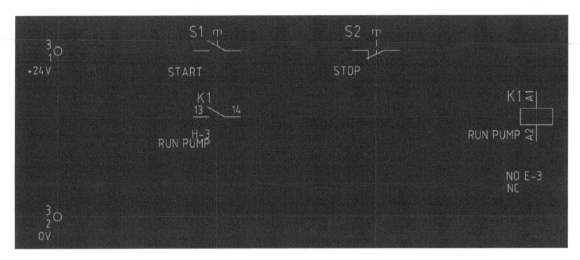

7.3   Wires

Next we will join up the components with wires. We have drawn all of the components first for ease of explanation. Normally you would draw a few components, join them with wires, then add more components.

We will discuss tools to move wires and components in a moment so do not worry if your components are not perfectly aligned or your wires have steps in them.

Click the **Wire** button in the **Schematic** tab of the ribbon.

Move the cursor over the edge of one of the switches, where you would expect to connect a wire. The cursor shows a small hourglass, indicating the connection point.

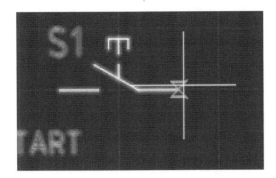

Click to start the wire. It will snap to the connection point. Then move to the connection point of the next component and click again. If you move the cursor diagonally, AutoCAD will automatically put a right angle bend in the wire. Wires do not have to stop on components. You can click on empty parts of the drawing, either to force a bend in the wire at a particular place or to add components later.

If you click to end on another wire, the wires will be classed as joining. If you cross over a wire they will not join. Your drawing/project settings for wires determine if dots or loops are used to show this.

Each time you press the left mouse button you fix a corner in your wire. Press the right button (on a blank area of the drawing) to stop drawing that wire. A new wire will start next time you click the left mouse button. You do not have to keep selecting the **Wire** button to draw a new wire.

To stop drawing wires press **<Esc>** or press the right mouse button again and select **Enter** from the menu that appears.

Add wires to join all of the components in the way shown below. Then save your drawing.

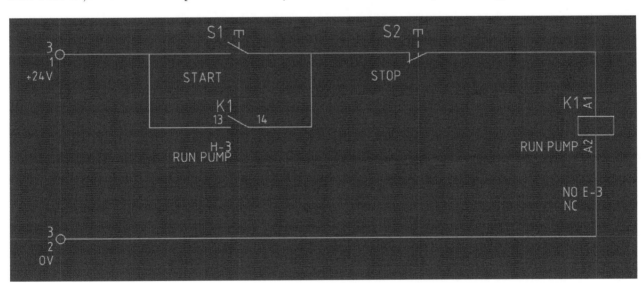

7.4   Working with wires and components

Before going further we will look at some tools to tidy your drawings and make modifying them easier. After saving a copy of your drawing you can use it to try the following actions and then close it without saving.

Remember you can press **CTRL+Z** to undo changes and **CTRL+Y** to redo them. You cannot undo actions after you have saved the drawing.

Selecting wires and components

In chapter 2 we learned that defining a rectangular area by dragging the mouse from bottom right to top left, with the left button depressed, selected everything the rectangle touched. Dragging from top left to bottom right only selected items completely enclosed within the rectangle. Now that you have a schematic containing many components and wires you will find these selection rules very useful.

Deleting and moving objects

Select some wires and components. Press **<Delete>** on your keyboard and they are removed. Press **CTRL + Z** to undo this and get them back.

If you right click the mouse after selecting some items you get a menu:

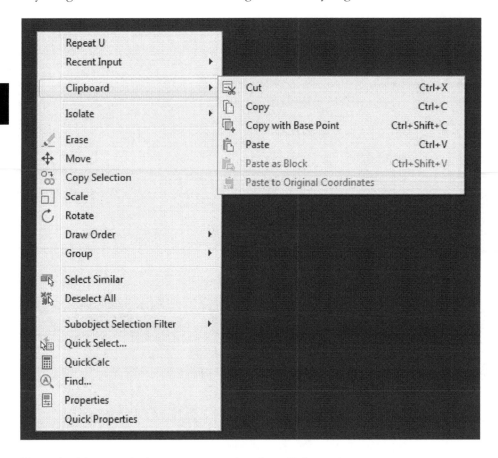

Erase in this menu is the same as pressing the **<Delete>** button.

The **Move** command moves the selected items. Click on the screen to set a start reference point. Then click again and the selected components will all be moved by an amount equal to the displacement between the two points. Very occasionally, when using **Move**, the items vanish completely. If this happens use **CTRL+Z** to undo the action then try again.

Hovering over the **Clipboard** item gives a submenu with further options for cutting, pasting and copying. When copying or moving from one drawing to another the functions using the clipboard work best. Those in the main part of the menu prevent you switching between drawings while they are in progress.

7.5   Moving wires

If you select some wires you will see they are highlighted with small blue squares at their ends and centres.

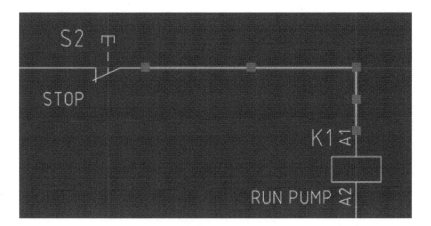

Click once on these boxes with the left mouse button, then click again away from the wire. The end you clicked on will move, changing the angle of the wire if necessary, while the other end remains in place. If you click on the centre, the wire can be moved without changing its orientation. If you wish to join the ends of two wires, select them both and then move the box at the end of one wire to be on top of the box at the end of the other wire.

Highlighting wires in this way also shows if what appears to be a single wire actually consists of two segments. This can be useful when using the **Scoot** command (discussed next) which will refuse to slide a component past a joint in a wire.

7.6   Scoot

While you can move components and wires manually, the **Scoot** command is faster and keeps everything lined up. Press **<Esc>** to ensure nothing is selected and no commands are running. Select the **Scoot** button from the **Schematic** tab of the ribbon. The cursor will change to a small hollow square.

Hold this cursor over a component and click once with the left mouse button. The component will now be highlighted with a box. Moving the mouse will slide the component along its wires. Left click again to place the component in its new position. If you find it hard to select a component you can temporarily turn off snap to grid at the bottom of the screen before selecting the component. Turn it on again before completing the **Scoot** command so that the component's new position is still aligned with the grid.

If you select a wire instead of a component, you can slide the whole wire at 90 degrees to its direction. This also moves any components in the wire. For example, if you click the wire above **K1** using the **Scoot** command, you can slide **K1** and the wires above and below it, left and right. The other, horizontal, wires will be adjusted to suit.

Scoot cannot go past components or over joints in a wire made from several small wires laid end to end. Try and have the whole wire visible on the screen when using **Scoot** to move a wire. If you zoom in too far, AutoCAD will zoom out before letting you use **Scoot**.

Press **<Esc>** to end the **Scoot** command. If necessary use **CTRL + Z** to undo the changes to your drawing.

7.7　Editing components and attributes

Press **<Esc>** to ensure nothing is selected and no commands are running. Left click relay coil **K1** to select it. Ensure nothing else is selected. Now right click on the drawing and the following menu will appear.

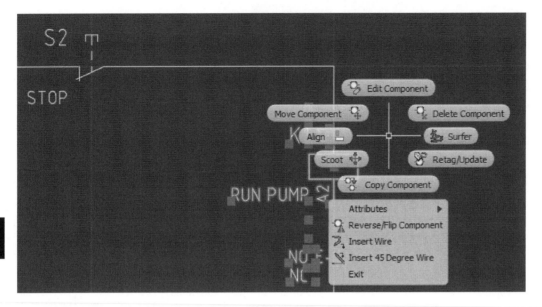

Copy Component, **Move Component** and **Delete Component** are self-explanatory and we have already covered **Scoot**.

Edit Component brings up the component details screen you saw when you inserted the component. Use this to change the descriptions, the component tag or other component information.

If several components exist with the same tag, AutoCAD will ask if you want to update the others when you edit one of them. For example, you could change the relay coil description from **"Run Pump"** to something else and the child contact for that relay would also be updated. Ensure the project you are working on is the active project so that things like this update properly.

Attribute list/edit

If you hover the mouse over **Attributes** you will get a submenu.

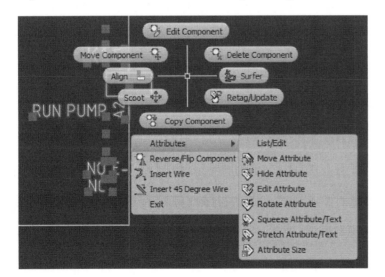

These functions allow you to alter the text labels on components. They are useful to tidy your drawing but can be tricky to use. Selecting **List/Edit** gives the following screen:

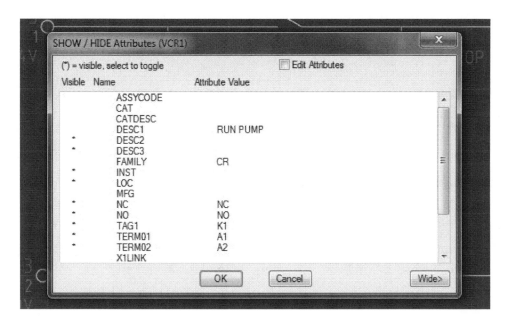

The small * at the left under **Visible** indicates that the attribute is displayed. Use the left mouse button to toggle it on or off, hiding any information you don't want to see on your drawing. The **Attribute Value** column shows the text assigned to each attribute. If you click the **Edit Attributes** box at the top of the window, you can then click on items in the list and edit the text directly. It is best, if possible, to use the **Edit Component** dialogue box and other tools that produce this information, rather than manually altering the end result with **Edit Attributes**.

Hide attribute

Selecting **Hide Attribute** changes the cursor to a small, hollow square. Each attribute you click with this cursor will be hidden. This has the same effect as removing the * in the **List/Edit** attribute dialogue box but is faster if you wish to hide many attributes belonging to different components.

Move attribute

Selecting **Move Attribute** from the menu allows you to reposition attributes, avoiding wires and other components. It is very useful but can cause confusion. After selecting this menu item the cursor will change to a small, hollow square. Carefully select a text attribute, making sure you do not click on empty background. The attribute text will be highlighted when you are over it.

Left click to select your next attribute. This can be from a different component. Each time you select an attribute, AutoCAD will draw a box around that piece of text.

When you have selected all of the attributes you wish to move, left click once on empty background to tell AutoCAD you are finished selecting things. The cursor will change from a hollow square to a large cross-hair. It is easy to do this accidentally.

Now left click once anywhere on the screen to specify the start co-ordinates. Move the cursor away from this point and the attributes will all move by the same amount. Left click again to fix them in position.

By allowing many attributes to be moved at once, even attributes belonging to different components, and by allowing you to start and stop the movement by clicking reference points (which could be wire ends or other items in your schematic) you can move attributes out of the way while still maintaining a uniform appearance.

It can be difficult to select attributes without selecting empty space by mistake. Temporarily turning off snap to grid can make this easier. Note that you can turn snap off at the start while selecting components then turn it on while still in the middle of the **Move Attribute** command to select the start and end coordinates.

7.8 Attribute size

Selecting **Attribute Size** from the menu gives the following dialogue box:

The value **Size** (**5** in the above example) is the new size you want an attribute to be. It defaults to the value set for text in your drawing using **TEXTSIZE** (see page 23). You can type a different value. Alternatively click **Pick>>** and select an existing attribute whose size you wish to copy.

Width is actually a width factor rather than an absolute value. Leave it as **1** unless you want the shape of the characters to be extra wide or extra narrow.

After setting **Size** to the value you want, click **Single**. The dialogue box will disappear and the cursor will change to a small hollow square. Now click on the attributes you wish to alter. Each will change to the new size when you click on them. When you have finished click on an empty area of the drawing or press **<Esc>** to exit the command.

The **By Name** command needs some explanation. It allows you to change the properties of a particular attribute tag name. This is most easily explained with an example:

Set the attribute **Size** and **Width** values. Then click the **By Name** button. The dialogue box disappears and you will see the small hollow square cursor. Click once on the **RUN PUMP** text attribute of **K1** relay coil. Now press **<Enter>**. This tells AutoCAD you wish to change all the attributes with the attribute name **DESC1** (the attribute that contains the text **RUN PUMP**).

Now drag the cursor to select all objects in your drawing. Press **<Enter>** again and the **DESC1** attribute of each selected component will change in size.

The **Type it** button allows you to type the name of the attributes to modify. You need to type the name of the attribute (for example **DESC1**), not the text contained in the attributes (for example **RUN PUMP**). You can use ***** as a wildcard.

As an example, to change all the component description attributes (**DESC1, DESC2** etc.) to a new size, click **Type it**. When prompted type **DES*** which tells AutoCAD to change all attributes with names starting **DES**. Now drag the cursor to select all components in your drawing and press **<Enter>**.

"Window the entire drawing?"

In the help files, AutoCAD refers to this process of selecting components using the confusing term "Window the entire drawing". Selecting components by dragging the cursor to define opposite corners of a rectangle is referred to as "windowing". "Window the entire drawing" just means "drag the cursor to select everything".

7.9   Attribute rotation

Rotate Attribute is very simple. Select this to get the small hollow square cursor. Each attribute you click will rotate 90 degrees anti-clockwise. You may need to follow this with the **Move Attribute** command to put the rotated item in its proper position relative to the symbol.

7.10   Aligning components

While drawing your control circuit you may have found it difficult to get your push buttons lined up. If they were not at exactly the same height you will have a step in the wire that joins them. AutoCAD has an alignment tool to help. Try the following example in a blank part of your drawing and delete it when finished. Alternatively, if your control circuit needs tidying up, you could try the tool while doing that.

First draw two push buttons which are not aligned vertically or horizontally.

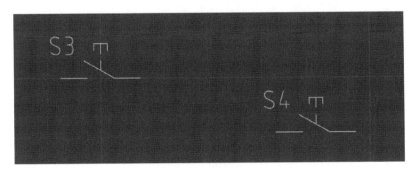

Click the **Align** tool. It is in the **Schematic** tab of the ribbon in a drop down menu shared with the **Scoot** button.

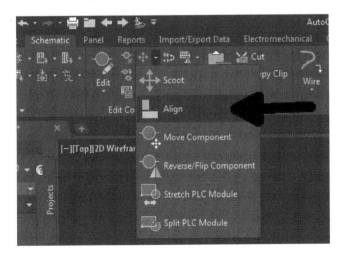

The cursor will change to a small hollow square. You will be asked in the command line if you want **horizontal** (same level) or **vertical** (one below the other) alignment.

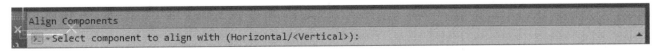

Type **h** to align horizontally or **v** to align vertically and press **<Enter>**.

Click on the symbol you want to align other components with. It will be highlighted and a small horizontal or vertical bar drawn on it to show which alignment will take place. Next click on each of the symbols you wish to align. They will be highlighted.

Finally press **<Enter>** and the symbols will be moved. If necessary, any attached wires will move with them.

Close **sheet 2**. If you have been experimenting with various commands you may wish to close it without saving. It should look like this:

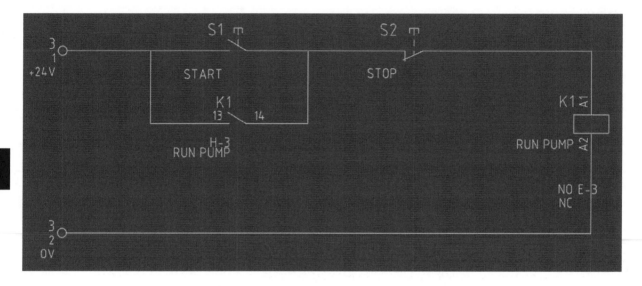

7.11   Draw the power circuit

Now we will draw the power circuit. This will help you practice what you have learned. It also lets us see how commands such as cross-referencing work across multiple sheets. It will look like this:

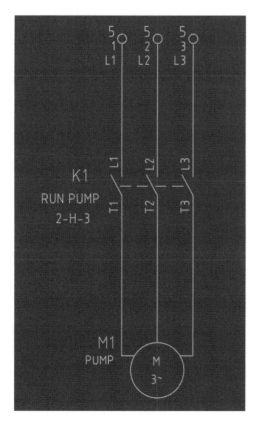

Open **sheet 3**.

Start by drawing the motor. (**Icon menu: Motor Control > 3 phase motor > 3 phase motor**) Make sure the **Vertical** box is ticked so that the connections are at the top of the motor.

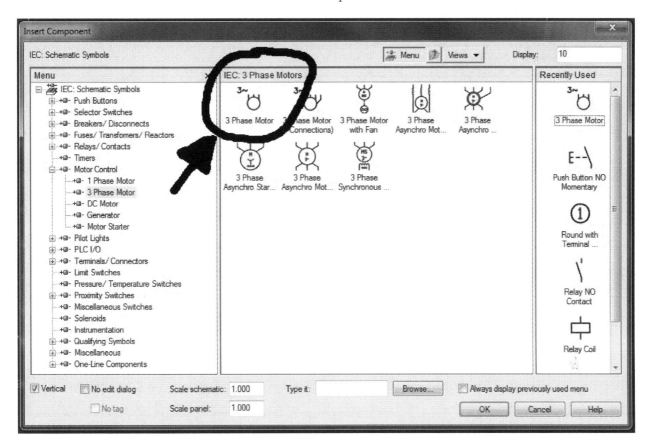

Accept the suggested tag of **M1** and add the name **Pump** as the first line of the motor description.

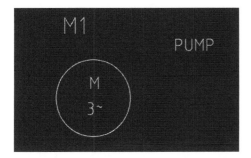

Next draw the vertical wires. Start the wires above the motor, near the top of the drawing. As you draw the wire down towards the motor, you will see green crosses highlighted on the motor's connection points when the cursor approaches the motor symbol. It is not an easy symbol to connect wires to so you may need to tidy your wires using the wire manipulation tools mentioned earlier.

You can also reduce the snap to grid distance or turn off snap after starting the wire but before finishing it at the motor. A snap setting of **2.5** should be sufficiently small to avoid problems.

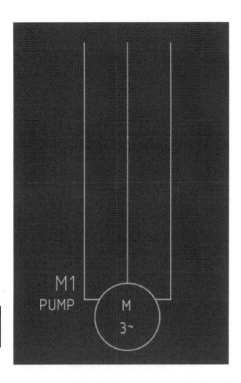

7

Next we will add three terminals. Use the **Round with Terminal Number, Block HT0002** symbol as before.

Place the first at the top of the left wire. Number it tag strip **5**, terminal **1**. Give it the description **L1**. Instead of clicking **OK** in the **Insert / Edit Terminal Symbol** dialogue box, use the **OK-Repeat** button to insert it.

AutoCAD returns to your drawing. Click the position for the second terminal, at the top of the centre wire. The dialogue box will reappear ready to insert a second terminal. Its terminal number will be incremented automatically to tag strip **5**, terminal **2**. You just need to change its description to **L2**.

Press **OK-Repeat** again and insert a third terminal, tag strip **5**, terminal **3,** description **L3,** on the last wire. Finish inserting terminals by using **OK**, rather than **OK-Repeat** after entering its details.

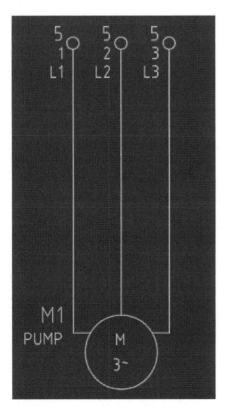

Adding contactor/relay K1

Now we will insert relay contacts from **K1** to allow it to control the motor.

Click the **Icon Menu** button in the **Schematic** tab. From the menu, select **Relays/Contacts > Relay NO contact**.

Insert this symbol on top of the first wire. The wire will automatically be broken to make a space for the contact. AutoCAD will automatically rotate the symbol to match the direction of the wire so you do not need to tick the **Vertical** box.

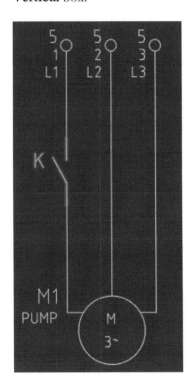

The **Insert / Edit Child Component** dialogue box will appear.

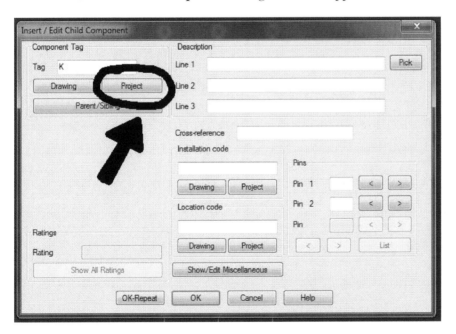

We want to make this a child contact belonging to the relay coil **K1** on **sheet 2**. The **Drawing** button would only give us a choice of components from this sheet. Instead, click the **Project** button (circled above). You will see a list of the components in your project which could be associated with a normally open contact. Other components are not shown. If you want to show every component, not just relay coils, then click the **Show all components for all families** box.

As with all cross-referencing tasks it is important to ensure the project you are working on is the active project. Use the **Freshen** button to update the database if you cannot see a recently added component.

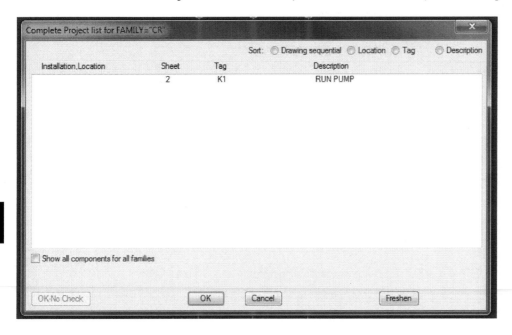

Click the line with **K1** to highlight it then click **OK**. The component details for the contact will be updated.

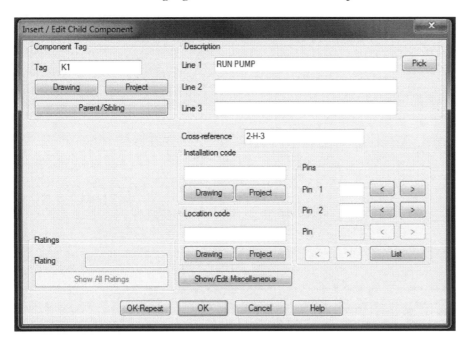

As with the coil, we are going to label the pins of our contacts. In the **Pins** area at the bottom right set **Pin 1** to be **L1** and **Pin 2** to be **T1**. Click **OK** and the contact will be inserted.

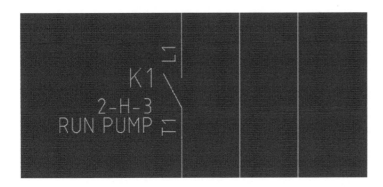

We will add the other two contacts by copying the first.

Left click on the contact to select it then right click and choose **Copy Component** from the menu that appears. Click on the middle wire to insert the second contact. The **Insert / Edit Child Component** dialogue box appears. Make this contact's pins **L2** and **T2**. Then press **OK-Repeat** to insert the third contact. Make its pins **L3** and **T3**.

The only change you need to make to the copies is to increment **L1** and **T1** to **L2**, **T2** and **L3**, **T3**. Instead of typing you can change them quickly by clicking the increment arrows in the **Insert / Edit Child Component** box.

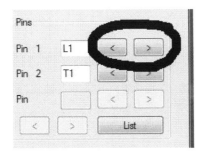

If the contacts are not quite level you can use the **Align** function to line them up.

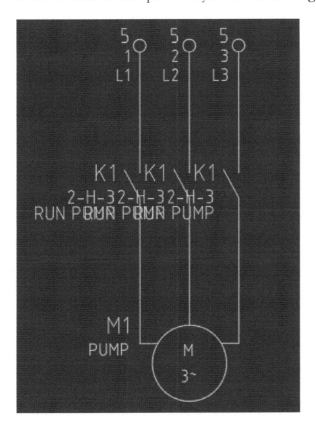

Each contact will be labelled with the description **RUN PUMP**. This looks messy and has pieces of text which overlap each other. You could use the **Hide Attribute** tool we discussed earlier to hide the **RUN PUMP** and **K1** attributes for the centre and right contacts.

Instead we will use the AutoCAD dashed line tool to link the components with a dashed line. This function hides the surplus labels automatically.

Linking components with a dashed line

On the **Schematic** tab click the **Link Components with Dashed Line** button.

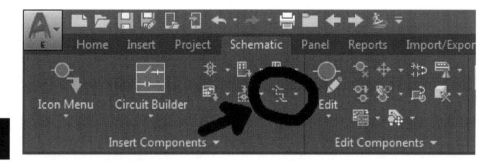

The cursor will change to a small hollow square. Click on each of the three **K1** contacts in turn. You may find this easier to do if you turn off snap to grid. After selecting all three, press **<Enter>**. The components will be linked with dashed lines and the surplus attributes hidden.

If you repeat this process on components that are already linked, in the same order as originally applied, the links are removed and the hidden attributes made visible again.

The linking process may leave the **Run Pump** and **K1** text on top of the symbol.

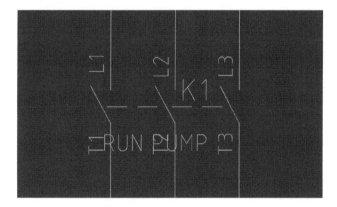

Use the **Move Attribute** function described earlier in this chapter to place them to one side of the symbol.

You may also find that the **Link Components with Dashed Line** has completely hidden the cross-reference to the relay coil on **sheet 2**. To get this back, select the left contact and right click to bring up the component menu.

Select **Attributes > List / Edit**. You will find that the attribute **XREF**, at the bottom of the list, does not have a * in the **Visible** column. Click this column to replace the * and make the cross-reference for the contact visible again. Then click **OK**. Move the **XREF** attribute if necessary to tidy the drawing.

Save your drawing. It should look like this:

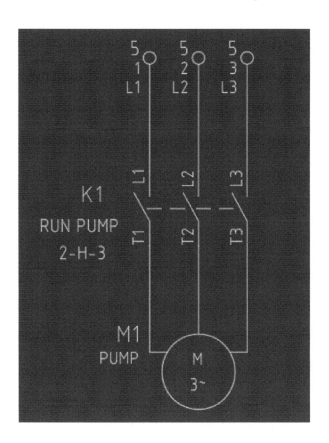

7.12 Updating cross-references

You will see that the contacts in the power circuit have a cross-reference to sheet 2, column H, row 3 which is the position of the relay coil.

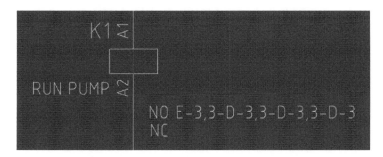

If you look at the coil on **sheet 2** you will see it has normally open (NO) contacts at E3 (on the same sheet) and three contacts at 3-D3 (on **sheet 3**). If the attributes overlap the wire you can tidy them with the move attribute tool to be as shown. You may have different values on your own drawing if you drew components at slightly different grid references. Depending on whether you included a '-' as a separator in your X-Y grid settings (see page 67), grid references may be in either the format 3-D-3 or 3-D3.

If you move components, grid cross-reference attributes usually update automatically but sometimes they do not. You can force an update of cross-references using the **Update/Retag** tool in the **Project** tab of the ribbon.

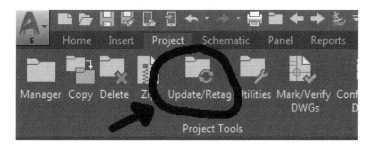

This will open the **Project-Wide Update or Retag** dialogue box.

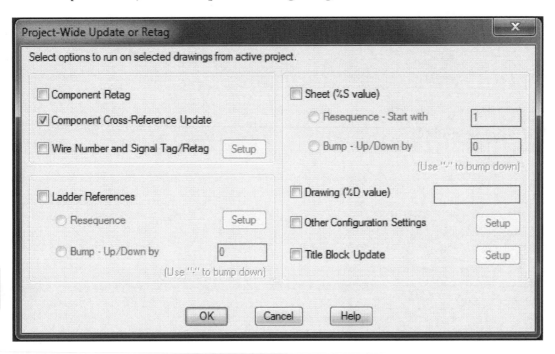

Tick **Component Cross-Reference Update**. Ensure the other boxes are not ticked and press **OK**. Select **Do All** when prompted and click **OK** to update component cross-references throughout your project.

Be careful with this tool. You could accidently retag all of your wire numbers or components.

8. Wire numbers, types and cross-references (45 minutes)

In this chapter we look at more advanced features of wires. Topics covered are:

- Adding and modifying wire numbers
- Assigning wire types
- Tracing connections in wire networks
- Wires that run between different drawings
- The surfer tool

8.1 Wire numbers

We will now add wire numbers to the drawing. Each wire number relates to a set of linked conductors so if several wires are connected together they all have the same number.

Go to **sheet 2** of your drawing. On the **Schematic** tab of the ribbon select the **Wire Numbers** button.

The **Wire Tagging** dialogue box will be displayed.

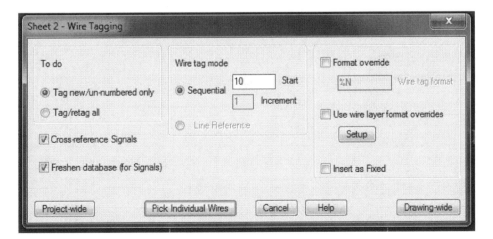

This box contains a number of important options. Under **To do** at the top left you will normally select **Tag new/un-numbered only**. This means any existing wire numbers will be left alone. **Tag/retag all** will replace existing wire numbers with new numbers. This could be disastrous if you have already started using the existing numbers in documents or assembly work.

First we will try adding wire numbers to some individual wires and start our numbering at the number 10. You might do this to fit a numbering system or to match numbers on external wiring coming into your project.

For **Wire tag mode** select **Sequential** and enter the **Start** number as **10**. Other information should be as in the dialogue box pictured above. Click the **Pick Individual Wires** button.

The dialogue box will close and the cursor will become a small hollow square. Use this to select the two wires on each side of switch **S1** and press **<Enter>.** These two wires will now be numbered with green text showing their wire number.

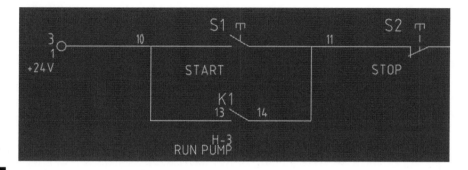

8

Next we will automatically number the remaining wires. Click the **Wire Numbers** button again in the ribbon. This time, in the dialogue box, set the sequential numbering to start at **1**. Ensure **Tag new/un-numbered only** is selected so you do not change wires **10** and **11**.

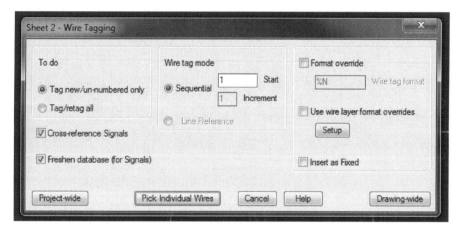

Now click the **Project-wide** button. The following box is displayed:

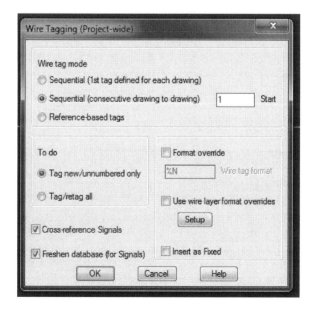

This contains further options to tweak the numbering. We are going to number every wire, starting at **1** in the first drawing and continuing the numbering in subsequent drawings where we left off in the previous one. Click **OK** and you will be asked which drawings you want to process:

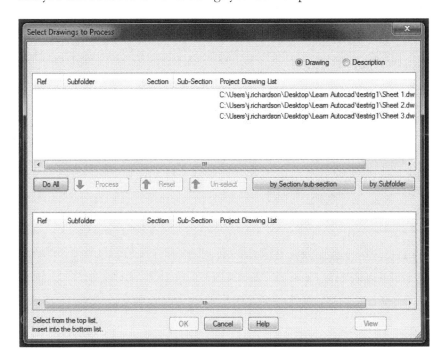

Click **Do All** to add wire numbers in every drawing of your project. Then click **OK**.

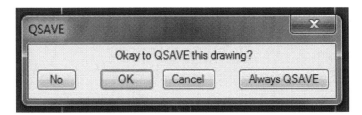

The AutoCAD Electrical software will ask permission to save the drawing before carrying out this operation. Click **OK**.

After a moment of processing, AutoCAD will add wire numbers to all of your wires on sheets 2 and 3. The numbering works from left to right as wires are found on the drawing, then from top to bottom. Wires **10** and **11** that we added earlier should be unchanged with the new wire numbers starting from **1**. AutoCAD ensures existing wire numbers are not duplicated.

Fixing wire numbers

Sometime you do not want a wire number to be changed accidentally. In this case you can set it to be fixed. On the **Schematic** tab of the ribbon select **Fix**. It is in the drop down menu that normally starts with **Edit Wire Number**.

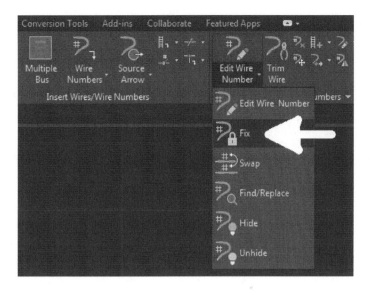

The cursor will change to a small, hollow square. Click on a few wire numbers and then press **<Enter>**. The selected wires will change from green to white to indicate they are fixed.

8 Edit and unfix wire number

Select a wire number then right click on the drawing. A menu is displayed.

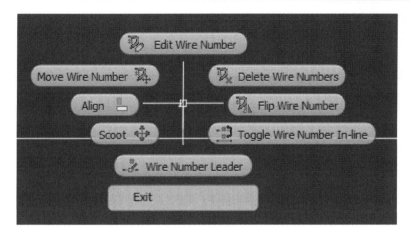

Select **Edit Wire Number** and the following box will open.

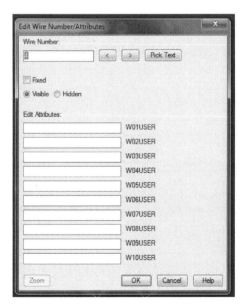

You can change the wire number to any number or text you like. When you click **OK** the new number will be assigned. Editing a wire number automatically changes it to fixed (white text).

If you edit a wire which is already fixed you will find the **Fixed** box ticked in the above screen. Untick it and the wire will revert to automatic (non-fixed) in green text when you click **OK**.

If a wire has no visible wire number you can still use the **Edit Wire Number** tool by selecting the wire, right clicking and choosing **Edit Wire Number** from the **Wire Numbers** submenu. You can also select **Edit Wire Number** from the **Schematics** tab of the ribbon and then use the cursor to click the wire whose number you wish to edit.

If you try to assign a wire number that already exists elsewhere you will receive the following warning:

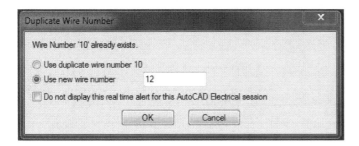

You can then either ignore the warning and have two wires with the same number or choose a different number. AutoCAD will suggest a number which is available. For the checking and automatic numbering to work it is important that the project you are working on is set as the active project in the **Project Manager** window.

Copy wire number

Sometimes one wire may be long with many branches. You can add extra copies of the wire number and these copies will update automatically if the number changes. Click the **Copy Wire Number** button in the **Schematic** tab of the ribbon.

The cursor will change to a small hollow square. Click on some wires. Each time you do you will get a copy of that wire's number placed near where you click. Press **<Esc>** to exit this function.

The copies of the wire number are green and change automatically to match the main number.

Deleting wire numbers

You can select a wire number then right click and choose **Delete Wire Numbers** from the menu that appears. Alternatively you can just select the numbers you want rid of and press **<Delete>** on the keyboard. You can also select multiple wire numbers then right click and choose **Erase**.

The **Delete Wire Numbers** command deletes copies of the wire number one at a time but if you use it on the original wire number, all of the copies are deleted. With the other methods you must get rid of every copy manually.

8.2 Resolving wire network problems

In more complex circuits you may find problems occurring with wire numbers. This may be due to wires joining when you do not intend them to or wires that you think join but which do not.

Using the **Edit Wire Number** tool you can see what wire number, if any, AutoCAD has assigned to a wire.

To further investigate you can use the **Check/Trace Wire** tool. This is on the **Schematic** tab of the ribbon in a drop down menu under the **Stretch Wire** button.

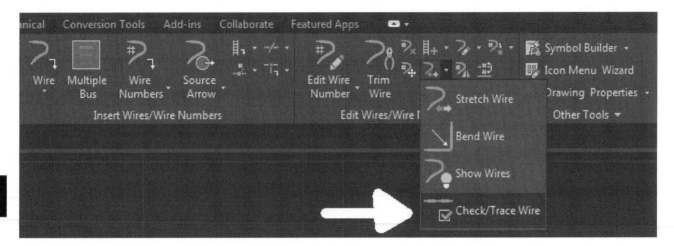

Click this button. The cursor becomes a small hollow square. Click on a wire in your drawing. It will be highlighted.

Pressing **<Space>** will show you which wires are connected to it. Keep pressing **<Space>** to see more connected wires. Alternatively press **'a'** to highlight all connected wires in one go.

Press **<Esc>** to exit the **Check/Trace Wire** tool.

8.3 Creating new wire types

By default, AutoCAD Electrical uses a layer called **WIRES** for electrical wires. When setting up the template we added further wire types. These are defined by a colour and size which are incorporated into the layer name, for example **BU_1.5mm**. The layer can also be assigned a plotting colour so that it appears, for example, blue on the drawing.

If you did not create sufficient wires in your template, or you find you need a new type, you can create an extra layer using the **Create/Edit Wire Type** button. This is explained in detail on page 77 in the template creation chapter. This new layer will only exist on the drawing you alter. Page 81 explains how to copy wire types between drawings.

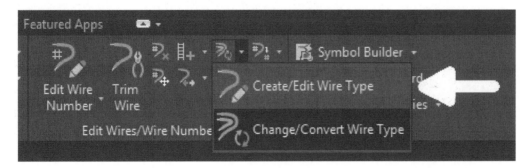

8.4   Assigning wire types to the schematic

Now we are ready to assign types to the wires in our schematic. Click the **Change/Convert Wire Type** button. It shares the same drop down menu as **Create/Edit Wire Type**.

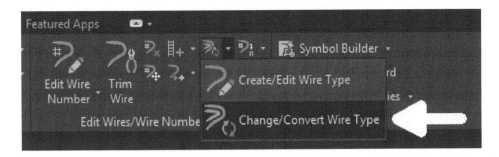

You will see a list of your wire types, rather like the one on the **Create/Edit Wire Type** screen.

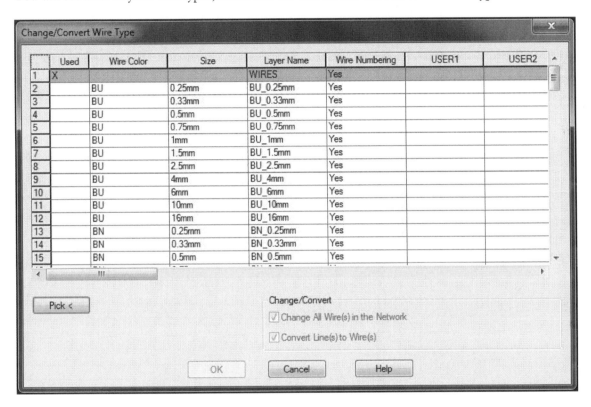

Click on a wire type to highlight it, for example **BU_1.5mm**. Then click **OK**. The box will disappear and you will see the familiar small hollow square cursor.

Use this to select several wires on your schematic by clicking on them. Then press **<Enter>**. The selected wires will change colour to blue, assuming that is the colour you chose for the selected wire type layer.

By default increased wire thicknesses are not shown on screen, even though they print correctly. Page 80 explains how change this.

8.5   Wire colour/gauge labels

While the colours of the wires are helpful, they do not tell us the wire's size and are no use if we later print the drawing in monochrome. We will now label the wires with their type. Click the **Wire Color/Gauge Labels** button in the **Schematic** tab of the ribbon.

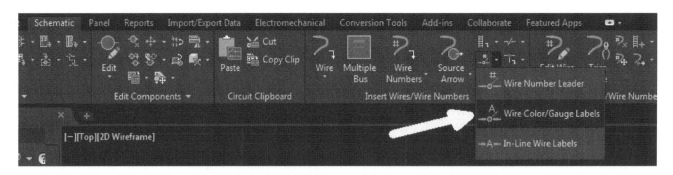

You will see the **Insert Wire Color/Gauge Labels** dialogue box.

Click the **Setup** button to get the following window.

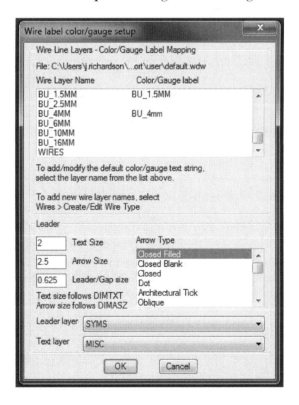

In this setup box you could, if you wanted, change the label for individual wire layers by clicking on the list in the top part of the box. We will keep the default and use the layer name which has the format **Colour_Size**.

In the lower left part of the box set **Text Size** to **2**.

Click **OK** to go back to the **Insert Wire Color/Gauge Labels** box.

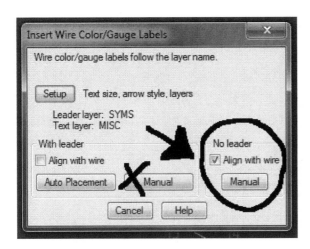

Ensure the tick boxes are as shown. A leader is a small arrow which points from the text to the wire itself. We will use the button in the **No Leader** section to label the wires without using a leader. Ticking **Align with wire** will rotate the text for vertical wires.

Click the **Manual** button at the right (not the **Manual** button in the centre which is for including a leader) and you will get the small hollow square cursor. Use this to click on wires. Each time you do they will be labelled at that point.

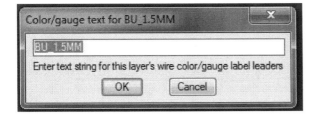

The very first time you use a particular wire layer, AutoCAD will ask you to confirm the label for that layer. Click **OK** to accept the default which uses the colour and size, for example **BU_1.5mm**.

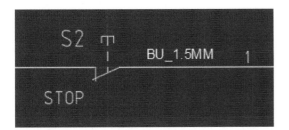

You can label the wires more than once if they have corners or joints. Each straight section can only have one colour/gauge label. This is useful if you change the text size since re-inserting a label with your preferred format will replace the existing label.

8.6   Wire cross-references

Often you want to show a wire leaving one place and heading for a distant destination, either on a different part of the same sheet or on another sheet. AutoCAD uses source/destination arrows to do this. These show signals leaving for another place and can automatically update wire numbers. By using the X-Y grid we set up around our template, they also tell the person using the drawing where in the drawings to find an arrow's source or destination.

For our example we will add an extra stop button to the control circuit. This might be a local stop button next to the machine so we will show it on **sheet 3** beside the motor.

Open **sheet 3**. Draw a normally closed, twist to release, latching pushbutton. Label it as **Local stop**. Add wires heading left as shown below.

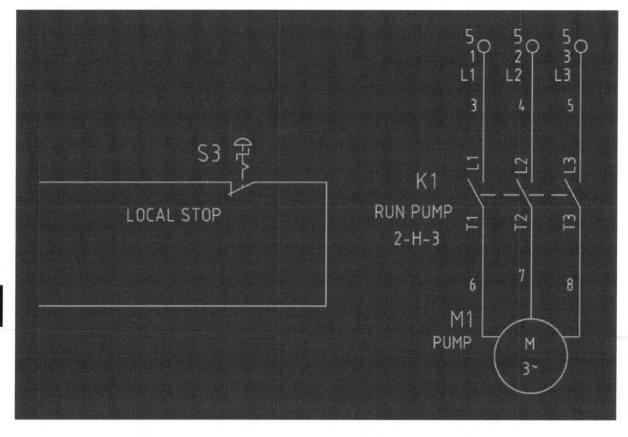

Now go to **sheet 2**. Make a break in the wire above relay coil **K1** by deleting the vertical section of wire. Add horizontal wires heading to the right from each side of this break as shown below. Using the tools explained earlier, ensure both sides of this break have wire numbers and wire types. Mark the wire types with wire colour/gauge labels. Use **Scoot** and the other tools to move components, wire numbers and wires if required. Make sure there is space beside the end of the wires for the source arrows and their information.

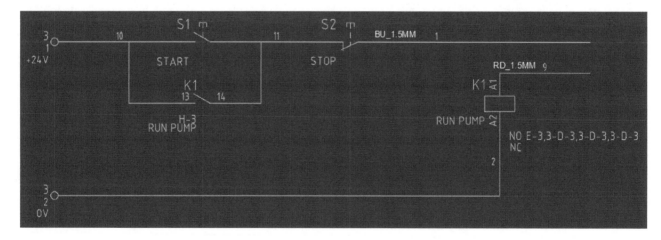

Add source arrows

In the **Schematic** tab of the ribbon select **Source Arrow**.

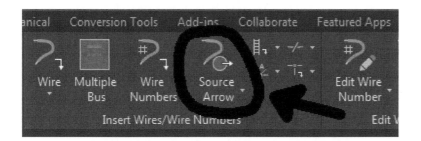

You will get the small hollow square cursor. Click near the end of the top wire which will connect switch **S2** to the **Local Stop** button. The following dialogue is displayed:

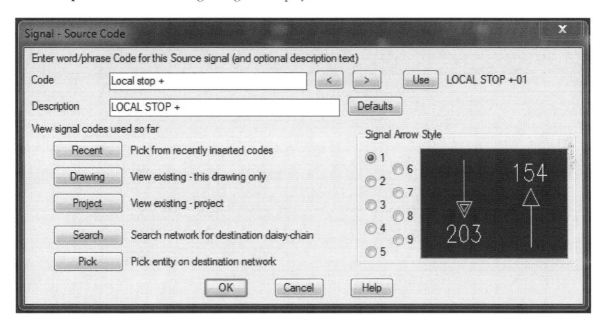

In the empty box **Code**, type a short, unique code that will refer to this wire end. For example **Local stop +**.
In the **Description** box below it you can write a longer, more informative explanation which will be used to label the arrow on the drawing. For this example just type **Local stop +** again. Click **OK** and you will be asked if you want to insert a destination arrow now.

You could click **OK** but in this example we will click **No** so we can learn how to insert destination arrows later. An arrow will be drawn at the end of the wire.

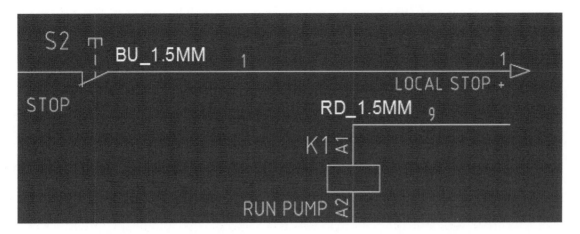

The arrow is labelled with the description and also the wire number. Now repeat the process to add a source arrow to the second wire. Label this one with both **Code** and **Description** entered as **Local stop -**.

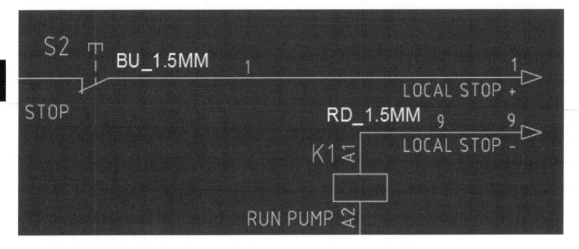

You can see the wire number, **9** in this example, next to the second arrow. Save your drawings.

Add destination arrows

Go to **sheet 3**. Click the **Destination Arrow** button. It is on a drop down menu below the **Source Arrow** button in the **Schematic** tab of the ribbon.

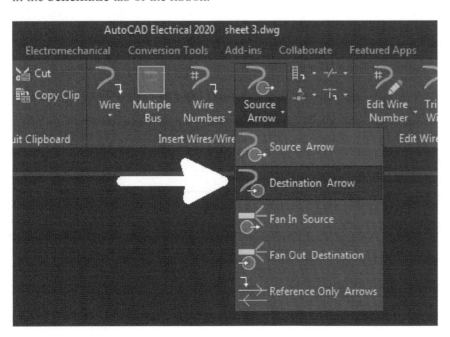

The small square cursor will appear. Click on the end of the top wire going to the **Local Stop** button. You will be asked for the source/destination arrow details.

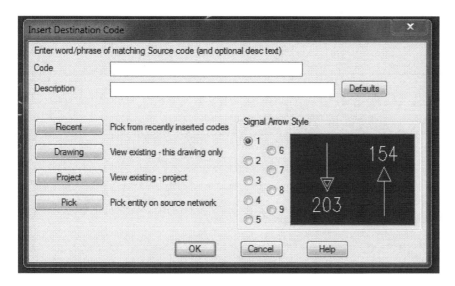

Click the **Project** button to see a list of all source arrows in the project. The **Freshen** button can be used to update this list if required.

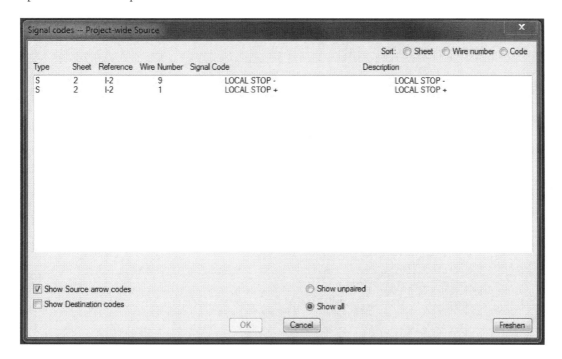

Click on **LOCAL STOP +** to select it and press **OK**.

This will return you to the **Insert Destination Code** dialogue box which now has the **Code** and **Description** fields filled in.

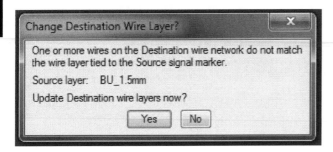

Press **OK** and the destination arrow will be inserted. AutoCAD will update the destination wires with the wire number and wire type of the source. If there is a mismatch between the wire types of the source and destination, it will warn you and ask if you want to change the destination wire to match the source.

8

In this case the mismatch is because we have not yet chosen a wire type or size for the destination wire. Press **Yes** and the destination will be updated.

The wire number and wire type are updated to match the source arrow on **sheet 2**. If the wire was set to a different colour then the **sheet 3** wire will change to match this. You can confirm the wire type has changed for the wire on **sheet 3** by adding a wire colour/gauge label to it. The label **2-I2** is the reference to the source arrow position, in this example grid reference **I2** on **sheet 2**.

Now add the second destination arrow to connect to the other source arrow on **sheet 2**. The finished product will look like this. Wire colour/gauge labels have been added manually to show the wire types.

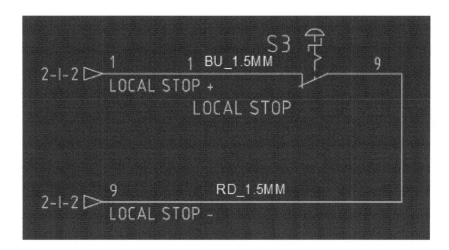

You may find the text overlaps the wires or other items. If so, use the **Scoot** and **Align** commands to tidy your drawing.

A wire with a destination arrow has the same wire number as its corresponding source arrow. You cannot insert a destination arrow on a wire with a fixed wire number. In this case delete or unfix the wire number on the destination wire before adding a destination arrow.

Now return to **sheet 2**. The source arrows will have been updated with the grid references of the destination arrows.

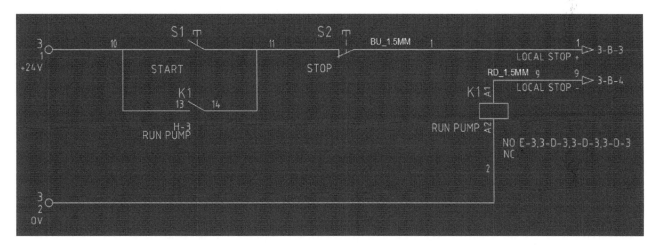

Save both drawings.

8.7   Surfer tool

Left click on one of the source or destination arrows to select it. Then right click on the drawing to get a menu. Choose **Surfer** from this menu. The **Surf** dialogue box appears.

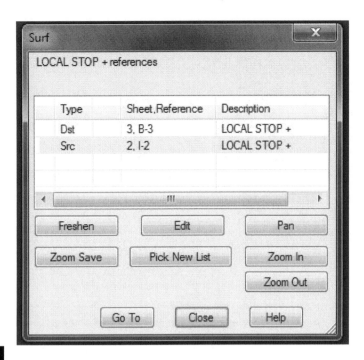

8

This box will show you matching source and destination arrows and allow you to jump between them in your drawings. Note that one source arrow can have multiple destinations but a destination cannot be linked to more than one source.

Updating cross-references

These tools work nicely when producing a new drawing but sometimes you may make changes after the source and destination arrows are inserted.

Go to **sheet 2**. Use the **Edit Wire Number** tool to change the wire feeding into the top source arrow to **99**. Change the wire to a different wire type, for example **OR_0.5mm**. You will see that the source arrow has updated to the new wire number.

Now go to **sheet 3**. The destination wire will be unchanged.

We have already seen the **Update/Retag** tool in the **Project** tab of the ribbon which can update component X-Y grid position references. To update the wire numbers we need to use the **Update Signal References** tool. This is quite hard to find.

To access it click the small drop down arrow beside **Edit Wires/Wire Numbers** in the **Schematic** tab of the ribbon.

Click the grey **Update Signal References** symbol shown below.

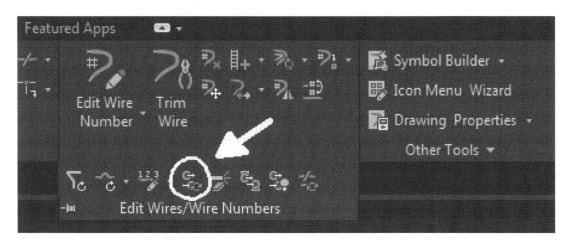

The **Update Wire Signal and Stand-Alone Cross-References** dialogue box will appear.

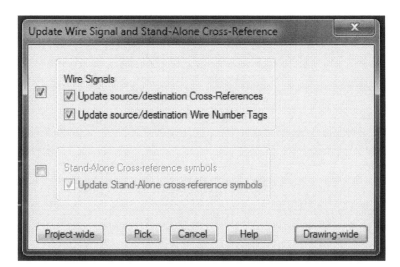

Ensure **Update source/destination Cross-References** and **Update source/destination Wire Number Tags** are both ticked. Click the **Project-wide** button.

You will be asked which drawings to process. Select **Do All** and click **OK**. Any modified wire numbers will now be carried across to the destination arrows. The X-Y grid references will also be updated.

Unfortunately the wire colour/gauge is not carried across. This is a limitation in AutoCAD. The wire gauge is only carried across to destination arrows at the time they are inserted. It is not updated after that.

The only way to force a wire colour/gauge to carry across is to delete the destination arrow then insert it again. You could also change the wire gauge/colour of the destination wire manually with the **Change/Convert Wire Type** tool.

For neatness, change the wire type on **sheet 2** back to its original value so that there is not a discrepancy between wire types across the source / destination arrows.

9. Terminals (30 minutes)

In this chapter we will introduce the **Terminal Strip Editor**. This edits the terminals in your drawing and produces physical layouts of the terminal blocks. We will use it in a very basic way at first and cover more advanced features in later chapters. We will also use a fused terminal symbol which cannot be found in the **Icon Menu**.

Topics covered:

- The fused terminal symbol
- Component symbol files
- The **Reverse/Flip Component** tool
- An introduction to the **Terminal Strip Editor**

9.1   Fused terminals

Before describing the **Terminal Strip Editor** I wish to highlight a useful symbol which is hard to find, that for a fused terminal.

On **sheet 2** add a wire from the positive side of **K1** relay coil as shown below. We want to place a fused terminal on this, perhaps to drive an indication lamp showing the state of the coil. You may need to select the top or bottom half of your circuit and move it to make space. If you do this you will need to update the signal references and component cross-references as described in previous chapters.

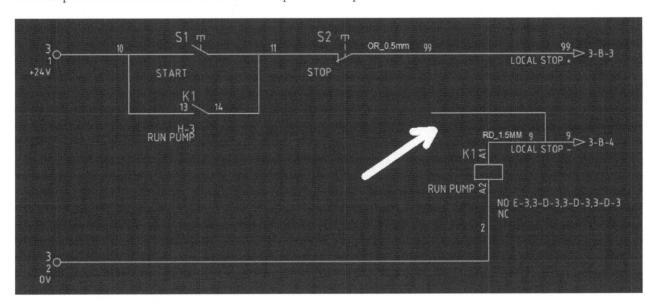

Now click the **Icon Menu** button in the **Schematic** tab of the ribbon, as though you were going to insert a component from the **Icon Menu**.

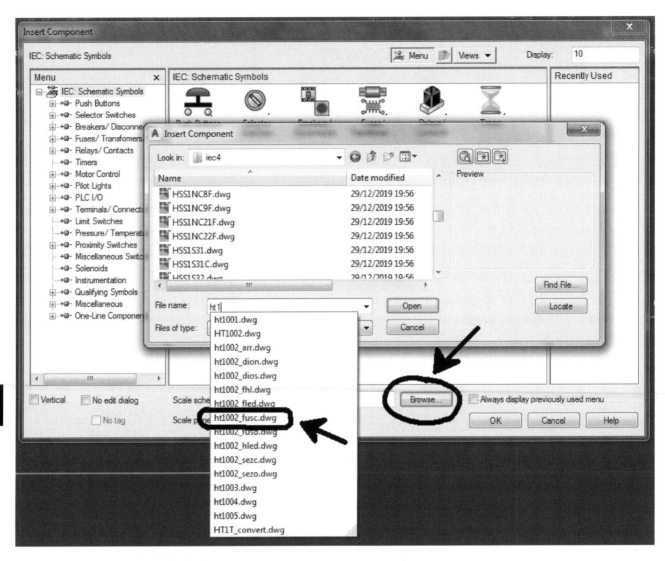

Instead of selecting a symbol, click the **Browse** button at the bottom of the dialogue box. An **Insert Component** dialogue window appears as shown above. In this window navigate to the **IEC4** library.

This will involve you going up to the root directory. On an individual PC this will usually be drive **C:** From the root directory, navigate down the file structure to the **IEC4** library. The path you need is:

C:/Users/Public/Public Documents/Autodesk/Acade 2020/Libs/iec4

As a general rule, the libraries for the AutoCAD Electrical software are all stored in the **Users/Public/Public Documents** part of the structure.

Once you have navigated so that **Look in:** at the top of the dialogue box is pointing at the right folder, you will see the files inside the **IEC4** library.

AutoCAD Electrical has strict naming conventions for the files in the libraries.

Those starting **AT** are component templates. We will use these later to develop our own symbols. Those starting **Bb** are wire connection drawings which are also used when creating new component symbols.

The component symbols themselves begin **H** for horizontal or **V** for vertical and end with **.dwg**. While you could scroll through the list there is a faster way if you know what you want.

In the **File name** box type **ht1** (do not press **<Enter>**). A list appears showing only the files starting **ht1.** The box ignores whether capitals are used.

H means a horizontal component, **T** stands for terminal and the **1** means wire numbers change on wires passing through the terminal, as one would expect for a fused terminal.

From the list, select fused terminal component **ht1002_fusc.dwg** and click **Open.** Insert the fused terminal at the end of the wire we drew earlier.

The **Insert/Edit Component** dialogue box will appear. Set the terminal to be **Tag strip 3,** terminal **Number 3** and click **OK.**

If you had wanted to insert a second fuse you could have used **OK-Repeat** instead of **OK**. You could also have inserted from the **Recently Used** pane of the **Icon Menu** dialogue box. The fuse will appear here as a picture of a keyboard with the words **typed it**.

If you need to search again for the library you will find the path to the folder for **IEC4** remains selected until you close down AutoCAD.

For our example we will only insert one fused terminal so your drawing should be as below.

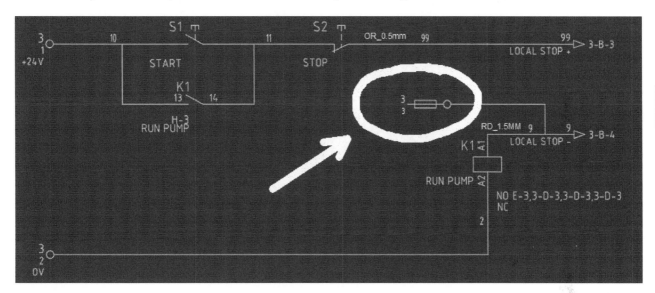

It is possible to add extra symbols, such as this fused terminal, to the **Icon Menu**. We will see how to do this in chapter 10.

Reverse/Flip component

Unfortunately the fused terminal is the wrong way round. It would be preferable to have the circle for the terminal at the left and the fuse part on the right. We can correct this with the **Reverse/Flip Component** tool.

On the **Schematic** tab of the ribbon, select the drop down arrow next to the **Scoot** button. Select **Reverse/Flip Component**.

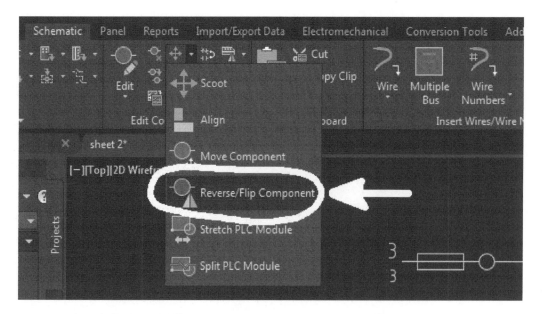

The **Reverse / Flip Component** dialogue box appears.

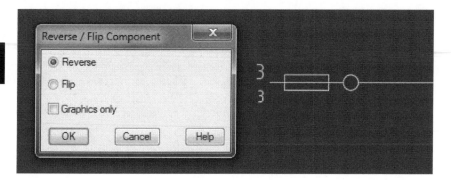

Ensure **Reverse** is selected. Tick the **Graphics only** box and press **OK**.

The cursor will change to a small hollow square. Use this to click on the fused terminal. It will be reversed as shown below. Press **<Esc>** when finished.

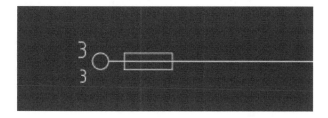

By selecting **Graphics only**, we left the attribute text unchanged at the left, rather than flipping it to the right of the symbol.

Save the drawing.

9.2   Terminal Strip Editor

The rest of this chapter will introduce the **Terminal Strip Editor**. To use it fully you need to understand component catalogue entries and panel layouts which are discussed later in the book. For now we will use it in a very basic way, introducing the tool and providing some useful functions.

Terminal layouts

A typical electrical panel contains numerous terminals mounted on DIN rail. The terminals are grouped into blocks with each terminal within a block given an individual number. On our symbols we have used an attribute, **Tag Strip**, for the block and another attribute, **Number**, for the individual terminals.

In a complex panel the terminals in a block might be scattered throughout the schematic, possibly on different pages. To assist wiring and panel layout you might supplement the schematic with a physical representation of the terminal blocks. You could do this using rectangles and lines as shown below:

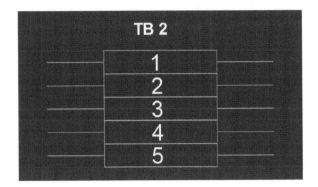

The **Terminal Strip Editor** does this automatically by searching through your schematics. This is faster than using unintelligent shapes. It can be updated easily when the schematic changes and can also show connecting wire numbers. By generating it automatically you will detect errors that you might miss when creating terminal layouts manually.

In this chapter we will use a default footprint block to show the terminals and their connections. Later chapters will add actual terminal part numbers to produce realistic images and scale panel layouts.

9.3   Open the Terminal Strip Editor

Open **sheet 3** of your drawing. Open the **Terminal Strip Editor** by clicking the **Editor** button in the **Terminal Footprints** section in the **Panel** tab of the ribbon.

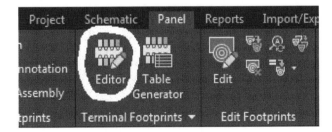

The **Terminal Strip Selection** window opens. It lists each terminal strip in your project and the number of terminals in each strip.

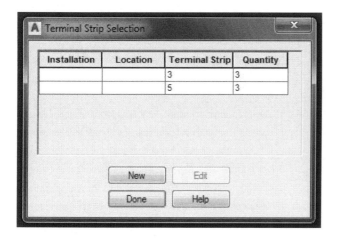

Click the row for terminal strip **5** to highlight it. Then click the **Edit** button. The **Terminal Strip Editor** window will open. This has a number of tabs. The three individual terminals within terminal strip **5** will be listed in a table on the **Terminal Strip** tab as shown below.

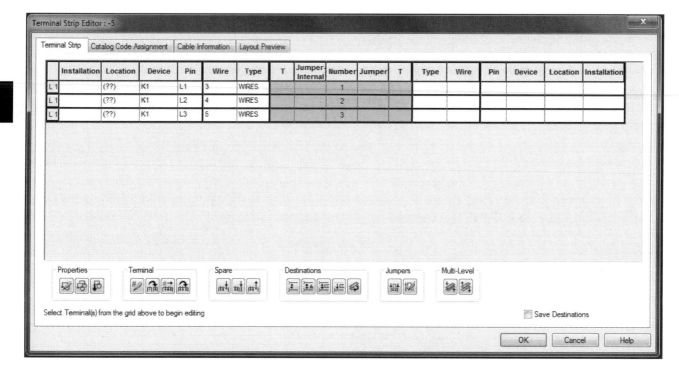

In the centre of the table is the column **"Number"**. In our simple example the terminals are listed in order from **1** to **3**. For more complex schematics the terminals might be listed in a random sequence, depending on the order in which AutoCAD found them when searching the drawings. If this is the case then clicking the heading of the **Number** column will sort the terminals into numerical order. Not only will this give a neater display and make it easy to spot missing or duplicated terminals, it sets the order in which the terminals will be placed in the panel when we move to the **Layout** section.

When you are happy the terminals are in the correct order, click the **Layout Preview** tab.

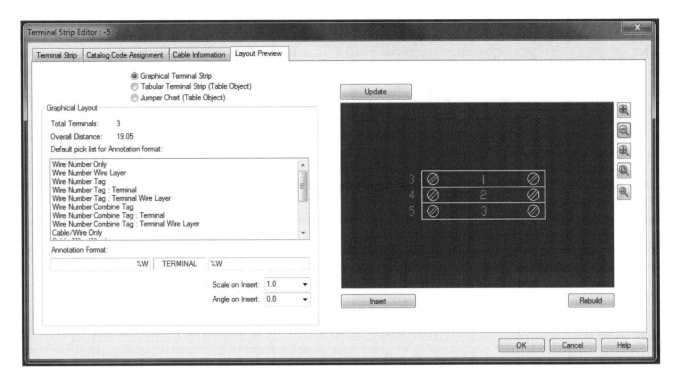

This tab defines the way the terminal layout is displayed. Select **Wire Number Only** on the left of the box. This will display the wire numbers of any wires going to the terminals. Other options let you display different information.

The attribute for wire numbers (**%W**), and any other attributes to be displayed, are shown under the heading **Annotation Format**, based on your selections. The **Annotation Format** codes can also be edited directly.

Clicking the **Update** button updates a preview at the right of the dialogue box. You can use the magnifying glass buttons at the far right to zoom in and out.

For now we are using the default terminal footprint. If you are using a metric drawing and have selected **panel_mm** as your schematic footprint library then each terminal will be drawn as a box 50.8 wide by 6.35 high when placed on your drawing. For an imperial scaled drawing you should use the **panel** library and the default terminal footprint will be 2 x 0.25 inches.

Scale on Insert changes the size of the inserted terminal footprint. Provided you are using the correct library, you can set **Scale on Insert** to **1.0**.

If you are using the wrong library for the units (inch or mm) of your drawing you may find the terminals too large or small by a factor of 25.4. You can use the scaling factor to correct this but it is better to use the correct library. Otherwise you may have problems with the text not scaling correctly or the spacing between terminals being wrong. It may also cause difficulties when you try drawing your own terminal footprints.

Angle on insert determines whether the terminal rail is horizontal or vertical. Set it to **0** and click the **Update** button. The terminals in the preview window will be shown horizontal (mounted on vertical DIN rail) as in the image above.

To place the terminal blocks on your drawing, click **Insert**. Then click on a blank area of your drawing to position the terminal layout. It should appear as below. The numbers **3**, **4** and **5** to the left of the terminals are wire numbers which may be different in your drawing.

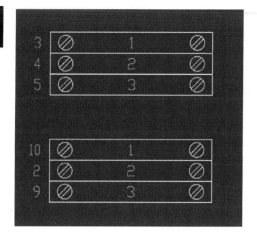

After placing the terminals, the **Terminal Strip Editor** dialogue box reappears. If you make further changes you can click **Rebuild**, rather than inserting the terminals again. Note that **Rebuild** only updates the terminals after you close the editor so do not worry if it appears to do nothing.

When you have finished, click **OK**.

You will return to the **Terminal Strip Selection** dialogue box. Highlight terminal strip **3** and click **Edit**. Ensure the terminals for this strip are listed in numerical order. If not, click the **Number** column header to rearrange them. Then use the **Layout Preview** tab to insert them on your drawing.

Click **OK** to get back to the **Terminal Strip Selection** dialogue box and exit by clicking **Done**.

The finished drawing should look like this. You can see the wire numbers **10**, **2** and **9** on terminal block **3**. Your numbers may be different.

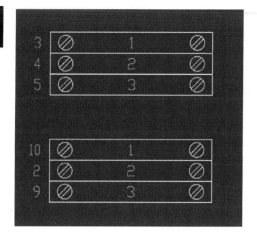

Save your drawings.

Using the automation

These terminal blocks are linked with the schematic drawing. If you select one of the terminals in the layout drawing of terminal block **5** and then right click, you will see a menu.

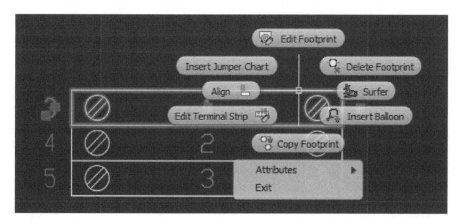

On this menu click **Surfer**.

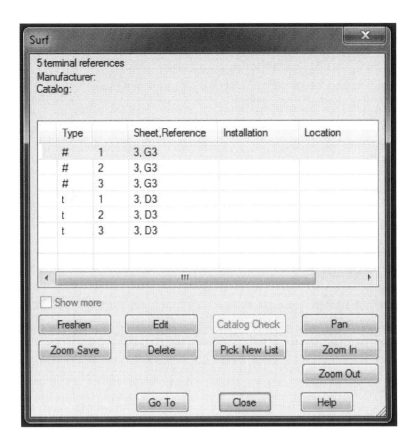

The **Surfer** tool lists every terminal in your drawings which belongs to terminal block **5**. If you cannot see all of the entries, click **Freshen**. The items marked **#** are the terminal footprints we have just drawn. The items marked 't' are the schematic symbols for those same terminals. You can use this **Surf** window to jump to any of these items. To do this highlight a line and click **Go To**.

If you draw your terminal layout and find you have more or less terminals than you expected then you can use this tool to trace the cause of the error.

9

Limitations of the Terminal Strip Editor

There are a few things to be wary of with the **Terminal Strip Editor**.

The first is an inconvenience. It would be nice if the terminal strip was labelled with the title **"Terminal Block 5"**. One way to achieve this is to unhide the **P_TAGSTRIP** attribute for the first terminal in the strip. This will display the number **'5'** above the strip.

You can make your drawings even clearer by using the value **"TB5"** rather than just **'5'** for your terminal **Tag Strip** value. This will also make your schematic drawings clearer but at the cost of cluttering the space around the terminals. The images below show what this would look like.

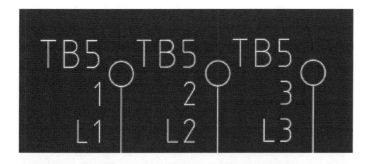

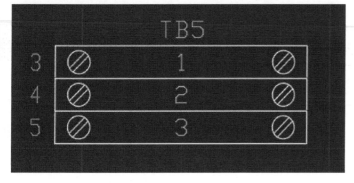

To display the **"TB 5"** you would first put the block on your drawing with **Terminal Strip Editor**. After leaving the editor, right click on the first terminal in the layout drawing of the block. Select **Attributes > List/Edit**.

The list of attributes is displayed.

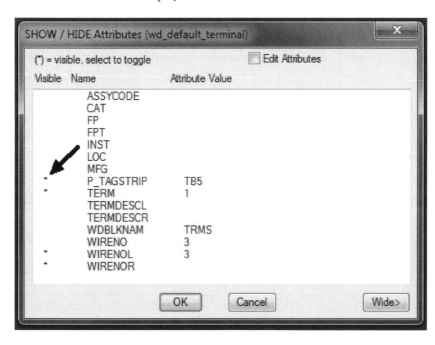

Click under the visible column next to **P_TAGSTRIP** to place an asterisk (*****) in this column. Then click **OK**. The terminal **Tag Strip** value will now be displayed on your drawing.

A second issue is that the wire numbers on the terminal block do not update when you change them in the schematic. For this reason you must rebuild your terminal blocks in **Terminal Strip Editor** after making wiring changes and before releasing the finished drawings. If you used the attribute editing screen to unhide the terminal block numbers then you must now redo this too, since the rebuild resets the **P_TAGSTRIP** attribute to hidden.

9.4   Changing terminal block numbers

You may sometimes wish to change the **Tag Strip** value of a whole block of terminals, for example changing **TB5** to **TB6**. It would be time consuming to edit each terminal individually.

You might be tempted to select multiple terminals and use the **Properties** window to change the **P_TAGSTRIP** attribute. Unfortunately this method does not always update the information used in reports properly unless you open the individual terminals for editing afterwards.

A better way is to use the **Find/Edit/Replace Component Text** tool. This is in the **Schematic** tab of the ribbon. It is accessed from the drop down menu beside the **Retag Components** button in the **Edit Components** panel.

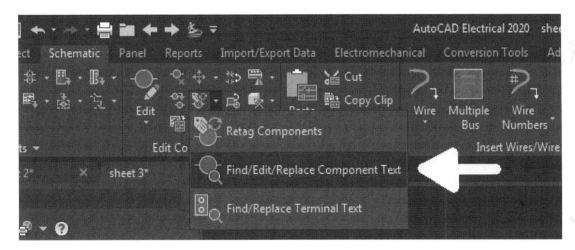

To use the tool, first select all of the terminals you wish to re-tag. Select the **Find/Edit/Replace Component Text** tool on the ribbon. The following box is displayed.

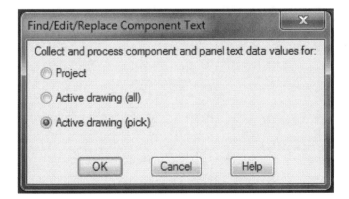

Choose **Active drawing (pick)** to only modify the terminals you have selected. You will see the **Find/Edit/Replace** dialogue box. To change terminal strip **TB5** to be **TB6** you would tick **Find** and **Replace** and enter the text to be modified as shown below.

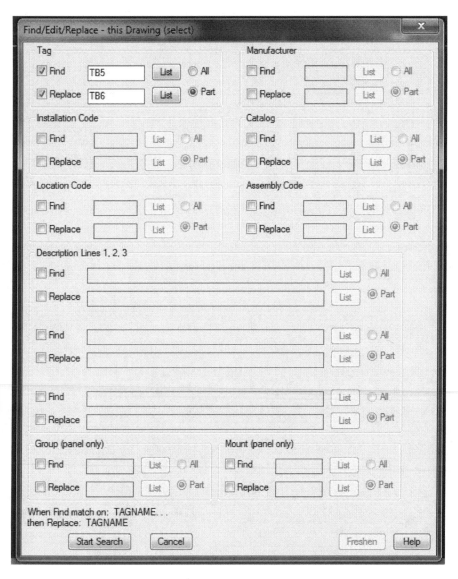

You would then click **Start Search** and choose **Replace All** when prompted. There is no need to actually do this for our example drawing. From the above image you can see there are many other useful options for modifying components and terminals.

The option **All** requires the whole string to match. If **All** was selected the tool would change **TB5** but ignore a terminal labelled **TB50** for example. If **Part** was selected then the **TB5** string at the start of a terminal labelled **TB50** would be changed, giving **TB60**.

The **Terminal Strip Editor** also provides a way to change the **Tag Strip** value for terminals by using the **Reassign Terminal** button shown below. This can be used on multiple terminals by selecting more than one line with **CTRL + click** or **Shift + click**.

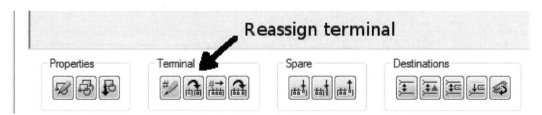

10. Custom symbols (1½ hours)

You will sometimes need components that are not in the symbol library.

One solution is to draw the symbols using shapes such as lines, boxes and text. Component terminals can be represented with circles or using discrete terminals. This is not using the AutoCAD Electrical software properly but is a fast method and may be sufficient.

You can also look in the **Miscellaneous > Generic Boxes** folder of the **Icon Menu** for general purpose component symbols. These are square boxes with two, three or four terminals.

A better way is to define your own AutoCAD symbols. This is fast and simple once you know how. Unfortunately it is also easy to make mistakes. Once you do that and get on the wrong path it can be very frustrating. The walk-through in this chapter explains what to do but follow the instructions carefully.

This chapter covers the following topics:

- How the AutoCAD Electrical symbol libraries work
- Making a custom symbol library
- Creating a new schematic symbol
- Adding symbols to the **Icon Menu**
- Purging blocks from drawings

We will create a symbol for a DC/DC converter as shown below.

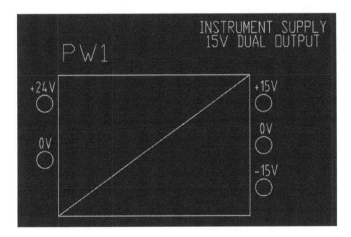

Before creating the actual symbol, the next section will explain how AutoCAD symbols and libraries work. This will make it clear what is happening in the subsequent sections when we make our symbol.

After creating the symbol we will insert it into one of our **TestRig1** drawings. We will then add it to the **Icon Menu** so it can be used in other projects.

10.1   Understanding AutoCAD Electrical symbols

It is important to understand how the symbol libraries work and how their folders are structured. Neglect this and you might save your beautiful new symbol and never find the file again. AutoCAD also has strict naming conventions. Ignore them and some of its features will not work properly.

Use Microsoft Windows Explorer to navigate to the AutoCAD symbol libraries. These are found at the following path:

C:/Users/Public/Public Documents/Autodesk/Acade 2020/Libs

Note that when browsing for this folder, **"Public Documents"** may sometimes be shown as just **"Documents"**.

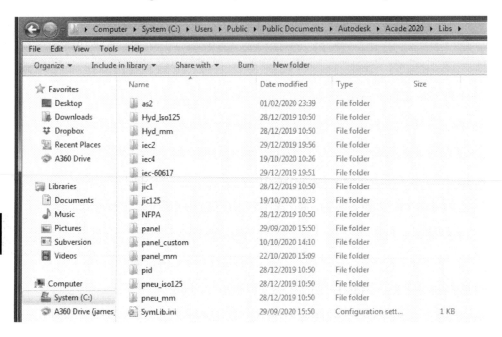

Each of the folders in the **Libs** directory shown above is an AutoCAD Electrical library. **"panel"** is the imperial scaled footprint library which is used for panel layout drawings. **"panel_mm"** is the metric footprint library. Those starting **"pneu"** and **"Hyd"** are pneumatic and hydraulic symbols which we are not interested in in this book.

"iec2", **"iec4"** and **"iec-60617"** are the metric symbol libraries. **"jic1"** and **"jic125"** are imperial scaled symbol libraries.

In this book we are using the **IEC4** library. Open this folder now in Microsoft Windows Explorer. You will see a huge selection of cryptically named files. Some of them are shown in the next four screenshots.

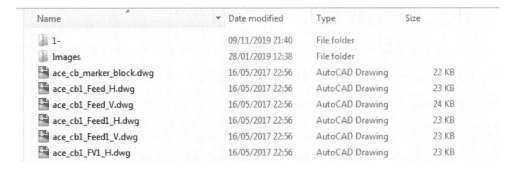

The folder **"1-"** holds another symbol library for single line diagrams. These are used in the power distribution industry to represent transformers, circuit breakers, etc. as two wire components, even though they are actually three phase devices.

AT_HC_CB.dwg	16/05/2017 22:56	AutoCAD Drawing	20 KB
AT_HC_CR.dwg	16/05/2017 22:56	AutoCAD Drawing	20 KB
AT_HC_DS.dwg	16/05/2017 22:56	AutoCAD Drawing	20 KB
AT_HC_FU.dwg	16/05/2017 22:56	AutoCAD Drawing	21 KB
AT_HC_GNR.dwg	16/05/2017 22:56	AutoCAD Drawing	21 KB
AT_HC_LR.dwg	16/05/2017 22:56	AutoCAD Drawing	20 KB
AT_HC_LS.dwg	16/05/2017 22:56	AutoCAD Drawing	20 KB

The files with names beginning **"AT_"** are attribute template files. These are used to create your own symbols. The different template files give you a head start by having appropriate attributes set up for certain types of component. For example **AT_HC_GNR.dwg** is the template for a generic component and **AT_HC_FU.dwg** is the template for a fuse.

Bb000.dwg	16/05/2017 22:56	AutoCAD Drawing	20 KB
Bb012.dwg	16/05/2017 22:56	AutoCAD Drawing	20 KB
Bb021.dwg	16/05/2017 22:56	AutoCAD Drawing	20 KB
Bb023.dwg	16/05/2017 22:56	AutoCAD Drawing	20 KB
Bb032.dwg	16/05/2017 22:56	AutoCAD Drawing	20 KB
Bb111.dwg	16/05/2017 22:56	AutoCAD Drawing	20 KB
Bb112.dwg	16/05/2017 22:56	AutoCAD Drawing	20 KB

The files starting **"Bb"** are definitions of connection points. Later in this chapter, when we add terminals to our custom components, we will need these files to be present.

HTS11S59.dwg	16/05/2017 22:56	AutoCAD Drawing	28 KB
HTS11S74.dwg	16/05/2017 22:56	AutoCAD Drawing	29 KB
HTS12.dwg	16/05/2017 22:56	AutoCAD Drawing	27 KB
HTS12S18.dwg	16/05/2017 22:56	AutoCAD Drawing	21 KB
HTS12S18C.dwg	16/05/2017 22:56	AutoCAD Drawing	21 KB
HTS12S59C.dwg	16/05/2017 22:56	AutoCAD Drawing	28 KB
HTS12S74.dwg	16/05/2017 22:56	AutoCAD Drawing	29 KB
HTS12S74C.dwg	16/05/2017 22:56	AutoCAD Drawing	29 KB
HTS21.dwg	16/05/2017 22:56	AutoCAD Drawing	20 KB

The .dwg files starting **H** or **V** are the drawings which define the symbols themselves. When you create a new symbol you produce one of these files. Most supplied symbols have a drawing for both the horizontal (starting with the letter **H**) and vertical (starting with the letter **V**) form. When creating a custom symbol you may wish to produce both.

Symbol naming conventions

AutoCAD has a strict naming convention for component symbol files.

This tells AutoCAD if a symbol is a parent or child component, whether it should be rotated to fit on a vertical wire, whether to change wire numbers on wires that pass through the symbol, etc. If you ignore these conventions then your symbol may work at first but it will cause problems later with automated tools and reports.

The **Symbol Builder** tool allows you to choose properties, for example parent or child, from drop down menus. It will then suggest suitable characters for the start of the filename which meet the naming conventions.

The naming rules are as follows and affect the first five characters of the filename:

- The first character should be **H** or **V**, depending on whether you have drawn a horizontal or vertical version of your symbol.

- The second and third characters are a family name, either existing or one you have made up. For custom symbols the default is **DV**. Do not use **H** or **V** for the second character of the filename (the first letter of the family name) since this causes AutoCAD problems.

- If you want a symbol where wire numbers do not change as they pass through it, for example a terminal, use a one letter family name for the second letter and make the third character zero.

- The forth character should be **1** for a parent or stand-alone component. For child components it should be **2**. This ensures the right options are provided when inserting and editing the component.

- If the symbol is a contact then the fifth character should be **1** for a normally open contact and **2** for a normally closed contact.

The remaining characters can be anything you like to give the symbol a unique name.

This book explains only how to create ordinary components. The AutoCAD naming convention extends further should you wish define things like your own cable markers. See the section **"About symbol naming conventions"** in the AutoCAD Electrical help files.

Libraries assigned to a project

In AutoCAD, open your **TestRig1** project and look at the **Project Properties**.

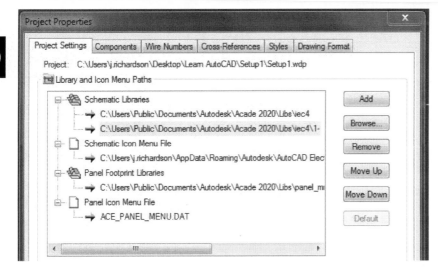

Chapter 3 (page 41) explained how to select the libraries. In the above example we are using the **"iec4"** library. This is the top line under **Schematic Libraries**. We have also included the library **"1-"** which we saw inside the **iec4** folder. When a library folder is added to this list AutoCAD only uses the top level files in that library. Any subfolders, for example the **"1-"** folder containing single line components, must be included as separate library entries. If you only included the **iec4** library folder then everything would work until you selected one of the single line components, at which point AutoCAD would display an error message.

The hydraulic and pneumatic libraries are not shown. If you left them installed in chapter 3, they will also be listed.

Add a custom folder

When you create your custom symbol you could stick it in the **iec4** folder with all of the other files but this causes several problems. Much of the filename is dictated by the AutoCAD symbol naming rules so it may be hard to find your file again after saving it. It will also be hard to group your custom symbols together, either to give to another user or to transfer to another folder when upgrading to a different version of AutoCAD.

10

The solution is to create a new folder to store your custom symbols. This can be anywhere but for our example we will create it inside the **iec4** directory. Do this now using Microsoft Windows Explorer to create the folder **CustomSymbols** as shown below.

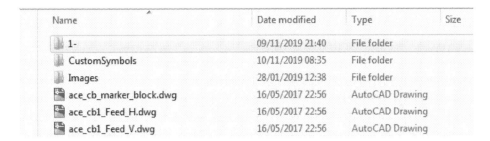

In **Project Properties** add this **CustomSymbols** folder as a schematic library. Move it to the top of the list with the **Move Up** button.

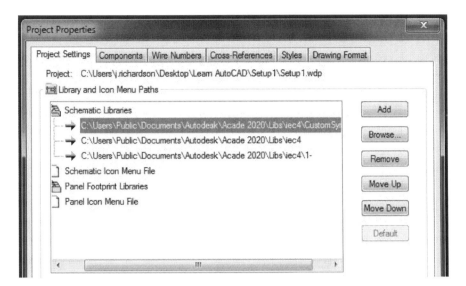

Click **OK** to exit the **Project Properties** dialogue box and save your changes.

When you insert a schematic symbol from the **Icon Menu**, the picture you click is linked to a filename. AutoCAD will search for a symbol with that filename in each library listed, starting with the one at the top.

If you wish to change a supplied symbol you can do this by placing a modified symbol file in your **CustomSymbols** folder while leaving the original symbol unchanged. Both will have the same filename but because your custom library is at the top of the list, the modified one will be found first.

If you produce completely new symbols they will have unique filenames but having them in a custom symbols folder is still a useful way to keep them together.

Attribute templates and connection points

Before creating our symbols there is a final caution about the attribute templates (the files starting **AT_**) and the connection point templates (the files starting **Bb**). AutoCAD symbol builder needs these files. You could copy them to your **CustomSymbols** folder. Alternatively, you could ensure that while the **Symbol Builder** program stores your new symbols in the **CustomSymbols** folder, it looks in the **iec4** folder for the templates.

For the examples in this book we will take the second approach and not copy them.

If you ever get a **"Selected folder does not contain any attribute template drawings"** error then **Symbol Builder** is not finding the attribute template files it needs.

10.2   Making a custom symbol

Draw a shape and open the Symbol Builder tool

Go to **sheet 2** of the **TestRig1** project. Draw a rectangle in a spare area of your drawing. This will be the outline of the new symbol. If you are using the metric template then 35mm wide by 25mm high is a good size. Add a diagonal line as shown.

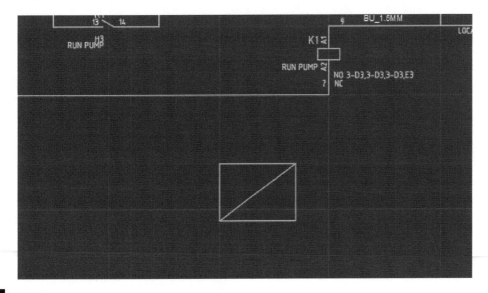

Click **Symbol Builder** in the **Schematic** tab of the ribbon.

You will see the **Select Symbol/Objects** dialogue box.

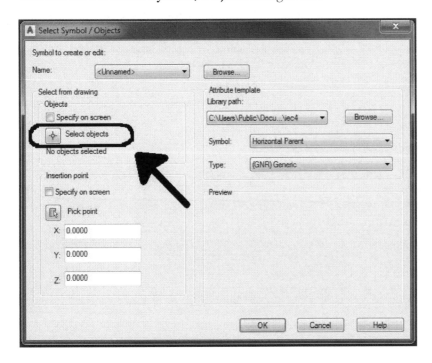

Click on the **Select Objects** button in the top left of this box. The dialogue box disappears and you will get the small hollow square cursor. Use this to click on the shapes you wish to use for your symbol. You can also drag the cursor to select all of the objects within a rectangular area.

For our example select the box and diagonal line.

When you have selected the shapes press **<Enter>**. The dialogue box reappears and now includes your selected shapes in its preview window.

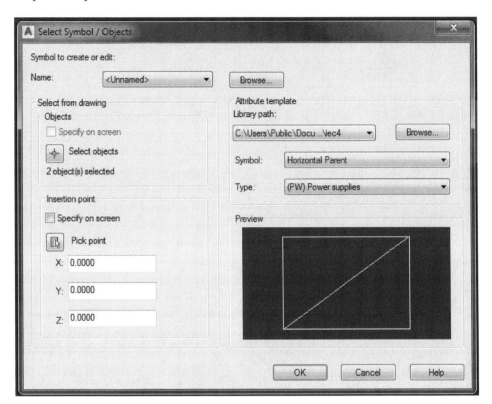

Set **Symbol** to **Horizontal Parent**. In this example we will not bother drawing a vertical version.

Set **Type** to the type of symbol you are creating. In our case we will choose **(PW) Power Supplies**. If your version of AutoCAD has problems with the **PW** template (see page 187) then you can use the **GNR** template for a generic symbol instead.

Do not alter the **Library path** on this page which refers to the folder with the attribute templates, not the place where you plan to save the symbol.

In our example, it points to the **iec4** symbol library folder which contains the templates. Even if you plan to put your custom symbols in their own folder you should leave the path on this screen pointing to one of the symbol libraries supplied with AutoCAD. Only change it if you have actually copied the attribute templates elsewhere.

If you set it to a folder with no templates you will get the error **"Selected folder does not contain any attribute template drawings"**.

Do not worry about the **Insertion point** at this stage.

Click **OK**.

You will now enter the AutoCAD Electrical **Symbol Builder** tool. In the drawing area you will see a large copy of the shapes you selected. At the left of the screen is the **Symbol Builder Attribute Editor** window shown below. (Its name is on the vertical text at the left of the window.)

10 You can close this window by clicking the **X** in its top corner but you might then wonder how to get it back. To get it back go to the **Symbol Builder** tab on the ribbon and click the **Palette Visibility Toggle** button.

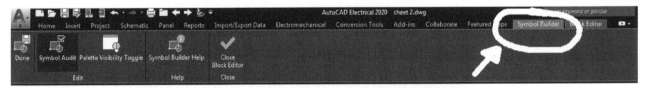

You can also undock the **Symbol Builder Attribute Editor** window from the edge of the screen by clicking on the vertical bar with its name (at the left) and dragging it away with the left mouse button held down.

The **Block Authoring Palettes** window (below) may also be open. We are not using this window so you can close it. You might also wish to close the **Project Manager** window to give yourself a less cluttered screen.

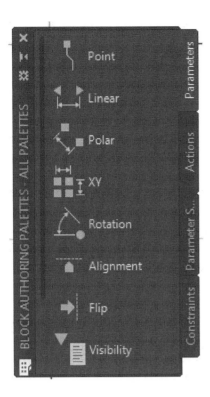

Set up your attributes

At the top of the **Symbol Builder Attribute Editor** window are three lists, **Required**, **Optional** and **Rating**. The items listed are the attributes you have already seen on other components.

It is compulsory to have a tag to identify the component. The other attributes labelled as **"Required"** are not compulsory. They are recommended however, particularly if you want your components to show up properly in a bill of material or other report. The **Rating** attributes are also useful as they are used in the component catalogue.

The items listed under **"Optional"** are less important so you can ignore them if you wish.

The list of required attributes is created by the attribute template files mentioned earlier. If you do not have any attributes listed then it may be due to a problem in these template files. For example, in AutoCAD Electrical 2018, the power supply template appears to be labelled as **PS**, rather than **PSU** which stops it working.

If you are using an older version of AutoCAD and have problems you can create your power supply as a generic symbol (**GNR**) rather than using the power supply template.

If you wish to make more advanced use of the **Symbol Builder** tool, you can add new attributes using the **Add Attribute** button shown below:

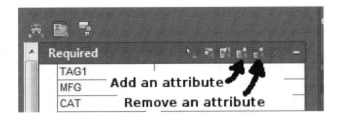

You can also create your own symbol attribute templates. See the AutoCAD help for further guidance on this subject. In this book we will just use the supplied templates.

We are going to leave the list of **Required** tags as it is and add each one to our power supply symbol.

Highlight **TAG1** in the **Symbol Builder Attribute Editor** window. When you have done this, click the **Insert Attribute** button as shown below.

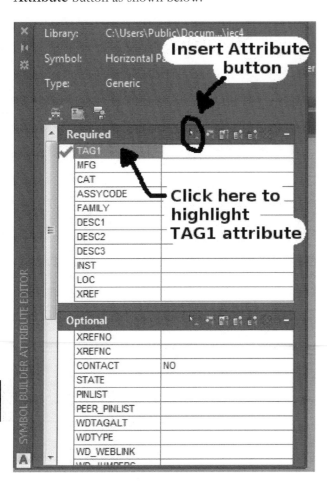

Move the mouse over the symbol in the drawing window. You will see the word **TAG1** at the cursor. Position this above your symbol and left click the mouse to place the **TAG1** attribute.

You will now see that there is a green tick next to **TAG1** in the **Symbol Builder Attribute Editor** window.

You may have a problem with the size of the attribute text, particularly if you are using a metric drawing. If the attribute template has the text set for a drawing scaled in inches it will be so small that it is almost invisible.

To correct this highlight the **TAG1** attribute in the **Symbol Builder Attribute Editor** window and click the **Properties** button.

The **Attribute Properties** window will appear:

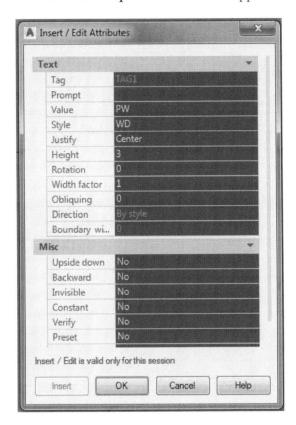

Change the value for height to be **3** (for a metric drawing) and click **OK**. **TAG1** will now be shown at a sensible size relative to your symbol.

You can select multiple attributes at once by pressing **<CTRL>** while selecting them and then use the **Properties** button to change them all. In the screen shots for this example **TAG1** has been set to a height of **3** and the other attributes to a height of **2**.

Now repeat this process to add all of the other **Required** attributes next to your symbol. Add the **Rating** attributes too. It will look like the image below.

Do not worry too much about the appearance of the attributes but put them above the symbol so we have space at the left and right sides to add terminals. Note that there are two identical sets of buttons in the **Symbol Builder Attribute Editor** window. One set is for the **Required** attributes and one set is for the **Optional** and **Rating** attributes.

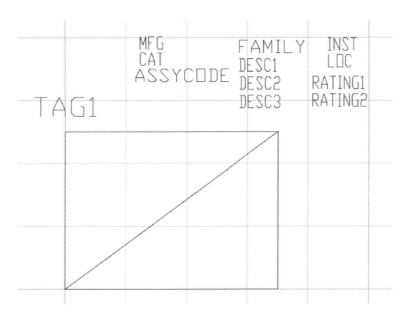

All of the **Required** attributes will now have a tick, as will the two **Rating** attributes.

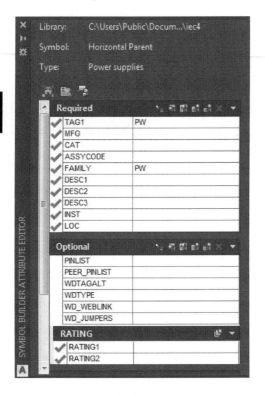

You can add default data for the attributes. If you are using the power supply template you will see **PW** in the box next to **TAG1**. When the symbol is used the tag name will start with the letters **PW** by default. If you are using a different template you may wish to type your desired tag prefix.

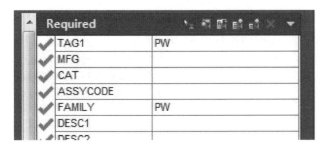

Set up wire connection points

Next we will set up the wire connection points for your new symbol. Make sure snap to grid is on so the finished symbol will be easy to line up with wires.

In the **Symbol Builder Attribute Editor** scroll down, past the attributes you have just set up, to the **Wire Connection** section which looks like this:

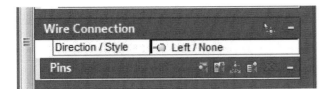

You may find this section minimised as shown below, in which case click the **+** to expand it.

Click on the box with the current style. In the above example this is the text "**Left/None**". This produces a drop down menu.

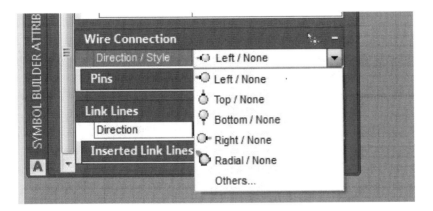

Choose **Others...** from this menu. This opens a dialogue box that configures your wire connections.

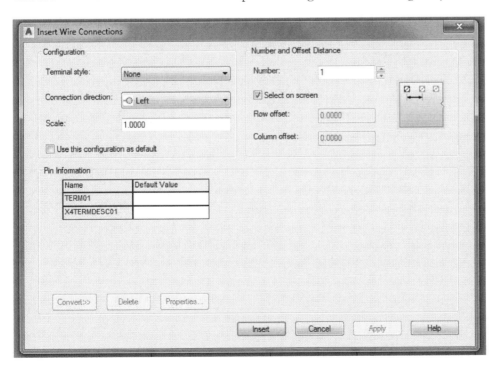

If you click on the **Terminal style** drop down menu at the top left of this dialogue box, you can select the terminal's appearance. The **Connection direction** drop down menu selects which directions wires can join this terminal from.

Choosing different values for the **Terminal style** affects which options AutoCAD offers you for the connections. You can also tick the box **"Use this configuration as default"** if you want to use a particular setting a lot.

For our example symbol:

Choose **Terminal style** to be **Circle, number inside**.
Set **Connection direction** to **left**.
Set **Number** to **'1'**.

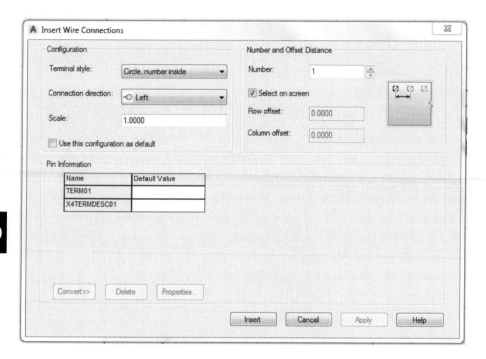

Click **Insert**. Use the cursor to position the terminal on the left side of the symbol, near the top.

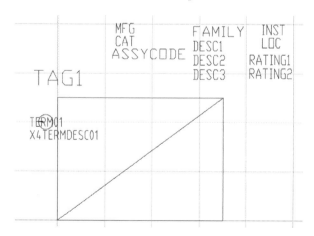

Now click the drawing again to add terminal **2** below it. Choose the **Right** symbol in the **Connection direction** box to add terminals **3**, **4** and **5** at the right of the symbol. Your symbol will now look like this:

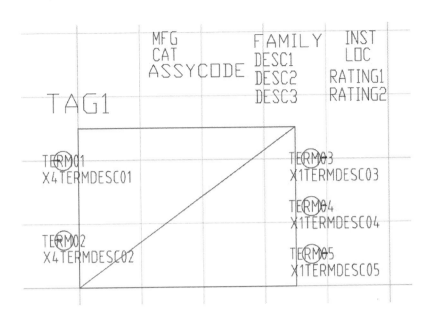

Saving the symbol

Close the **Symbol Builder Attribute Editor** window with the **X** so you can see the ribbon. Double-click on **Done**. Do not click **Close Block Editor**.

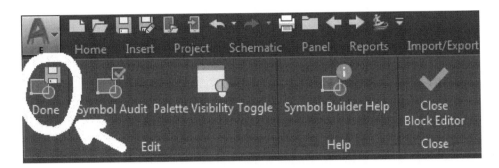

You will get the **Close Block Editor: Save Symbol** box.

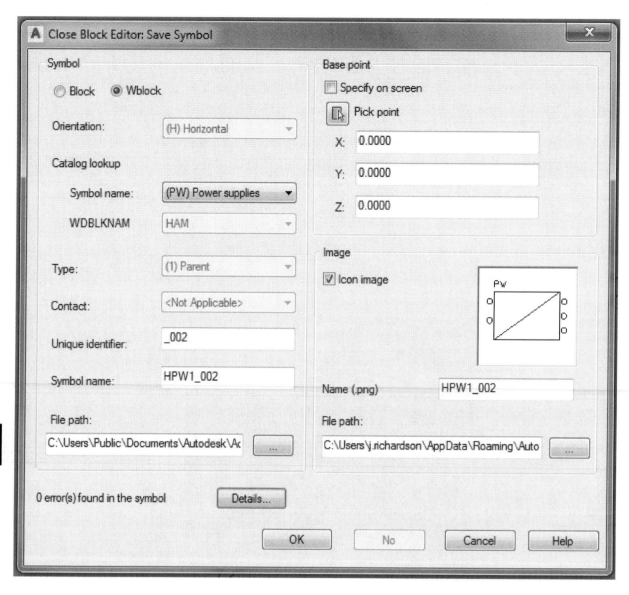

Take care with this box as there are many pitfalls.

Block or Wblock?

If you save as **Block**, the new symbol can only be used in this drawing. Instead we will save as **Wblock** which will save the symbol as a file, allowing it to be used in other drawings.

Base point

When you click to insert a symbol you expect it to be inserted at the point where you click. Failure to set up the base point can result in it being inserted somewhere else, far past the edge of your drawing.

To set the base point click the **Pick point** button under **Specify base point**. The dialogue box will be hidden to show the screen where you were drawing your new symbol. Click the point on your symbol which you wish to be at the cursor when you insert it, typically pick either the top left corner or one of the wire terminal connections.

After selecting a point the **Close Block Editor: Save Symbol** dialogue box returns and the correct coordinates will be entered in the **Base point** boxes

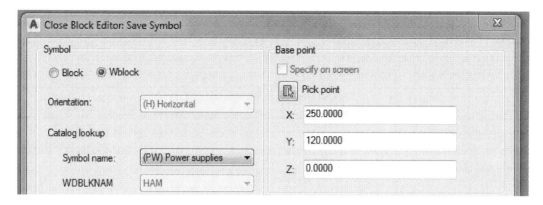

Symbol name

Symbol name is the filename for the new symbol. The first few letters must follow the AutoCAD Electrical naming rules. This is ensured by not typing in this box directly. Instead, this box is updated automatically from the boxes and drop down menus above it.

On earlier screens we already defined our symbol to be horizontal and a parent/stand alone component so these boxes cannot be changed here. The component category is **Power supplies** and this sets the family name to **PW**.

Unique identifier is suggested as **_002** in the screenshot. You may see another number. You can type anything you like in this box and it will be added to the codes at the start to form the full filename.

For our example there is no need to change the suggested value. If you do, remember what it is so you can find the file later.

For our new power supply symbol the file name will be **HPW1_002** so it will be saved as **HPW1_002.dwg**

Image

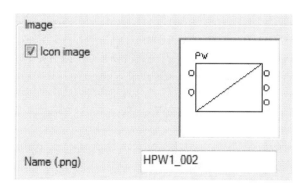

Under **Image**, ensure that the **Icon image** box is ticked. This creates an image (**.png** file format) of the symbol which we will need later to add the symbol into the **Icon Menu**.

A small drawing shows what our new symbol will look like. Below this is a box, **Name (.png)** which is the name for the image file. Leave this box alone. It will be filled in automatically to the same value as the symbol filename.

Filepath

There are two boxes asking for a file path. The one on the left is the location where the symbol itself will be saved. The one on the right, below the image, is the place where the image file is saved.

First we will set up the **File path** value at the left. Left click the box and hold down the mouse button while moving sideways to see the full content that is already in this box. By default it points to the folder for whichever symbol library you are using. In our examples this is **iec4**:

C:\Users\Public\Documents\Autodesk\Acade 2020\Libs\iec4

Use the **Browse** button (labelled "...") to point this path at the **CustomSymbols** folder you created earlier. If you did not create this folder you can create it now from within the **Browse** function.

Our new symbol will be saved here as a **.dwg** file.

Now click on the file path on the right under **Image**. This is the location where AutoCAD will save a **.png** image of your symbol for use in the **Icon Menu**. You will see the following default path:

C:\Users*your windows user name*\AppData\Roaming\Autodesk\AutoCAD Electrical 2020\R23.1\\enu\Support\IMAGES

Leave this path alone. It is the place to go if you ever want to find the image files for your custom symbols. The value **R23.1** will change for different versions of AutoCAD.

Before going further be sure you understand where your files are being saved. If necessary make a careful note of each file path and the symbol name. It is easy to create a symbol and not be able to find either the symbol file or its icon image when you come to add it to the **Icon Menu** in the next section.

Error(s) found in symbol

At the bottom left of the box is a warning of any errors in your symbol. Some of these can be very minor suggestions so will not necessarily be a problem for your symbol. Click **Details** to see the cause of any errors present.

Closing the window

When you are happy with the above information, click **OK**.

You will be asked if you want to insert the symbol.

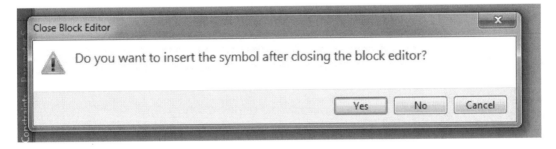

Click **Yes**.

You will find yourself back in your original drawing with your new symbol at the cursor ready for insertion. Left click on a blank space to the left of your drawing to insert the symbol as shown.

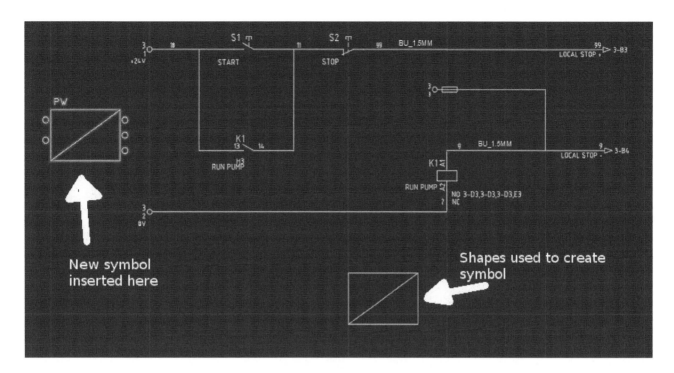

The **Insert / Edit Component** dialogue box will appear when you insert the symbol. The **Component Tag** value will default to **PW1**, since we included the letters **PW** as default data when we set up the **TAG1** attribute in the **Symbol Builder** tool.

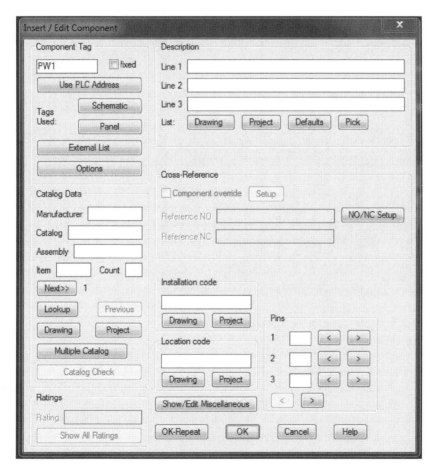

Type "**Instrument supply**" in **Description, Line 1**.
Type "**15V dual output**" in **Description, Line 2**.

Set the pin labels as follows:

Pin 1	+24V
Pin 2	0V
Pin 3	+15V
Pin 4	0V
Pin 5	-15V

You can use the **>** button to see pins 4 and 5.

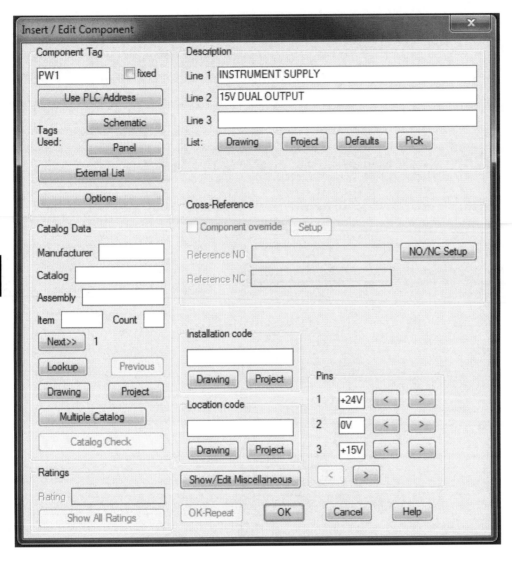

Click **OK**.

Your symbol will be inserted. When creating symbols try to avoid adding specific items like voltages or manufacturer's part numbers directly as text in **Symbol Builder**. Keep these as descriptions, ratings or other attributes so the same symbol can be reused in other projects.

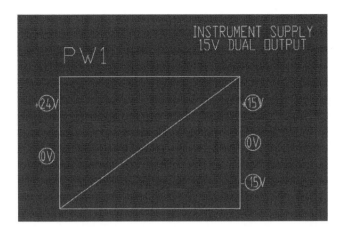

The attribute sizes and positions were set when you added them in the **Symbol Builder** tool. You can alter them after insertion as you would for any other symbol by selecting the component, right clicking and selecting **attributes** from the menu. In the screenshot below, the pin labels have been moved above the terminals.

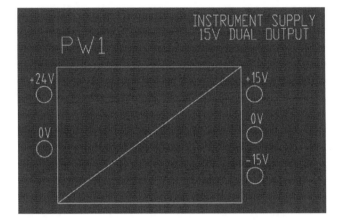

The initial drawing (the rectangle and diagonal line) that you produced for the symbol before entering **Symbol Builder** will still be present. You can delete it now.

Add two wires to the 24V side of the power supply. Use **Scoot** as required to move the existing supply terminals **3.1** (Terminal block **3**, terminal **1**) and **3.2** (Terminal block **3**, terminal **2**) to tidy up the drawing. It will now look like this.

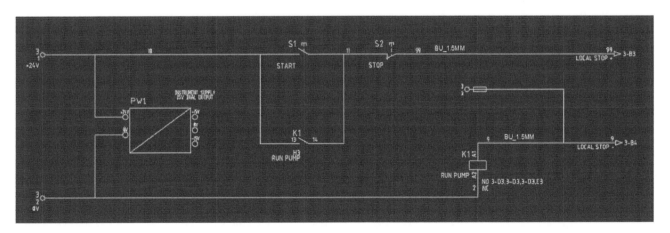

Save your drawing.

Finding your new symbol

You can use Microsoft Windows Explorer to check your new symbol file has been created.

You will find the file **HPW1_002.dwg** in the **CustomSymbols** folder you created at:

> **C:\Users\Public\Documents\Autodesk\Acade 2020\Libs\iec4\CustomSymbols**

This is the file for your custom component and contains all of the information required to use it in your drawings. You will also find a file called **HPW1_002.png** at the following location:

> **C:\Users\ *your windows user name* \AppData\Roaming\Autodesk\AutoCAD Electrical 2020\ R23.1\enu\Support\IMAGES**

This is a simple image file and you can open it with any software that views images or import it into Microsoft Word. Its purpose is to add a picture of your symbol to visual menus.

10.3   Modifying the Icon Menu

To re-use your new symbol easily in future drawings you can add it to the **Icon Menu**.

The details of this menu are stored in a **.DAT** file. For the**IEC4** symbol library used in this book we are using the **ACE_IEC_MENU.DAT** file.

This is a text file which includes links to the **IEC4** component **.dwg** files. These **.dwg** files are drawings which define the appearance, attributes and wire connections for the symbols. The power supply symbol we have just made is one such **.dwg** file.

The **.DAT** text file also includes a link to an image of each component. This is the small picture you see in the **Icon Menu** dialogue box when you insert a component. For our custom power supply this is a **.png** image file, a standard image format that you can view and edit in many non-Autodesk programs.

AutoCAD can also accept the images as slides, an AutoCAD file format with filename extension **.sld**. These can be grouped into one file as a slide library with filename extension **.slb**.

The supplied AutoCAD electrical component images are in libraries of this format, for example the **IEC4** images are in the slide library **iec1.slb**. Should you look at the **.DAT** files with a text editor you will see references to slides within a slide library file for these components, rather than a **.png** file.

The AutoCAD help documentation has information on creating and viewing slides but it is beyond the scope of this book.

Back up the .DAT file

Before altering the **Icon Menu** it is worth backing up the existing file.

You will find the **.DAT** files in the folder:

> **C:\Users\ *your windows user name* \AppData\Roaming\Autodesk\AutoCAD Electrical 2020\ R23.1\enu\Support**

The names **R23.1** and **enu** may be different if you are using a different version of AutoCAD or if you are using a version for a different language or country.

Find the **.DAT** file you are using. This is the one you have selected in your **Project Properties**. For the examples in this book it is **ACE_IEC_MENU.DAT**.

You can copy this file to a different name, for example **ACE_IEC_MENU_BACKUP_DAT**.

Alternatively make a copy and rename the copy as your custom menu, for example call it **CUSTOM_ACE_IEC_MENU.DAT**.

Then set your project properties to use **CUSTOM_ACE_IEC_MENU.DAT** for your project.

This menu would then be the one altered in the next section, leaving the original unchanged.

Adding a symbol to the Icon Menu

AutoCAD has a menu wizard tool which makes it easy to alter the supplied **Icon Menu**.

Click **Icon Menu Wizard** in the schematic tab.

You are asked to select a menu file to alter.

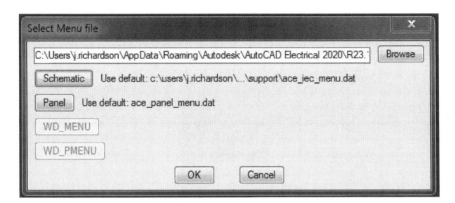

The box at the top shows which **.DAT** menu file will be changed.

The **Schematic** and **Panel** buttons provide a fast way of entering this file path. Clicking **Schematic** will enter the path of the schematic symbol menu currently assigned to the project in **Project Properties**. Clicking **Panel** will enter the path of the current panel footprint menu.

Click the **Schematic** button. Ensure the path shown is for the menu file you wish to alter.

Click **OK**. The **Icon Menu Wizard** appears. It looks like the menu you use to insert components.

Click **Add** and select **Component** from the submenu that appears

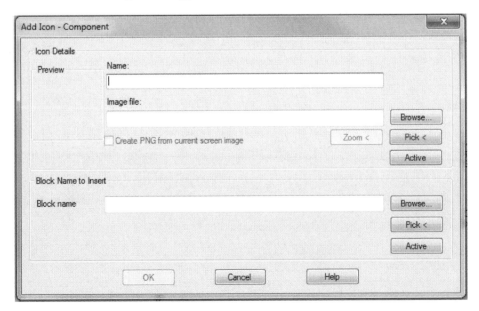

The **Add Icon** dialogue box appears

In the lower half of this box use the **Browse...** button to navigate to the place where you saved your new component as a **.dwg** file.

In the upper half of the box navigate to the place where you saved your image **.png** file. Once this is selected you will see a small preview of the symbol's image.

If you cannot find these then, provided you inserted a copy of the component when you closed the **Symbol Builder**, all is not lost. Use the **Pick <** button in each section to select the symbol on your drawing, both for the **Block Name to Insert** (the symbol) and the **Icon Details** (its picture for the menu).

In the very top box, **Name**, type the name you would like displayed beside your new symbol in the **Icon Menu**. For this example type **Dual PSU**.

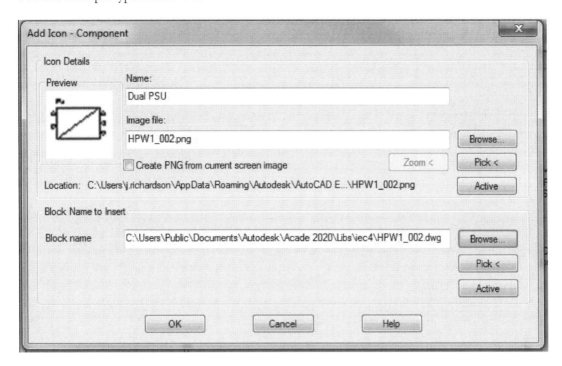

Click **OK** and you will see the **Icon Menu** with your new component added.

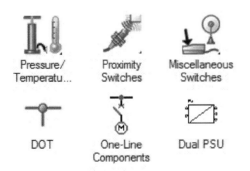

Click **OK** to exit the **Icon Menu Wizard**.

You can now insert your custom component from the **Icon Menu** as you would any other.

10.4   Tidying the Icon Menu

Adding components at the top level will soon make the menu messy.

If you double click on the existing folders (called submenus) for example **Relays / Contacts**, in the **Icon Menu Wizard,** you can navigate to lower levels of the menu and place your new components in the appropriate folder.

By selecting **New submenu** from the menu after clicking the **Add** button at the top right of the **Icon Menu Wizard** screen, you can create a new submenu, for example **Custom Symbols**, to store your components.

If you click a component or submenu once it will be selected. You can then right click the mouse to bring up a menu:

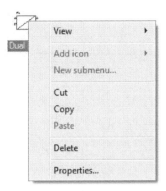

This allows you to delete symbols or submenus from the **Icon Menu** (the symbol files themselves will not be deleted). You can also cut and paste from one part of the menu structure to another. The **Properties...** option allows you to choose an image for a submenu, either using a file or by picking objects from your drawing.

When navigating through the structure you may wonder how to move up a level. This can be done by clicking in the **Menu** box on the left part of the **Icon Menu Wizard** shown below. Clicking **IEC: Schematic Symbols** in this box will take you to the top of the menu structure.

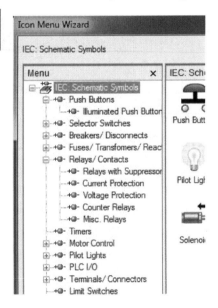

If you click the left mouse button over a component or submenu and hold it down, you can drag the symbols to an empty space (at the bottom of the box or between components). This lets you rearrange the order of components to put the most used ones at the top.

Modifying existing symbols

If you want to make a new symbol by modifying an existing one, you can open the existing symbol's **.dwg** file in the **Symbol Builder** tool and make changes. Save it in your custom library under a new filename and add it to the **Icon Menu**.

You will see a detailed walk-through for using the **Symbol Builder** in this way in chapter 17 when we create a new terminal footprint symbol by changing an existing one.

If your intention is to replace an existing symbol with a modified version then save the modified copy in your custom library under the same filename. You would not need to alter the **Icon Menu** in this case unless you wanted to change the icon image as well. Provided your custom library is listed first in **Project Properties**, AutoCAD will use the modified version instead of the original.

10.5 Purge command

When you insert a symbol or other block into an AutoCAD drawing, AutoCAD places the information about that block within the drawing. This information remains, even if you delete the symbol. This speeds up the software because it does not need to upload the information into memory when you next insert that symbol.

This process can create confusing side effects.

Suppose you create a new symbol, insert it into your drawing, and then decide you want to change it. When you insert the modified symbol you will get the old version because AutoCAD remembers the first time you used a symbol with that name. If you instead inserted it in a different drawing you would get the new version.

To fix this you must first ensure every instance of the old symbol has been deleted from the drawing and then purge the hidden information.

To do this select **Utilities** from the **Project** tab of the ribbon.

The **Project-Wide Utilities** box will open.

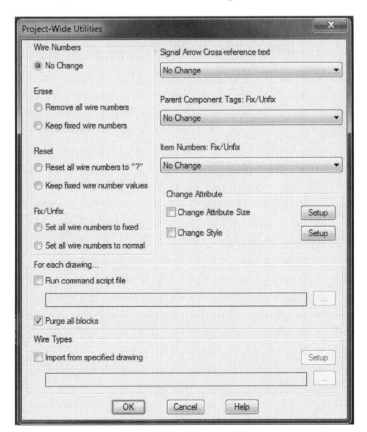

Tick the box **Purge all blocks**. Ensure nothing else is selected as shown above. Click **OK**. You will be asked if you wish to purge only the active drawing or every drawing in the project.

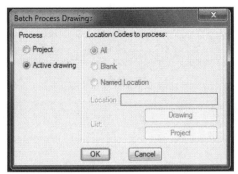

Select **Active drawing** and click **OK**.

If you wish to purge many drawings select **Project** instead of **Active drawing** and you will be asked which sheets to process.

There is no visible sign that anything has happened but the next blocks that are inserted will be loaded fresh from disk, rather than from within the drawing. Note that you cannot purge a component block unless every instance of that component has been deleted from the drawing first.

It is also possible to purge blocks by typing **PURGE** at the command line and selecting **Blocks** as the item to be purged. This is the underlying AutoCAD purge function, rather than the AutoCAD Electrical tool. It is safer to use the electrical version from the **Project** menu. This is less likely to accidently delete something needed by the AutoCAD Electrical system.

The command line version has the advantage that it lists the names of any blocks present which are allowed to be purged. This makes it is easier to see what is happening and whether a particular block is causing a problem. To see the list of blocks, click the **+** next to **Blocks** in the dialogue box of the command line version of the **Purge** command. If the **+** is not visible, there are no blocks to purge. Remember blocks are only available for purging if every instance of them in the drawing has first been deleted.

10

11. Connectors (15 minutes)

The AutoCAD Electrical program has a simple tool for drawing connectors. This tool will create connectors of any size as you need them.

In this chapter we will add a connector to the wires of the stop button on **sheet 3** of your project.

Open **sheet 3**.

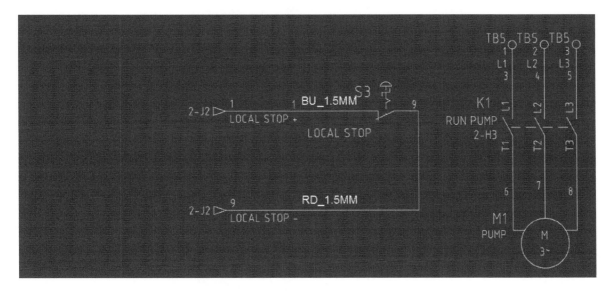

Select your components and move them to create some space at the left of the circuit. Then use **Scoot** to stretch the wires going to the stop button and move them closer together. If necessary use **Scoot** to move the wire numbers too. We want an uncluttered area where we can insert our connector.

You may need to update the signal and component cross-references so that the grid reference labels on components in your drawing remain correct.

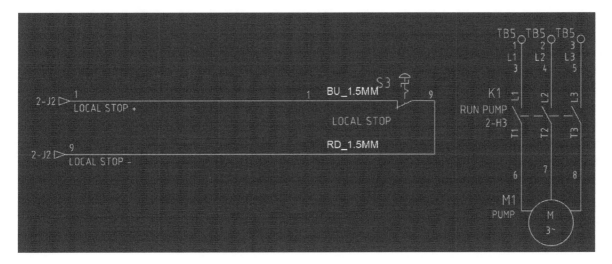

Click the **Insert Connector** button in the **Insert Components** panel of the **Schematic** tab.

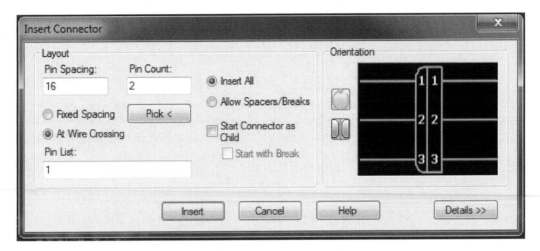

The **Insert Connector** dialogue box will be displayed.

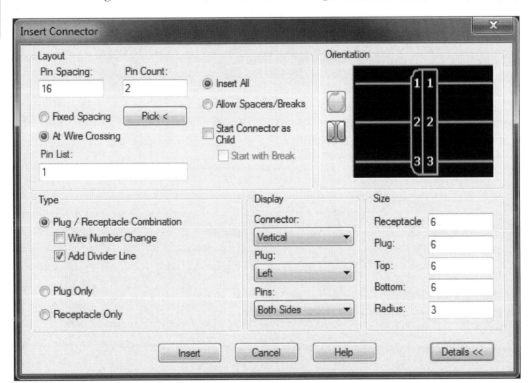

Part of this dialogue box is hidden. Click **Details >>** to get the full box.

We are going to draw a two pin connector so set **Pin Count** to **2**.

If you were to select **Fixed Spacing** then the connector would be drawn with equally spaced pins on a blank piece of your drawing. For a metric drawing, **5** is a sensible value for **Pin Spacing**.

Instead, for our example, select **At Wire Crossing**. This will let us insert the connector with spacing automatically adjusted to fit a set of existing wires.

Other settings

Using the settings shown above, AutoCAD will draw a plug and socket plugged into each other with wires coming out of each side. By unticking **Add Divider Line**, the vertical line between the two can be removed. The **Wire Number Change** tick box determines if AutoCAD considers the wire numbers to change when passing through the plug/socket combination.

Instead of selecting **Plug/Receptacle Combination** you can choose **Plug Only** or **Receptacle Only** to just draw one side of the connection. The plug is the side with the curved corners.

The pins are numbered starting with the value in the **Pin List** box. They normally start at **1** but you could add a list separated by commas, for example **L, N, E**.

The values on the bottom right are mostly cosmetic. You can have the connector **Vertical** or **Horizontal** with the plug on the **left** or **right**. The **Pins** item determines whether the pin labels are shown. The **Size** values for **Receptacle** and **Plug** determine the thickness of the symbol. **Top** and **Bottom** determine how far the ends of the connector stick out beyond the first and last pins. **Radius** controls how rounded the corners are. The values shown are reasonable settings to use on a metric drawing.

The preview picture shows the effect of your changes, except for the number of pins or changes to the **Size** values. The preview always shows a three pin connector with the same size settings. The buttons next to the preview picture allow you to flip and rotate the connector.

You can split large connectors into several parts which are in different places on your drawing. The points where a connector continues elsewhere can be shown with jagged lines at the break. There are also several tools to edit existing connectors. In this book we will only cover simple connectors but see the AutoCAD help for options if you want something more complicated.

11

Placing the connector

After entering your details in the **Insert Connector** dialogue box, click **Insert**.

Place the cursor over the top wire. You will see a dotted outline of the connector.

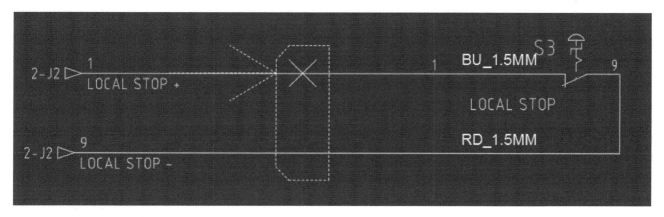

Left click the mouse to place the connector.

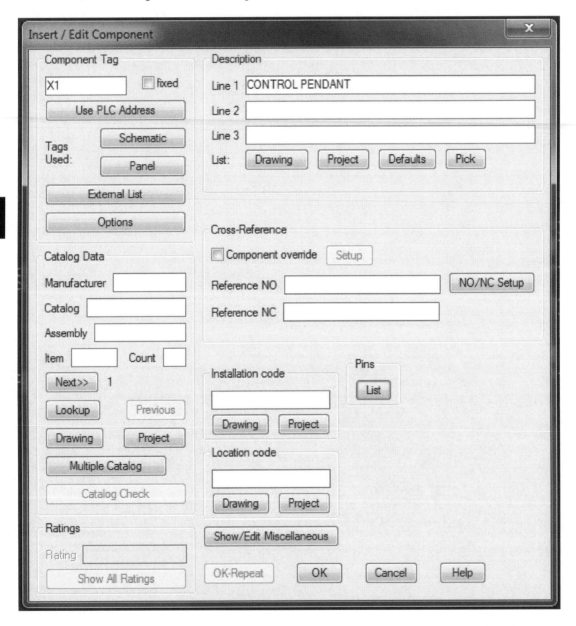

The **Insert/Edit Component** box will open.

Enter the description **Control Pendant** as a name for our connector. This will be shown as a label on the drawing.

If you want to edit the numbers or labels of the individual pins in a connector you can click the **List** button in the right hand part of the dialogue box under **Pins**. This will open the **Connector Pin Numbers In Use** dialogue.

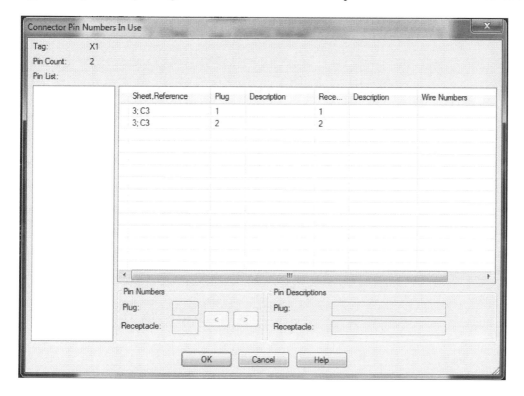

To use this dialogue box, click on a line at the top to highlight a particular pin. You can then change the pin number or add a pin description, for both plug and receptacle sides of the connector, by typing in the boxes at the bottom of the window.

Click **OK** to exit this box. Then click **OK** in the **Insert/Edit Component** dialogue box to finish inserting your connector. It should look like this:

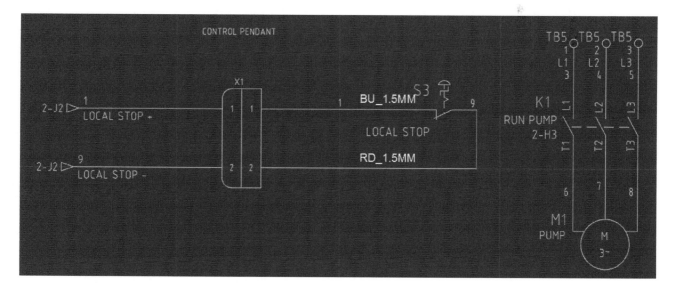

12. Location codes (30 minutes)

The electrical system you are designing might have equipment in several locations. In this chapter we look at:

- Location and installation codes
- Location boxes
- Project and drawing location settings

The AutoCAD Electrical software allows components to have an **installation code** and a **location code**. These can be combined with the component tag number to identify a specific component. If identical pieces of equipment exist in different places they could have the same component tags but be distinguished by different location or installation values.

If you were designing a large industrial facility, the **installation codes** might be substation, office, production line and pump house.

The **location codes** are below installation codes in the hierarchy. For example, individual panels within the substation or separate machines on the production line.

If you were designing a smaller piece of equipment then locations might be individual circuit boards or push button enclosures.

Since the AutoCAD tools can filter reports based on location and installation, you can also use these codes for more creative purposes. If you were designing a range of hydraulic power packs which could have one or two pumps, you might assign a separate installation code to all parts relating to the second pump.

12

Location codes would then be used alone to define physical positions. When a customer ordered a single pump model it would be easy to remove the parts for the second pump by excluding that installation from the bill of material report.

12.1 Entering location codes

Location codes can be entered in the **Insert/Edit Component** dialogue box.

Open **sheet 2** of your drawing. Select switch **S1**. Right click to bring up a menu and choose **Edit Component**.

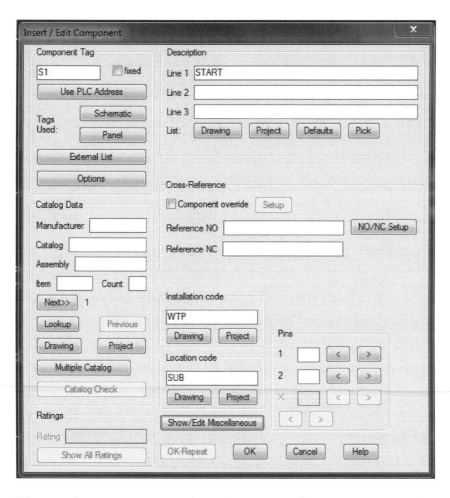

We are going to assume our schematics are part of a water treatment plant which we will assign as **installation** code **WTP**. This in turn might be part of a bigger facility with many installation codes. Within the water treatment plant we will have several **locations**, a substation (**SUB**), a pump room (**PR**) and a supervisor's office (**SOF**).

We want to show switch **S1** as being in the substation so enter the codes **WTP** and **SUB** in the **Installation** and **Location** code boxes for **S1** as shown above and click **OK**.

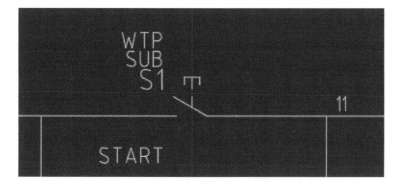

The switch, **S1,** is now assigned these location and installation codes. They are shown as attributes next to the switch symbol. You could enter installation and location codes using this method when you first insert your components. If you wish to change the location for many components there is a faster way, using the **Copy Installation/Location Values** tool.

On **sheet 2,** click the **Copy Installation/Location Values** button. This is in the drop down menu at the bottom of the **Edit Components** panel in the **Schematic** tab of the ribbon.

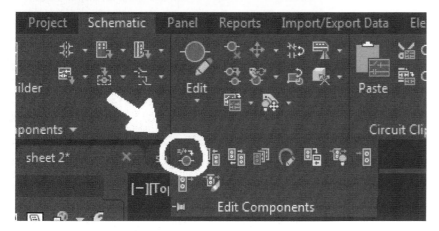

The **Copy Installation/Location to Component** dialogue box is shown.

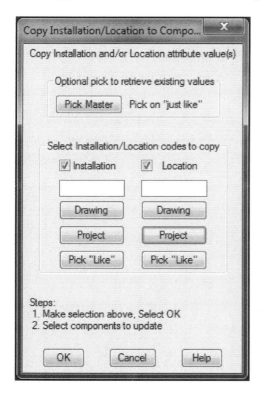

This box allows you to select a component whose installation and location codes you wish to copy using the **Pick Master** or **Pick "Like"** button. You can also select codes already used in the project or active drawing using the **Project** and **Drawing** buttons.

Alternatively, despite the name which implies always copying something, you can simply type the codes you want. If you leave the codes blank you can use the tool to remove codes from components. Tick boxes select whether you are changing the **Installation** code, the **Location** code or both.

For our example, ensure that both the **Installation** and the **Location** boxes are ticked. Type the codes **WTP** and **SUB** as shown below.

Click **OK**. You will be returned to your drawing with the cursor as a small hollow square. You must now select the components whose location you wish to change.

Select every component in **sheet 2** by dragging the mouse. Then press **<Enter>**. Since **K1** has a child contact on this sheet you are asked if you want to update it.

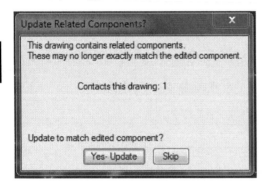

Click **Yes - Update**. You are also asked if you wish to update the related components on **sheet 3**.

Click **OK**. and agree when asked for permission to **QSAVE** the drawing. The attributes **WTP** and **SUB** will now be assigned to all components on **sheet 2**.

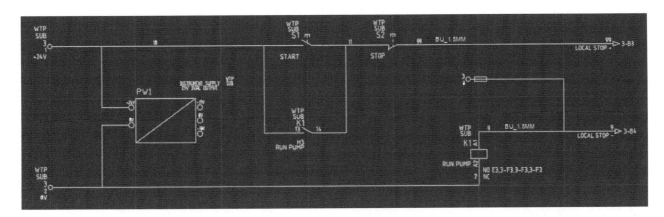

Depending on your version of AutoCAD, you might notice that location codes are not shown next to fused terminal **3.3**. In some versions of AutoCAD these attributes are set to hidden for this symbol. You can select this component, right click and use the **Attributes > List/Edit** function from the menu to fix this.

If you look at **sheet 3** you will see that the contacts for **K1** have also been updated. You may need to use **Move Attribute** to tidy the drawing if the text has been placed on top of the contact symbol.

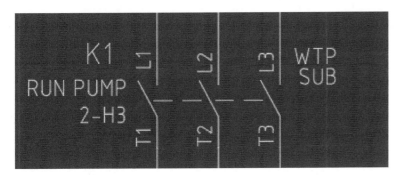

12.2   Location boxes

You might have a drawing where most components are in one place but a small group are located elsewhere. For this situation you can draw a **Location Box**.

On **sheet 2** we will use a **Location Box** to change the installation code of switches **S1** and **S2** to **SOF**, the code we are using for the supervisor's office.

Go to **sheet 2**. Click the **Location Box** button in the **Insert Components** panel of the **Schematic** tab of the ribbon.

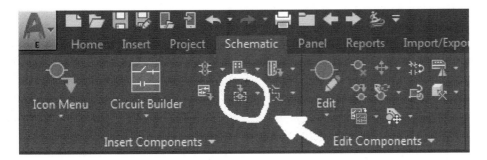

Left click on your drawing, above and to the left of **S1**, to mark one corner of the location box. Then click below and to the right of **S2** to mark the other corner. A dotted outline of the location box will be drawn and the **Location Box** dialogue window will appear.

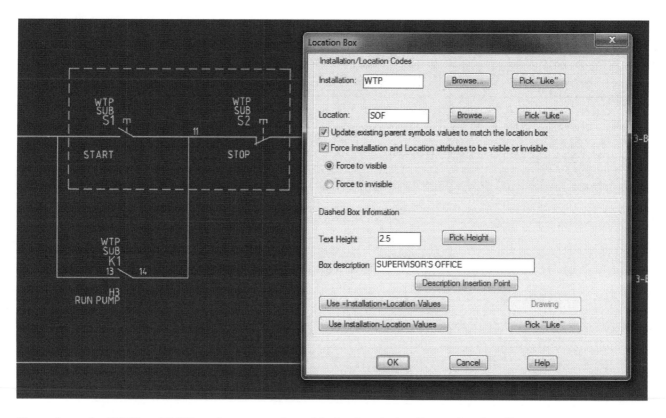

Enter the codes **WTP** and **SOF** as shown, together with the description **Supervisor's office**.

Tick the **Update existing parent symbols values to match the location box** option. Also tick **Force Installation and Location attributes to be visible or invisible** and set the selection below this to **Force to visible**. This will update the codes of the components inside the box and override individual visibility settings to ensure they are displayed.

Click **OK**. You will be asked if you want to scan for child components and update them. Agree to this although for these switches there aren't any.

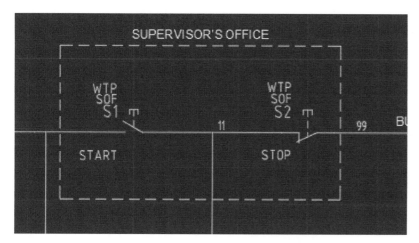

The location box will be drawn and the locations for switches **S1** and **S2** updated. The box is drawn using the **HIDDEN2** linetype.

If it is not drawn dashed then that is because you have not installed this linetype. See page 74.

Locations for sheet 3

Now go to **sheet 3**. Use the **Copy Installation/Location code values** button to set connector **X1**, **Local Stop** button **S3** and motor **M1** to have the location code **WTP** and the installation code **PR** (Pump Room).

The contacts for **K1** are already set to **WTP**, **SUB** because they are child components of the coil on **sheet 2**. Use a **Location Box** to emphasize this and also assign terminal block **TB5** as being in the substation with codes **WTP**, **SUB** and description **"Substation"**.

You drawing should be as below. In this image the location and installation codes within the location box are hidden but you could set them to be visible.

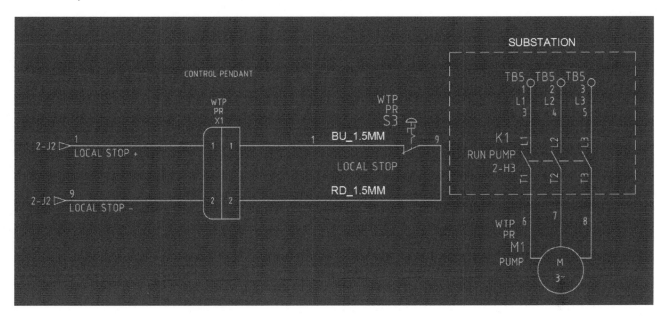

Save the **sheet 2** and **sheet 3** drawings.

12.3   Drawing location

In the **Drawing Settings** tab of **Drawing Properties** you can set an **Installation Code** or **Location Code** for a whole drawing.

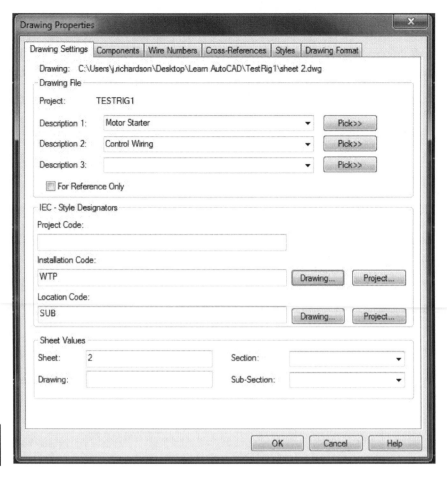

As with individual components, you can click the **Project** or **Drawing** buttons on this screen to select from a list of codes already used. When producing a title block template (Chapter 4) it is possible to display the drawing location and installation values as attributes on your title block in the same way that you included sheet number. The attribute for drawing **installation code** is **%I** and the attribute for drawing **location code** is **%L**.

Setting your drawing properties does not automatically update components already in the drawing to the new location codes. You must use either the **Copy Installation/Location Values** tool or the **Location Box** tool if you want to do this.

It is possible, however, to make new components default to the drawing location codes using an option in the project location settings described next.

12.4   Project location settings

In the **Components** tab of the **Project Properties** you will find a section for **Component TAG Options**. This section only exists at project level and is not present in the **Components** tab of the **Drawing Properties** for individual drawings.

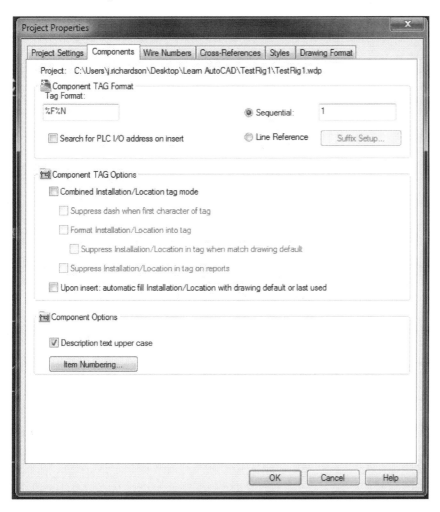

To allow duplicate component tags for components in different places, for example two switches called **S1** in different locations, tick the **Combined Installation/Location tag mode** box. You can then set the boxes below this to indicate whether you want the locations explicitly incorporated into the component tag text.

Leaving the **Combined Installation/Location tag mode** box unticked will keep all component tags in your project unique, regardless of location.

If you tick the **Upon insert: automatic fill Installation/Location with drawing default or last used** box then new components will have these location and installation values automatically entered in the **Insert/Edit Component** box when you create them.

This only applies when inserting new components. Existing components must be changed manually using other tools.

13. Wiring order (30 minutes)

Having drawn a schematic, it is possible to wire the equipment by printing the drawing and marking off each wire with a highlighter pen as it is fitted.

One problem with this is that a basic schematic only shows a number of points are connected together. It does not show the exact order in which the wires loop between them. Depending on how the person wiring the panel decides to fit the cables, several panels built from the same drawing could be wired in different ways.

The AutoCAD Electrical software can produce a from/to wiring list as a report, giving a neater way to instruct your panel wirers. It also allows you to incorporate the exact wiring order into the schematic.

This chapter covers the following topics:

- Creating a **From/To** wiring report
- Controlling the wiring sequence with the **Edit Wiring Sequence** and **Show Wiring Sequence** tools
- Use of **Angled Tees** to control and display wiring order
- Potential conflict between **Angled Tees** and other wiring sequence tools

13.1 Create a new drawing for the From/To report

Create a new drawing by right clicking the **TestRig1** project title in the **Project Manager** window and selecting **New Drawing...** from the menu that appears. Remember that you need to have a drawing already open to do this.

Call the new drawing **sheet 4** and use the **first_template.dwt** template. You can also type **Reports** for the **Description 1** value as shown below.

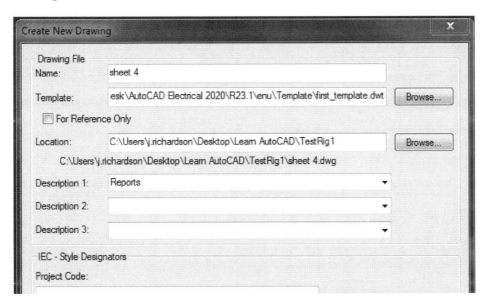

Click **OK** and, when prompted, click **Yes** to apply the project defaults to the new drawing. The new drawing will open and will be listed under **TestRig1** in the **Project Manager** window.

13.2   From/To wiring report

Click on **Reports** in the **Schematic** panel of the **Reports** tab of the ribbon. There are several **Reports** buttons so be sure to select the right one.

The **Schematic Reports** dialogue box will appear. At the left of this box, under the heading **Report Name**, click **From/To** to select a **From/To** wiring report as shown below.

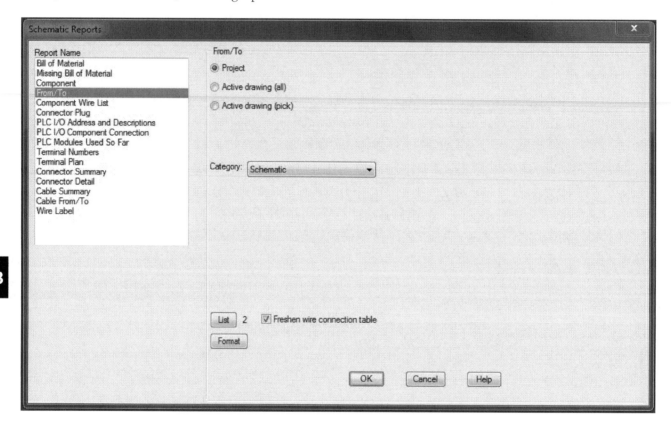

The tick box **Freshen wire connection table** ensures the report is up to date with the latest changes to your drawings. The number beside this, if present, indicates how many drawings AutoCAD thinks have changed since it last updated its database. Click the **List** button to see which sheets have changed.

The radio buttons at the top select whether to base the report on the whole project or the current drawing. For our example, select the whole project by clicking the **Project** radio button and click **OK**.

Agree when asked to **QSAVE** the drawing. When asked which drawings to process, select **Do All** and click **OK** again.

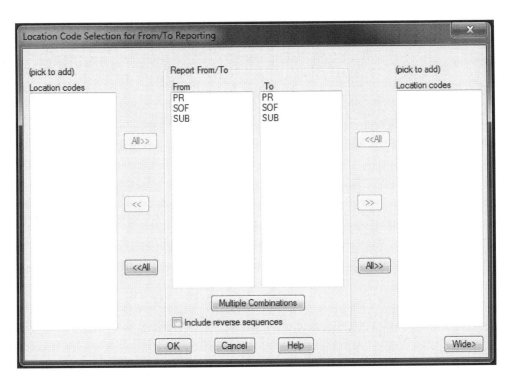

You are now asked which **Location codes** you want to include in the report. **Location codes** which could hold the ends of wires are listed at the far left and far right of the dialogue box. Click **All>>** and **<<All** to move these to the columns in the centre which are the locations to be included in the report. The screen should then be as shown above.

Click **OK**.

You will see the **Report Generator** window with a preview of your report.

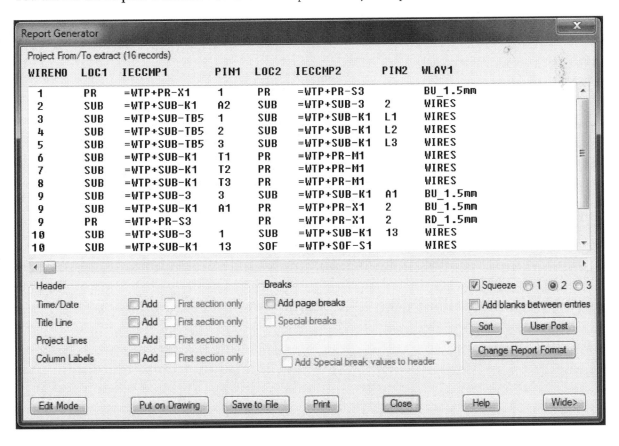

The **From/To** report lists every wire number. For each wire it gives the location and component at each end. The component tags have the **location** and **installation** codes included in the tag names. **Pin1** and **Pin2** give the component pins if they are included in the component symbols, for example pins **A1** and **A2** for relay coil **K1**.

Terminal blocks use the name of the block (**Tag strip**) as the component tag, for terminal block **5** we used **TB5** which makes the list very clear. For terminal block **3** we just used **3** as the **Tag strip** value so the report is less clear. The number of the individual terminal is used as the pin number, for example terminal **2** in block **3** is given as tag **WTP+SUB-3** and its pin as **2**.

Wires that connect more than two components are listed a number of times, once for each length of wire. For example wire **9** is in three sections:

1. **Terminal block 3, fused terminal 3** to relay **K1, pin A1** in blue 1.5mm² wire
2. **Relay K1, pin A1** to **connector X1 plug, pin 2** in blue 1.5mm² wire
3. **Switch S3** (pin not labelled) to **connector X1 socket, pin 2** in red 1.5mm² wire

When building the equipment, three lengths of wire would be used to achieve this. Note that you may have used different wire colours in your drawing.

There are some cosmetic options on the **Report Generator** screen to change the headings and spacing of the report.

If you wish instead to change which items of information are displayed, click **Change Report Format.** This opens the following box, allowing you to change which pieces of information (fields) are displayed for each wire.

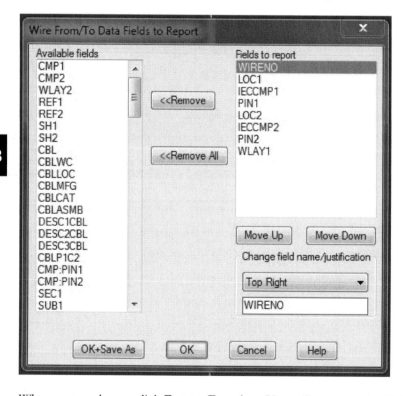

When you are happy click **Put on Drawing**. You will now see the **Table Generation Setup** screen.

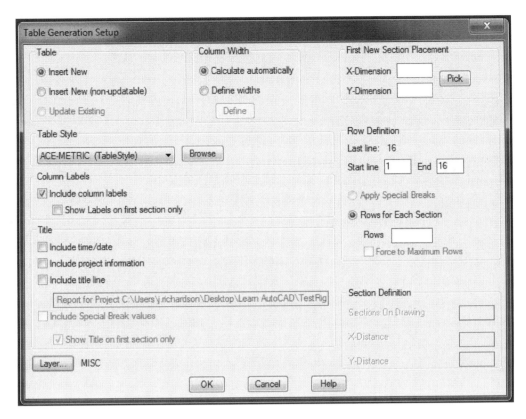

Ensure you select **ACE-METRIC (TableStyle)** under **Table Style** if you are using a metric template for your drawing. Otherwise your table will be tiny.

Click **OK** and then click on your drawing to place the table. It will look like this:

WIRENO	LOC1	IECCMP1	PIN1	LOC2	IECCMP2	PIN2	WLAY1
1	PR	=WTP+PR-X1	1	PR	=WTP+PR-S3		BU_1.5mm
2	SUB	=WTP+SUB-K1	A2	SUB	=WTP+SUB-3	2	WIRES
3	SUB	=WTP+SUB-TB5	1	SUB	=WTP+SUB-K1	L1	WIRES
4	SUB	=WTP+SUB-TB5	2	SUB	=WTP+SUB-K1	L2	WIRES
5	SUB	=WTP+SUB-TB5	3	SUB	=WTP+SUB-K1	L3	WIRES
6	SUB	=WTP+SUB-K1	T1	PR	=WTP+PR-M1		WIRES
7	SUB	=WTP+SUB-K1	T2	PR	=WTP+PR-M1		WIRES
8	SUB	=WTP+SUB-K1	T3	PR	=WTP+PR-M1		WIRES
9	SUB	=WTP+SUB-3	3	SUB	=WTP+SUB-K1	A1	BU_1.5mm
9	SUB	=WTP+SUB-K1	A1	PR	=WTP+PR-X1	2	BU_1.5mm
9	PR	=WTP+PR-S3		PR	=WTP+PR-X1	2	RD_1.5mm
10	SUB	=WTP+SUB-3	1	SUB	=WTP+SUB-K1	13	WIRES
10	SUB	=WTP+SUB-K1	13	SOF	=WTP+SOF-S1		WIRES
11	SOF	=WTP+SOF-S1		SOF	=WTP+SOF-S2		BU_1.5mm
11	SOF	=WTP+SOF-S2		SUB	=WTP+SUB-K1	14	BU_1.5mm
99	SOF	=WTP+SOF-S2		PR	=WTP+PR-X1	1	BU_1.5mm

After inserting the table the **Report Generator** dialogue will be re-displayed. If you are finished you can close this. The **Location Code Selection** screen will then appear. Click **Cancel** to close that screen as well and get back to your drawing.

To update the wiring **From/To** report just repeat the process of creating it and the new table will replace the old one. Save your drawings.

Saving to file

The **Report Generator** dialogue has an option to save to a file. Instead of **Put on Drawing**, click **Save to File**. The following box will be displayed:

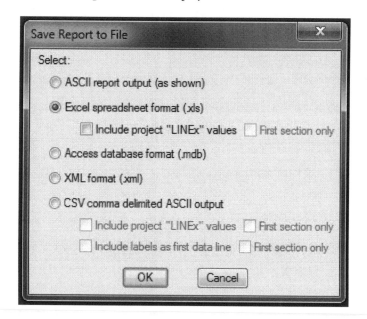

To save as a Microsoft Excel file, tick **Excel spreadsheet format (.xls)** and click **OK**. When asked, select a filename and location to save the file.

You will be asked if you wish to send the file to an automated script.

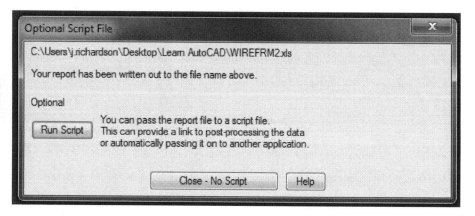

Click **Close - No Script**.

Then close the **Report Generator** dialogue box and click **Cancel** on the **Location Code Selection** screen to get back to your drawing.

You can now open the saved file in Microsoft Excel and use it to produce documents for your installation team.

13.3   Wiring order

Now that you can produce a **From/To** list, you may find the wiring is not happening in the order you would like. On the schematic you can check this order using the **Show Wire Sequence** tool.

Open **sheet 2**. Go to the **Edit Wires/Wire Numbers** panel on the **Schematic** tab of the ribbon. Click the drop down arrow at the bottom.

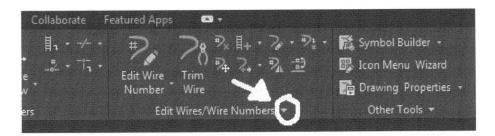

You will see a new row of buttons that were previously hidden. **Edit Wire Sequence** and **Show Wire Sequence** can be accessed here by a drop down menu next to whichever one is on top.

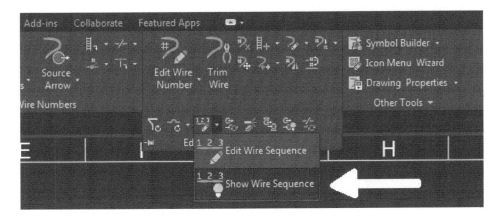

Start by choosing **Show Wire Sequence**. The cursor will change to a small hollow square. Left click on the wire network between switches **S1** and **S2**. AutoCAD will highlight the first direct connection with a series of small, green arrows between two components. Older versions of AutoCAD Electrical will use a thick line, rather than the arrows.

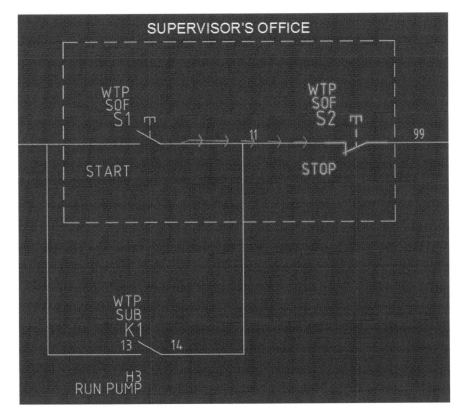

Now press **<Space>** (the command line will tell you to do this if it is open). A second set of green arrows will be drawn showing the second direct connection.

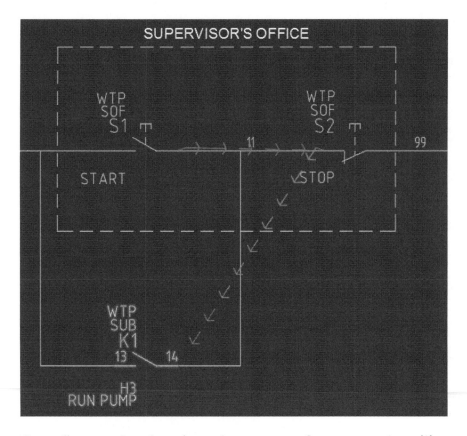

Once all connections have been shown, press **<Space>** to exit or **'1'** to cycle through them again. If the command line is visible you will be prompted to do this.

In the above example it can be seen that the actual wire goes from switch **S1** to **S2**, then from **S2** to **K1**.

If several panels are being built, the wiring sequence information in the **From/To** report can be used to wire them in identical ways. This information also lets the designer check practical aspects, for example, ensuring that the terminal of **S2** is big enough to take two wires and only having one core, not two, between the substation and the supervisor's office.

Changing wire sequence

The sequence assigned by AutoCAD may be undesirable. You might want to change it to reduce the amount of wire needed or to avoid multiple terminations at components best suited to a single wire.

To change the sequence select **Edit Wire Sequence** from the **Edit Wires/Wire Number** drop down on the **Schematic** tab.

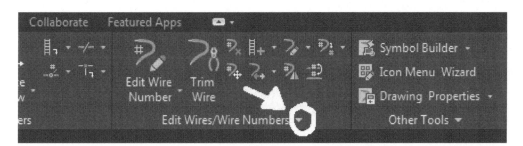

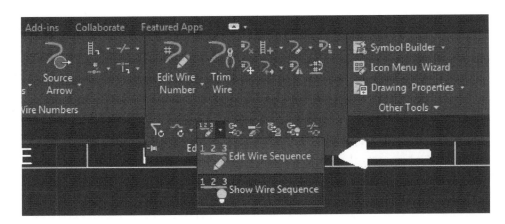

The cursor becomes a small hollow square. Click on the wire network between **S1** and **S2** again. A table is shown listing all connection points in the network. They are listed in the order that they are wired.

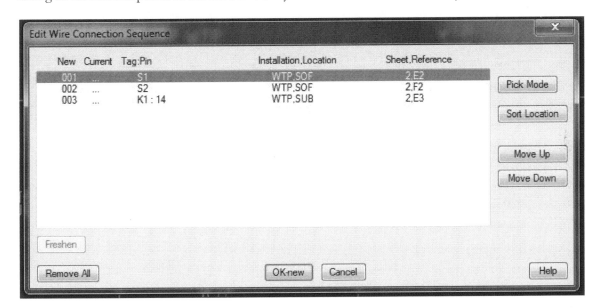

In the above example it can be seen that wiring starts at **S1** (the first line) and then goes next to **S2** (the second line). A wire then goes from **S2** to **K1, pin 14** (the final line).

To change the order, click on the last line to highlight it and click the **Move Up** button.

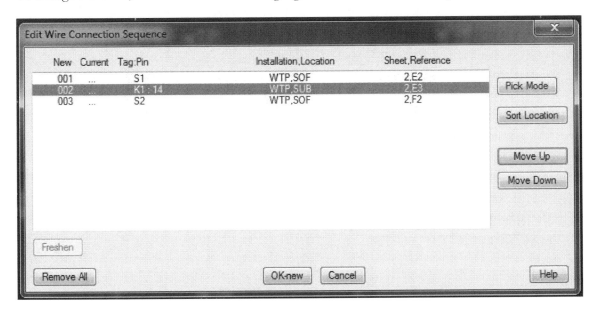

Wiring will now go first from **S1** to **K1** and then from **K1** to **S2**. After re-ordering click the **OK-new** button. This accepts your changes and goes back to the small, hollow square cursor, ready to edit the wire sequence of another network. If you do not want to edit any more networks, press **<Esc>** after getting back to the cursor to exit the tool.

If you have worked through this example you can now use the **Show Wire Sequence** tool to confirm your changes have worked.

13.4   Angled tees

By using angled tees instead of normal tees to join wires, you can make the wire sequence easily visible, even on printed copies of your schematic. To change a normal tee to an angled one, click on the **Insert Angled Tee Markers** button in the **Insert Wires/Wire Numbers** panel on the **Schematic** tab of the ribbon. It will be in a drop down menu under the **Insert Dot Tee Markers** button.

Click on the tee you want to modify (You must have the cursor very close to the point where the wires meet) and it will change to an angled one showing the sequence.

Try this on the wire beside terminal **3.1** as shown below.

Do not try it on a wire you have already modified using the **Edit Wire Sequence** tool as the two tools can conflict

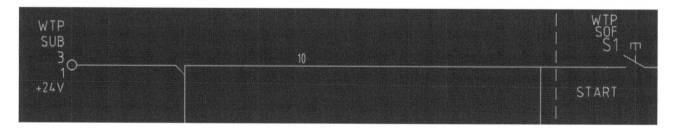

After inserting an angled tee you may wish to modify the wiring order it defines. Left click the tee to select it. Then right click on empty space on the drawing to bring up the following menu:

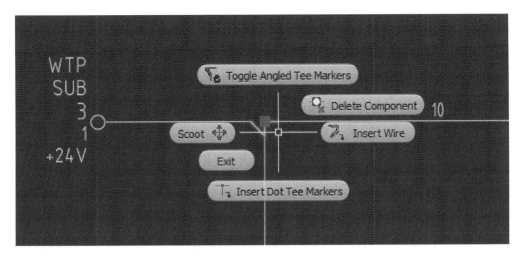

Select **Toggle Angled Tee Markers** from this menu to change the wiring order. You can then press **<Space>** to cycle through different orientations for the tee. If the command line is open you will be prompted to do this. Press **<Esc>** to stop altering the tee.

If you wish to remove the tee and go back to an ordinary wire joint you can select **Delete Component** from this menu and the tee will be removed.

You can try changing the tee marker and then updating the wire **From/To** report to see how the wire sequence changes.

13.5   Setting angled tees as a default

If you use angled tees all of the time you can set them as a default by selecting **Angle 1** or **Angle 2** in the **Styles** tab of **Drawing Properties** and **Project Properties**. This will draw an angled tee on each new wire joint you draw. Existing joints are not affected.

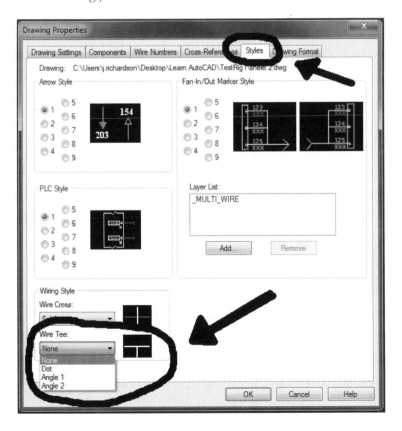

13.6   Conflict between Edit Wire Sequence and angled tees

You should avoid mixing the **Edit Wire Sequence** / **Show Wire Sequence** tools and angled tees.

If you use an angled tee the **Show Wire Sequence** tool will no-longer work on that wire network. It is not needed however as the tee itself shows the sequence.

If you add an angled tee to a network where you have already used the **Edit Wire Sequence** tool then the tee will be shown but will not change the wire sequence. In this case the **Show Wire Sequence** tool will ignore the tee and still work. The tee itself will have no effect and may show an incorrect wiring order that differs from that displayed by the **Show Wire Sequence** tool and the **From/To** report.

This behaviour is seen in AutoCAD Electrical 2020 and might change in other versions.

Generally you are advised to choose one method of defining the wire sequence and stick to it.

13

14. Cables (1½ hours)

The wires we have drawn so far are single core conductors, as might be found within a panel. Connections between panels are usually made with multicore cables containing several conductors. The AutoCAD Electrical software has tools to represent these.

This chapter explains how to:

- Mark a group of wires as a cable
- Add cable details from the AutoCAD catalogue
- Create cable reports
- Use the **Fan In / Fan Out** tool

It would be nice if you could just click on a group of wires, tell the AutoCAD Electrical software that they are a cable and then have the AutoCAD Electrical program do the rest. Unfortunately it is not that simple. Cables in AutoCAD are represented using a combination of wire layers and special components. You should understand the way that this representation works.

In AutoCAD Electrical, cables are shown by initially drawing the cable conductors as individual wires. A cable marker is inserted into the first core. This cable marker is actually a component. It has a symbol which looks like a cable marker but which can also be assigned catalogue data to represent the type of cable purchased and produce an entry in the bill of material. Cable markers are also inserted in the other cores. These look the same as the first marker but are child components linked to the marker on the first core.

This system is sufficient to record information about your cables. There is a further refinement that is purely cosmetic, the **Fan In / Fan Out** command. This joins the cores together into a single line representing the cable then fans them out again at the other end.

The important thing to remember about this command is that cables in AutoCAD are primarily handled using the cable marker method. The **Fan In / Fan Out** tool makes your drawing look nice but the intelligence that drives your reports and bill of material is in the cable markers.

The **Fan In / Fan Out** tool does the following things:

- It allows you to break the wires and continue them elsewhere. It adds source/destination references on the individual cores. These are similar to the source/destination arrows that we used in chapter 8.
- It draws a single line between these to make the drawing look nice
- It puts the single line on a layer defining it as a multicore cable

This system works once you realise what is happening but it is a complicated method and it can be difficult to make AutoCAD transfer all information across the **Fan In / Fan Out** section of the drawing automatically.

14.1   Drawing a cable

At the bottom of **sheet 2**, in a space below your motor starter circuit, draw two sets of four terminals as shown below.

Use the symbol **Round with terminal number**.

Number terminals on the left as tag strip **1** and those on the right as tag strip **2**.

Give the left terminals the **Installation** code **WTP** and **Location** code **SUB**. Give the right hand side terminals the **Installation** code **WTP** and **Location** code **PR**.

Join the pairs of terminals with wires and number these wires sequentially starting at **101**.

Scoot the wire numbers close to the terminals on the left and use the **Copy Wire Number** tool to place duplicate wire numbers at the other end. This will leave space in the middle for our cable markers.

From the **Schematic** tab of the ribbon, select **Cable Markers**.

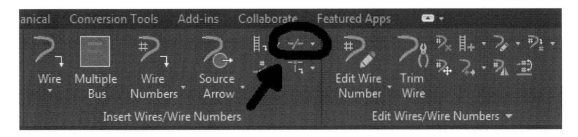

The insert cable marker dialogue box will appear.

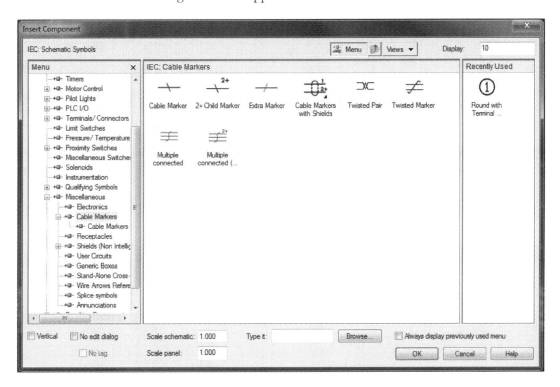

You will recognise this as the **Insert Component** dialogue box you have used for component symbols. In fact you could insert cable markers using the **Icon Menu** as you would for any other component if you preferred.

The **Cable Marker** components are simply schematic components with no wire number change and the correct letters in their symbol filename to tell AutoCAD they are cable markers. You will see there are several special cable marker symbols to show screened cables and twisted pairs. You could even create your own using the **Symbol Builder** tool if you follow the AutoCAD file naming convention correctly.

We are only going to use the most basic symbol, called **Cable Marker**.

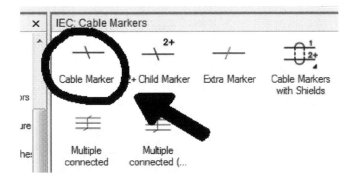

Choose this symbol and insert it on the top wire of the schematic with the cursor. Position it towards the left as shown below.

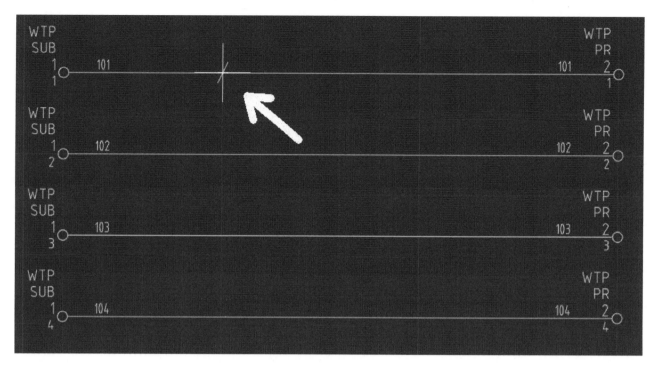

When you insert the marker the **Insert / Edit Cable Marker (Parent wire)** dialogue box will appear.

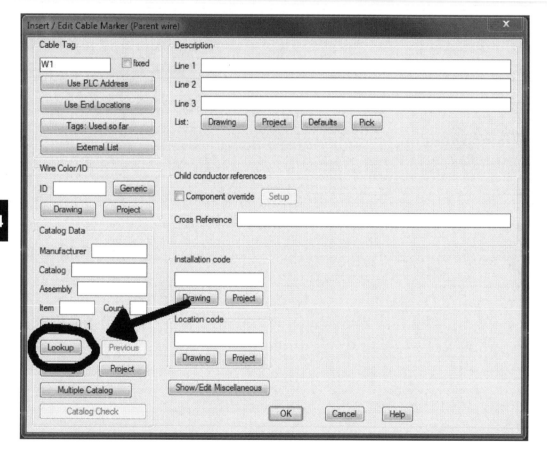

We are going to use a cable type from the AutoCAD Electrical catalogue of manufacturers' parts. To follow the example ensure you have the component database for the company **LAPP** included (see page 4).

Click **Lookup**. The **Catalog Browser** will open.

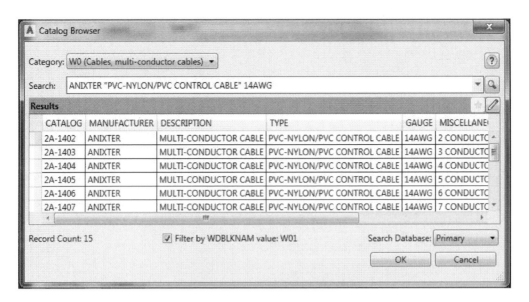

The cable we are going to use is from the LAPP Olflex 110 range. It is a 4 core 4mm² cable with manufacturer's part number **1120360**. This cable has three black numbered cores and one green/yellow earth core.

Ensure the category **W0 (Cables, multi-conductor cables)** is selected in the **Category** box.

In the search box type **Lapp 1120360**. This will search for entries containing the terms **"Lapp"** and **"1120360"** anywhere in their information. If you did not know the part number you could search for **Lapp Olflex 110**, which would give you a list of cables in that product range.

Click the magnifying glass button to carry out the search. You will see the cable type listed.

If the cable you wish to use is not included in the AutoCAD catalogue, you can create a new catalogue entry. Creating new catalogue entries will be covered in chapter 15.

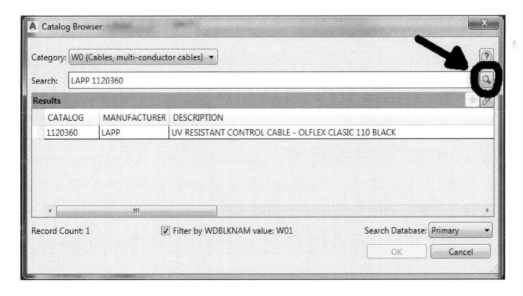

Left click the line in the catalogue with the desired part to select it. Then click **OK**.

It is easy to forget and click **OK** without selecting the line, in which case you will need to click **Lookup** once more and try again.

The **Insert / Edit Cable Marker (Parent wire)** box will reappear with the cable catalogue data filled in.

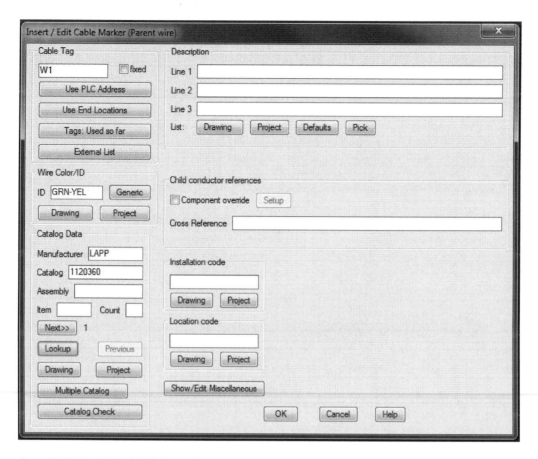

AutoCAD has identified from the catalogue information that the first core of the cable has a **Wire Color/ID** of green/yellow (**GRN-YEL**). You can change this by typing different text or by clicking the **Generic** button to get a list of suggested abbreviations for wire colours.

AutoCAD has assigned the cable with the component tag **W1**. '**W**' is the family code to represent a cable and the number '**1**' is an identification number for this particular cable. We could let AutoCAD assign cable tags sequentially as we create them on the drawing. Alternatively we might already have a number in mind for this cable. Let us assume we want this cable to be number **536**. We could leave '**W**' as the prefix or change this to a different letter code, either manually or by altering the family code AutoCAD uses for cables.

For our example, type the new tag name as **cable 536** and set this to **fixed**. Also add **Description** information in **Line 1** and **Line 2** as shown in the following image.

14

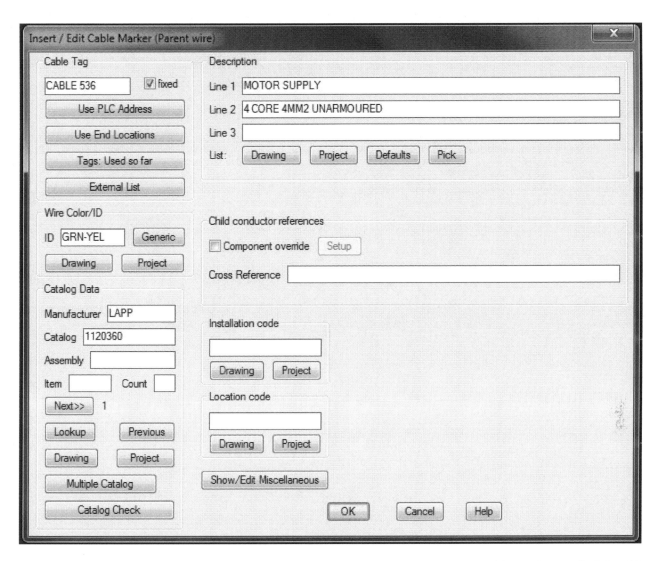

Click **OK** to insert the symbol. You will be asked if you always want to use this cable marker symbol for this catalogue item.

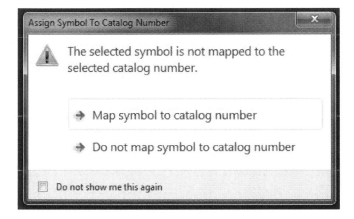

Since you probably will, you might as well click **Map symbol to catalog number**. If you were to enter the cable by choosing a catalogue part in the **Catalog Browser**, rather than by inserting a schematic symbol, AutoCAD would now use this cable marker as the default suggestion.

14

The cable symbol will be inserted. You are asked if you want to insert a child component.

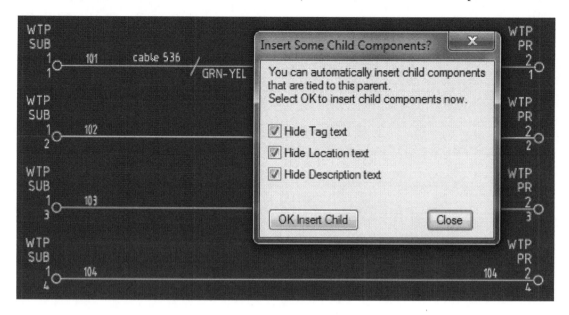

Child components are used for the other cores of the cable.

The **Hide Tag text, Hide Location text** and **Hide Description text** tick boxes in the **Insert Some Child Components?** dialogue window prevent the cable information being repeated for every core of the cable. Normally you will leave them ticked to avoid cluttering the drawing.

Click **OK Insert Child** and select the next wire to insert a cable marker below the first.

A marker will be placed on the second core and the **Insert / Edit Cable Marker (2nd+ wire of cable)** dialogue box will open.

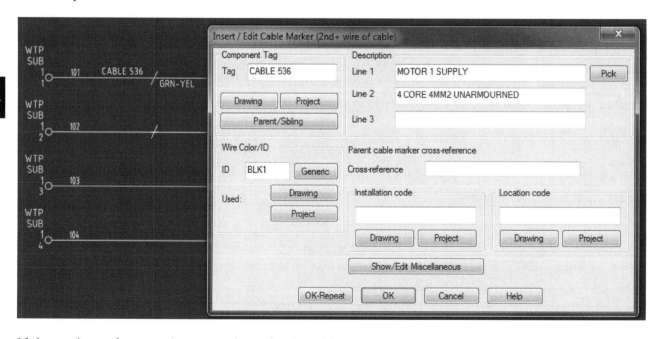

If the catalogue data contains core colours for the cable then these will be entered automatically in the **Wire Color/ID** field. For our example the second core of the cable is black and marked with a number 1 inside the cable. This is shown as **BLK1**.

Change the **Wire color/ID** if necessary, otherwise click **Ok-Repeat** and continue to insert markers for the third and fourth cores.

The finished cable will look like this.

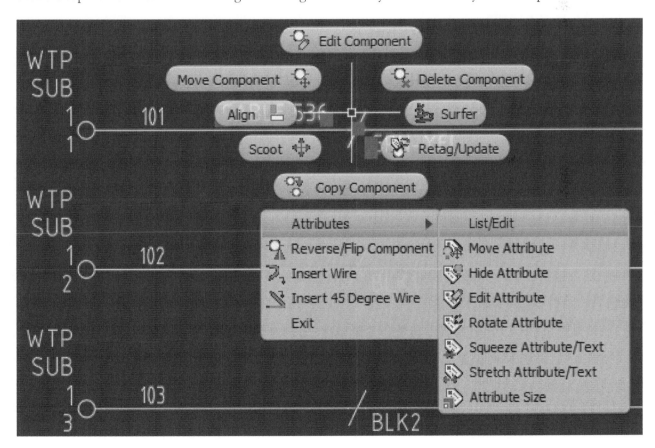

Our cable descriptions are invisible. If you have added descriptions you will need to unhide these attributes. Left click the top marker to select it. Then right click to get a menu as you would for any other component.

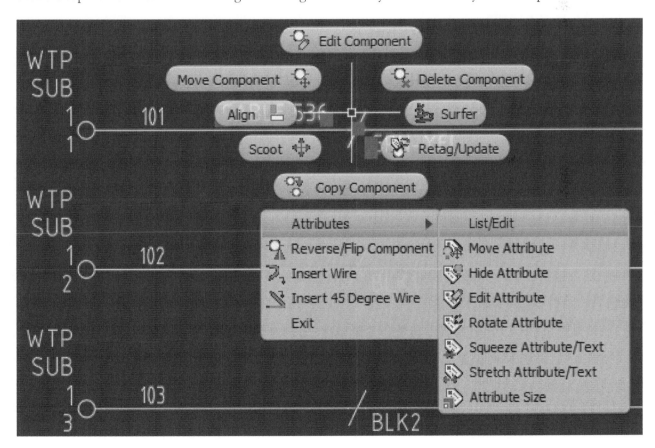

From here you could click **Edit Component** if you need to modify information about your cable after you have inserted it.

We are going to modify the attribute visibility. Hover the mouse over **Attributes** and select **List/Edit** from the sub-menu that appears. This will give a list of the attributes for the parent symbol of the cable.

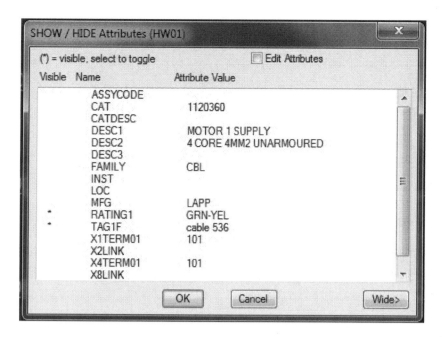

You can see that the **RATING1** and **TAG1** attributes are visible because they have an asterisk '*' in the **Visible** column. Click in the **Visible** column beside the **DESC1** and **DESC2** attributes to toggle these from invisible to visible. Press **OK** and you will see our descriptions on the finished cable.

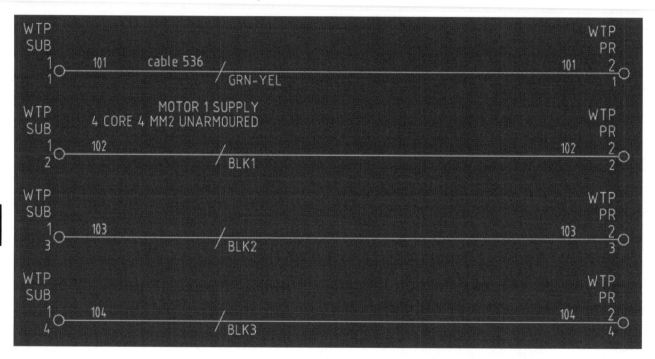

You can also move attributes as you would for any other component to make the drawing neater.

Save the drawing.

14.2   Cable reports

Now that we have correctly set up a cable, we can create cable reports. Ensure that the project you are working on is the active project, otherwise the reports will not be generated correctly. First we will generate a list of cables in the project. After that we will look at the more useful **Cable From/To** report.

We will put these on **sheet 4** of our drawing. Open **sheet 4** now.

Cable list report

Go to the **Reports** tab on the ribbon. Click the **Reports** button on the **Schematic** panel at the left. Do not confuse this with the other button, also called **Reports**, in the **Panel** section of the **Reports** tab.

The **Schematic Reports** dialogue box will open. Click on **Cable Summary** under the **Report Name** list on the left.

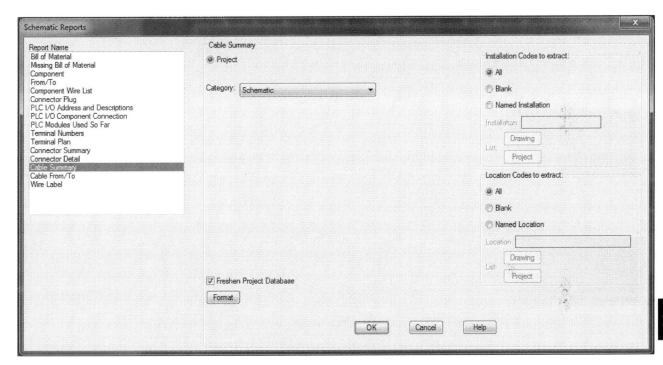

Leave **Category** as **Schematic** and keep **All** selected for **Installation codes to extract** and **Location codes to extract**. Ensure **Freshen Project Database** is ticked.

Click **OK**. You will be asked which drawings to process. Select **Do All** and click **OK** again. You will see a dialogue box containing a preview of the report.

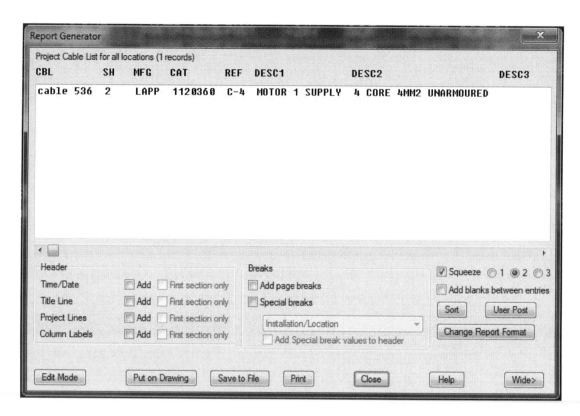

This report lists each cable in the drawings you selected. In this example our project only contains one cable.

The report gives its tag number (**cable 536**), its manufacturer and manufacturer's part number and the text we entered as a description for this particular cable. The sheet number (**SH**) of the drawing and the X-Y grid reference (**REF**) within that drawing, are also displayed.

Change Report Format allows you to alter which fields are displayed as columns in the report. Unfortunately it is not possible to add **count** (discussed next) as a field. **Edit Mode** allows you to manually adjust the order of cables in the report.

Click **Put on Drawing** and you will get the following dialogue box.

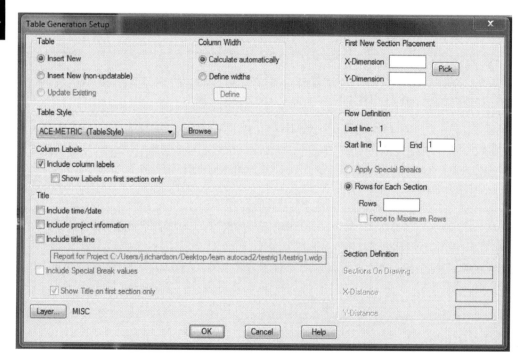

Ensure **Table Style** is set to **ACE-METRIC (TableStyle)** if you are using a metric drawing, otherwise your table will be drawn very small.

Click **OK** and select an empty area of your drawing to place the table. The table will be drawn but then the **Report Generator** dialogue box will open again. We do not want to generate the report again so click **Close**.

You can now see the report on your drawing.

CBL	SH	MFG	CAT	REF	DESC1	DESC2	DESC3
cable 536	2	LAPP	1120360	C-4	MOTOR 1 SUPPLY	4 CORE 4MM2 UNARMOURED	

Cable length

We can add length information to the cables in our schematic drawings. This will ensure our future bill of material (see chapter 15) indicates the correct amount of cable to purchase.

Go to **sheet 2**. Left click the parent cable marker (the top one with the text **cable 536**) on the schematic to highlight it. Then right click beside it to open the menu. Select **Edit Component** and the following dialogue box will open.

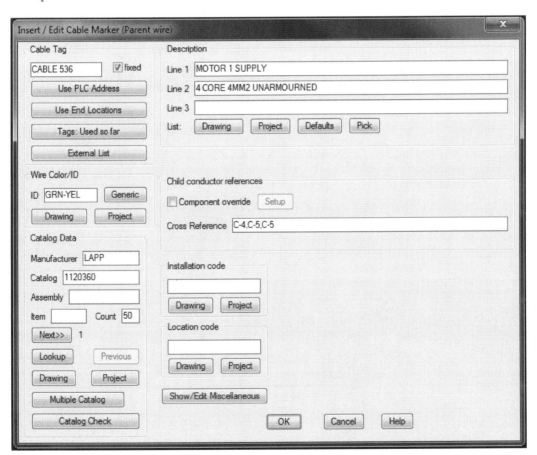

We want to record our **cable 536** as being 50 metres long. Do this by typing **50** in the box **Count** as shown. Click **OK**.

Save your drawing.

Cable From/To report

The **Cable From/To** report is more useful than the **Cable Summary**.

Open **sheet 4**. Select **Reports** from the **Schematic** panel of the **Reports** tab. In the **Schematic Reports** dialogue box, choose **Cable From/To**. Make sure you select **Cable From/To**, not **From/To** which shows single core wires that are not cables.

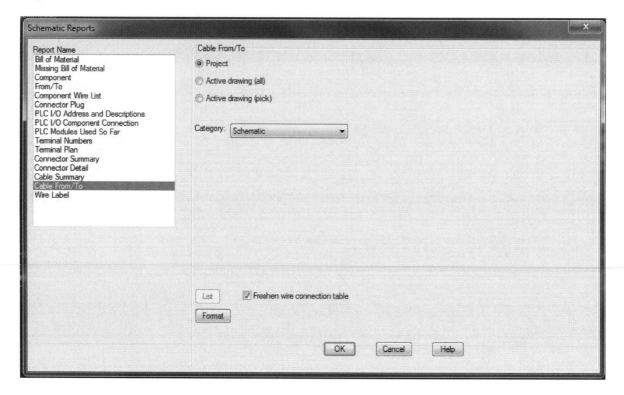

Set **Category** to **Schematic**. Remember to ensure your project is the active project before creating reports.

Select **Project** to include cables from every drawing. Ensure you tick **Freshen wire connection table** to refresh the database. Click **OK**.

14   Select **Do All** when asked which drawings to process and click **OK**. You will be asked to choose which locations to report on with the **Location Code Selection** window:

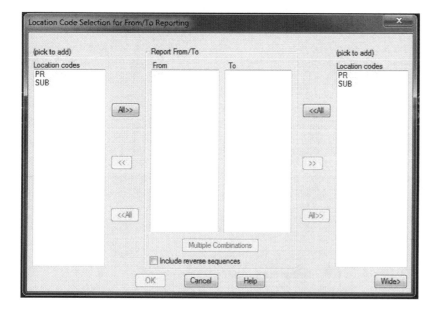

This screen lists the cable end locations in your project, allowing you to report only on cables to certain areas. For our report click **All>>** and **<<All** to include cables going to any location. This will add the selected locations to the columns in the centre of the dialogue box. Click **OK**.

A window will open showing the draft report. It includes one line for each core of the cable.

If there are too many columns to fit in the window, you can click **Wide>** to increase the window size or use the scroll bar to see more of the report.

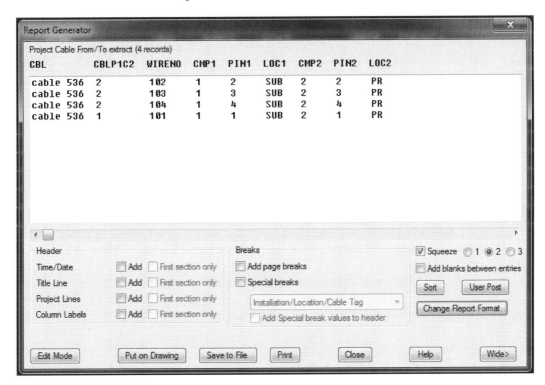

Click **Put on Drawing**.

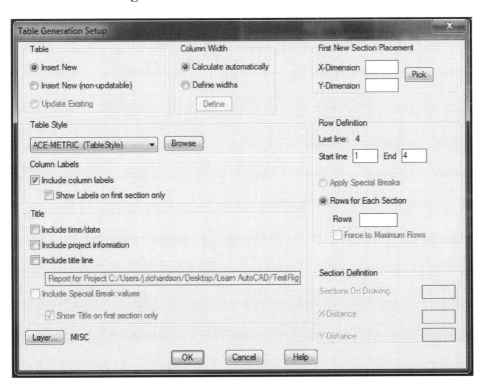

Select **ACE-METRIC (TableStyle)** (if you are using a metric scaled drawing) and click **OK**. Click your drawing to position the report table and the report will be produced.

CBL	CBLP1C2	WIRENO	CMP1	PIN1	LOC1	CMP2	PIN2	LOC2
cable 536	2	102	1	2	SUB	2	2	PR
cable 536	2	103	1	3	SUB	2	3	PR
cable 536	2	104	1	4	SUB	2	4	PR
cable 536	1	101	1	1	SUB	2	1	PR

The **Report Generator** dialogue box re-appears. Click **Close** then **Cancel** to avoid producing another report.

Improvements to the Cable From/To report

The default columns are not very useful but we can change them. Create a new report by clicking **Reports** and choosing the **Cable From/To** report again. Ensure the **Project** option is selected. Click **Do All** when asked which drawings to process.

Add all locations by clicking **All>>** and **<<All** as before to get to the report preview screen again.

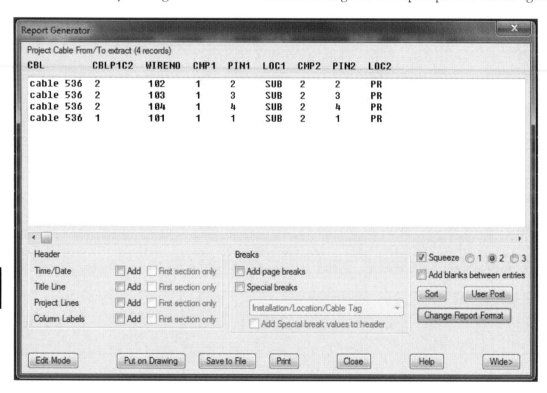

On this screen there are a few formatting options. The **Edit Mode** allows you to manually alter individual cable entries, delete entries and change the order of the report. You can use it to tidy up the presentation of your report but we will not bother with it here.

Instead click **Change Report Format**. This gives the following dialogue box which lets you change the table columns.

250

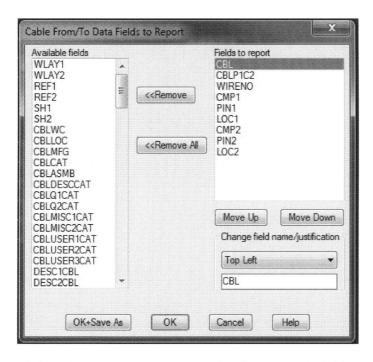

Click **Help** to see a list explaining what data is in each field. You can use the scroll bar to move through the list of available fields.

Where fields refer to each end of the cable they have the suffix **1** for the **"from"** end and **2** for the **"to"** end.

The most useful fields are as follows:

WIRENO   - wire number

LOC1   - Location value of "from" component
INST1   - Installation value of "from" component
CMP1   - Tag value of "from" component. This is the label of the component at the end of the cable. For example, if a cable was connected directly to relay **K1** then **CMP1** would have a value of **K1**. Usually cables will be connected to terminals in which case **CMP1** will be the **tag strip** value of the terminal block.

   For our example cable, **cable 536** the value of **CMP1** is **1**, since it is connected to terminals **1.1**, **1.2**, etc.

CMP:PIN1 - combined tag and terminal number of "from" component
PIN1   - Terminal value of "from" component

LOC2, INST2, CMP2, CMP:PIN2, PIN 2 - as above but for the "to" component

WLAY1, WLAY2   - wire layer
CBL   - cable tag
CBLWC   - cable core colour/ID
CBLMFG   - cable manufacturer
CBLCAT   - cable catalogue (manufacturer's) part number
DESC1CBL, DESC2CBL - cable descriptions 1 and 2
CBLP1C2   - This field is set to either **1** or **2** to indicate if a cable core is a parent (**1**) or child (**2**)
CLEN   - calculated length

I suggest you use the following codes in your report:

CBL	- cable tag
WIRENO	- wire number
CBLP1C2	- parent (1) or child (2)
DESC1CBL	- cable description 1
DESC2CBL	- cable description 2
CBLWC	- cable core colour/ID
INST1	- Installation code of "from" component
LOC1	- Location value of "from" component
CMP:PIN1	- combined tag and terminal number of "from" component
INST2	- Installation code of "to" component
LOC2	- Location value of " to" component
CMP:PIN2	- combined tag and terminal number of "to" component
CBLMFG	- cable manufacturer
CBLCAT	- cable catalogue (manufacturer's) part number

Enter these fields by clicking on them in the left part of the dialogue box. Remove unwanted fields by highlighting them in the right hand window and clicking **<<Remove**. You can change the order of columns using **Move Up** and **Move Down**. Note that the last item, **CBLCAT**, is not visible in the following screenshot since the dialogue window is too small to show the full list without moving the scroll bar.

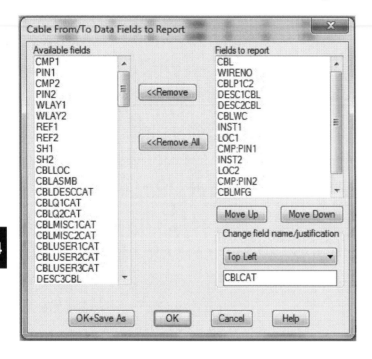

Click **OK**. Put the new report on the drawing. It will automatically replace the old one. Then close the report generator dialogue box.

This will produce the following report:

CBL	WIRENO	CBLP1C2	DESC1CBL	DESC2CBL	CBLWC	INST1	LOC1	CMP:PIN1	INST2	LOC2	CMP:PIN2	CBLMFG	CBLCAT
cable 536	102	2	MOTOR 1 SUPPLY	4 CORE 4 MM2 UNARMOURED	BLK1	WTP	SUB	1:2	WTP	PR	2:2		
cable 536	103	2	MOTOR 1 SUPPLY	4 CORE 4 MM2 UNARMOURED	BLK2	WTP	SUB	1:3	WTP	PR	2:3		
cable 536	104	2	MOTOR 1 SUPPLY	4 CORE 4 MM2 UNARMOURED	BLK3	WTP	SUB	1:4	WTP	PR	2:4		
cable 536	101	1	MOTOR 1 SUPPLY	4 CORE 4 MM2 UNARMOURED	GRN-YEL	WTP	SUB	1:1	WTP	PR	2:1	LAPP	1120360

This still has some issues. The first is that every conductor is listed. This is useful for wiring but often it is more desirable to produce two versions of the report.

One version would contain a single line for each cable. It would be used to order and install the cables but not to terminate the cores. A second version would include each conductor on a separate line and would be used to terminate the cores. This version would not necessarily need the manufacturer's details since it is intended only for terminating cores once the cable is in position.

A second problem is that it is not easy to include the **count** value in the report to indicate length. There is an attribute **CLEN** that is meant to represent length but this is difficult to update beyond simply typing it manually into the finished table.

As a beginner I suggest taking the basic cable schedule described and exporting to Microsoft Excel where it is trivial to both add length information and filter out the child conductors which have the **CBLP1C2** field as **2**. (For parent conductors the **CBLP1C2** field is **1**.) You can export the table by selecting **Save to File** in the **Report Generator** window instead of using **Put on Drawing**.

If required the report can then be re-imported into AutoCAD.

14.3   Fan In / Fan Out

It would be nice if you could select a group of wires, tell AutoCAD that they are a cable, and then have the software group them together into a single line, handling all of the intelligence about the cable automatically.

Looking at a drawing you might assume the **Fan In / Fan Out** command does this. Unfortunately it is really a cosmetic device. The cable markers already described are the fundamental method used to deal with cable information.

Fan In / Fan Out can still be a useful tool to make your drawings clearer. We will demonstrate its use now.

Trying Fan In / Fan Out

Go to **sheet 3** of the **TestRig1** project. We are going to draw a cable at the bottom of the sheet using **Fan In / Fan Out**. If necessary move your existing drawing on this page up a bit to make room.

Draw eight terminals as shown below using the **Round with Terminal Number** component symbol.

For the terminals on the left assign a **Tag Strip** value of **6** and number the individual terminals **1** to **4**. Give them an installation code of **WTP** and a location code of **SUB.** (Representing Water Treatment Plant, Substation).

Give the terminals on the right a **Tag Strip** value of **7** and a **Number** value from **1** to **4**. Give them an installation code of **WTP** and a location code of **PR**. (Representing Water Treatment Plant, Pump Room).

Add a length of wire to each terminal as shown. Assign each of the wires on the left a wire type. You will see the operation of the **Fan In / Fan Out** command best if this is a prominent colour - red, blue, yellow etc. Place a wire colour/gauge marker on each one.

Assign each of the wires on the left a wire number from **121** to **124** as shown. Leave the wires on the right as the default wire layer and do not assign them wire numbers.

Save your drawing.

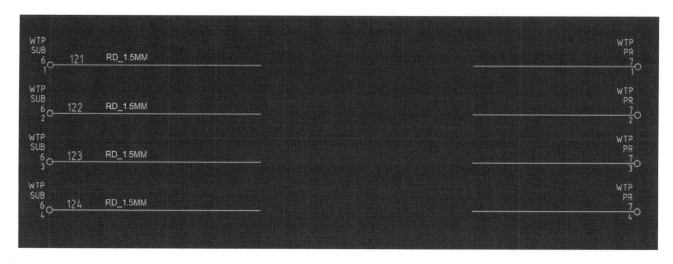

We are going to use the **Fan In / Fan Out** command to link these pairs of wires. First we will associate each wire with its opposite number. This will link the wire numbers across to the wires on the right as signal references did in chapter 8.

From the **Insert Wires/Wire Numbers** panel on the **Schematic** tab select **Fan In Source**. It is in a drop down menu which will probably have **Source Arrow** or **Destination Arrow** on top.

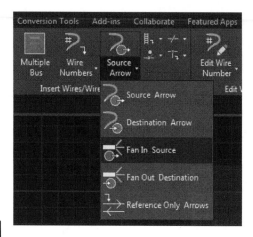

14

You will be asked to choose a style.

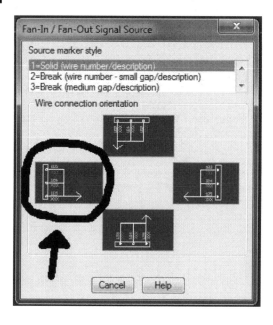

Select option **1=Solid (wire number/description).** This determines the appearance and position of the **Fan In / Fan Out** signal reference text.

Now click the left picture (circled in the image above) since we want our wires to converge from the left.

The dialogue box disappears and AutoCAD returns to your drawing. Click on the top wire some distance from its end to insert a source marker. The following box appears:

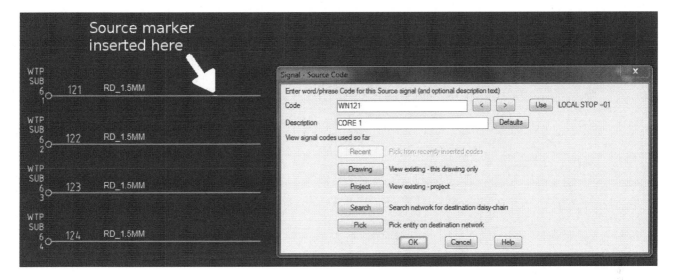

In the **Code** box you need to enter a signal reference. This is a unique value that you will use later to link a destination wire to this source wire. AutoCAD will give a suggested name based on recent references you have used in your project. In this case it has suggested **LOCAL STOP-01.** If you wish to use this automatically suggested name, press the **Use** button. It is best to end your **Code** value with a number. AutoCAD will then increment this number to suggest codes for the other cores automatically.

For our example we will base our code on the wire number. Enter a code value of **WN121.**

In **Description** type a label for this wire. For our example we will call it **CORE 1.**

Now press **OK.**

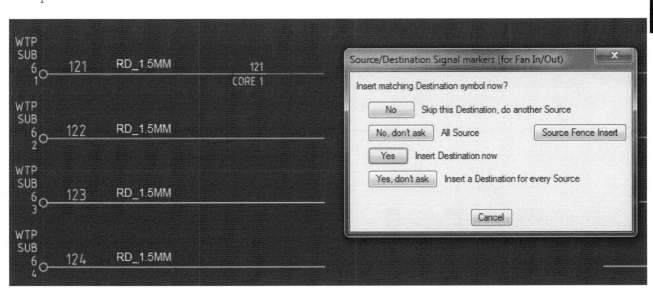

The **Fan In** source marker will be inserted. It is labelled with the wire number (**121**) and the description you entered (**CORE 1**). The wire to the right of the marker will be changed to a grey colour. How noticeable this is will depend on the colour of the original wire. This grey section of wire has been changed by the **Fan In / Fan Out** tool to a different wire layer called **_MULTI_WIRE**.

A dialogue box will also have appeared as shown above.

You now need to add **Fan In** source markers on the other cores of the cable at the left and place corresponding **Fan Out** destinations on the wires at the right. This dialogue box offers you several options. You could insert the destination marker now or continue adding sources and insert the destinations later.

We will instead choose another option to demonstrate its use, the **Source Fence** option. Click the **Source Fence Insert** button at the right of the dialogue box.

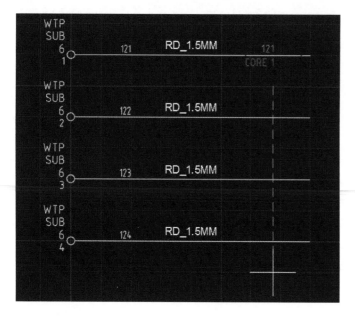

AutoCAD will return to your drawing. Left click once between the first and second wires at a point immediately below the source marker you inserted in the top wire. Then left click below the bottom wire. A dotted line will appear between the two points as shown above. This line becomes solid when you click the second point.

Now press **<Enter>** and a source **Fan In** reference will be inserted on the second wire. The following box appears.

Leave the selections as shown in the image above. Click **OK**.

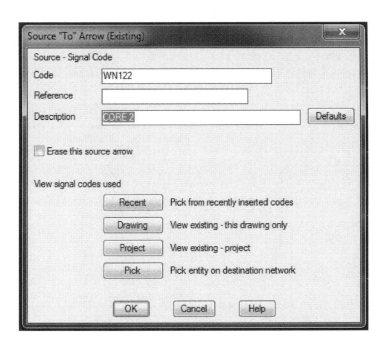

You will be asked for details of the source **Fan In** reference on the second wire. Provided you ended the **Code** value on the first reference with a number, AutoCAD will increment this by one to fill in the **Code** box automatically. The description is not incremented automatically. Manually change the description, in this case to **CORE 2**.

Press **OK**.

A reference will be inserted on the third wire and the **Keep?** dialogue box is shown again.

Since we are not changing the items in the **Keep?** dialogue box you can select **Keep all, don't ask**.

Choose this option and click **OK**. When prompted, update the **Description** information for cores 3 and 4 in the **Source "To" Arrow (Existing)** dialogue box as before.

After entering the information for the forth core, the command will end and all four source references will have been inserted as shown below.

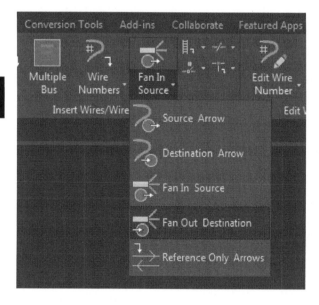

Insert Fan Out destinations

Now we will insert the **Fan Out Destination** markers.

Save your **sheet 3** drawing, otherwise the signal references may not appear when we match them with destinations later in this section.

Select **Fan Out Destination** from the **Schematic** tab on the ribbon.

As with the source markers you will be asked to choose a style.

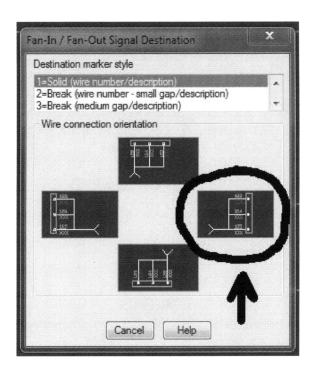

Select a style of **1=Solid (wire number/description)** and click the picture at the right (circled in the image above) to choose wires fanning out in that direction.

AutoCAD returns to your drawing. Click on the top wire at the right of your drawing to insert a destination marker. This should be some distance from the end. AutoCAD will draw a diamond around this point and bring up the **Destination "From" Arrow** dialogue box.

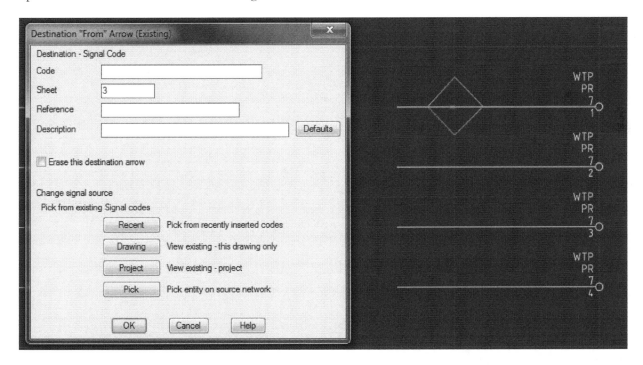

We now decide which source this destination will be linked to. Rather than remember the code we used, click the **Project** button for a list of all signal references in the project. Alternatively you can list those in the active drawing or click **Recent** for codes you have entered this session.

You should now see the four source markers we created earlier. If not, click the **Freshen** button. For tasks like this to work properly you must always ensure the project you are working on is the active project.

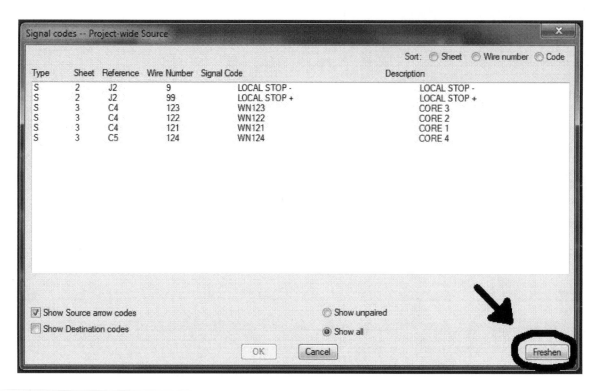

You will also see other signal references in the project which are nothing to do with the **Fan In / Fan Out** tool. In this case you can see the source arrows we used on wires going to our local stop pushbutton.

Click the line with wire **WN121, CORE 1** to highlight it and press **OK**. The **Destination "From" Arrow** dialogue box reappears, correctly populated.

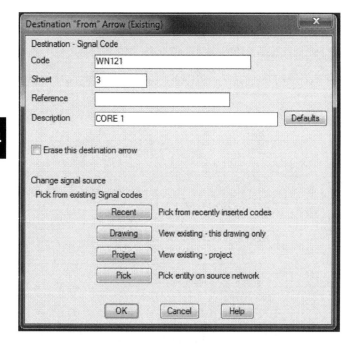

Click **OK** and the destination marker will be inserted.

AutoCAD will copy the cable number across to the destination wire. If you are using XY grid references it will also add corresponding references to the source and destination markers. In this example screenshot, these are **G4** and **C4** which are displayed immediately after the core description, **CORE 1**.

Click on the second destination wire to insert the next destination marker. You do not need to reselect the **Fan Out Destination** button.

Enter the details for the second marker. Repeat this process for the final two cores. Press **<Esc>** to cancel the command when you have inserted destination markers on all four cores.

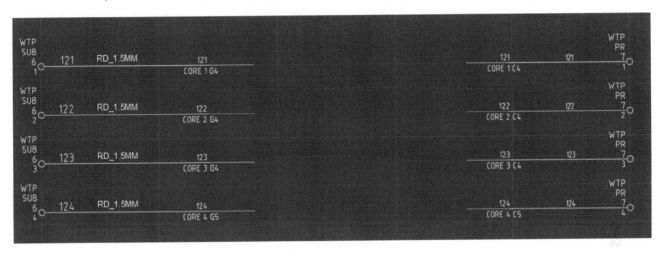

The wire numbers on the destination wires are copies. If you change the wire number on one of the source wires, the copy on the destination wire will change. Note that this change does not happen automatically, you must use the **Update Signal References** tool as described in chapter 8 on page 164 to update the destination wire.

Although wire numbers are carried across to the destination wires, wire types are not. These must be changed manually.

Also note that if you abandon inserting a destination arrow by clicking **Cancel** in the **Destination "From" Arrow** dialogue box, a destination marker may still be inserted but with no source attached. Since you cannot have two destinations on one wire you will need to remove this destination before you can add another destination marker. You can do this most easily by immediately pressing **CTRL + Z** to undo the last instruction.

The _MULTI_WIRE layer

We have now linked the ends of our cable. It may seem like a complicated process but with practice it will not take long. Now we must make the middle section look nice and also tie it into our cable reports.

If you look at the wire ends you will see that the sections to the right of the source markers and to the left of the destination markers are a grey colour. This is more noticeable if the original wire was a bright colour, rather than white. The **Fan In / Fan Out** command has changed these sections to the layer **_MULTI_WIRE**. You can verify this by hovering the cursor over one of these sections. A small information box appears showing the layer that the wire is on.

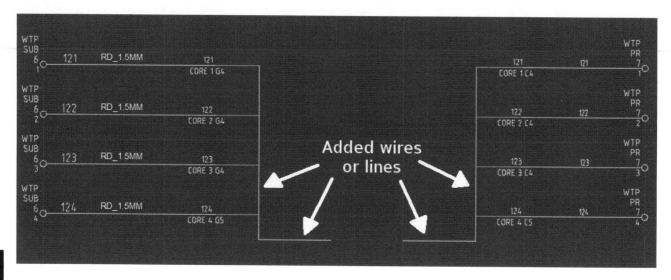

To complete the cable select the **Wire** tool from the schematic menu and draw wires to join the cables as shown below. You can also use the **Line** command in the **Home** tab of the ribbon to do this using ordinary lines. In either case we will be changing the layer of these lines/wires so the end result will be the same.

In this example we have included a gap in the bottom wire for demonstration purposes. This is to show what to do if the ends of the cable are widely separated or on different drawings. You could instead use a solid wire at the bottom if the cable ends are next to each other on your drawing as they are in this example.

Now we must move the wires/lines we have just added onto the **_MULTI_WIRE** layer. From the **Home** tab on the ribbon select **Match Properties**.

The cursor will turn into a small hollow square. Click on the small stub of wire to the right of one of the **Fan In** source markers as shown below. This will copy the properties of this wire, in particular its layer property of **_MULTI_WIRE.** After clicking it a small image of a paintbrush appears next to the cursor.

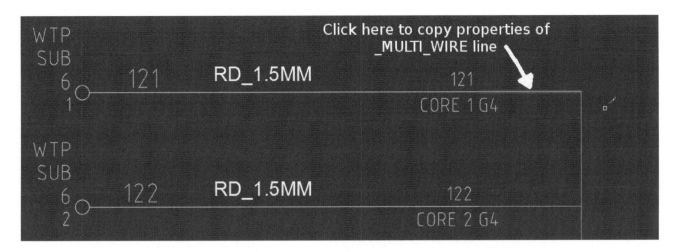

Click on the newly added wires as indicated in the image below. You should click four times, once on each straight section. After selecting them all press **<Enter>**. This will convert them to the **_MULTI_WIRE** layer.

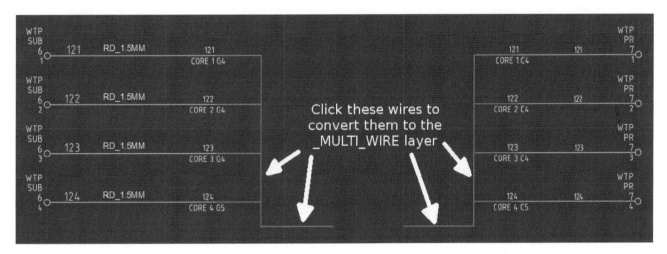

The wires representing the combined cores are now on the **_MULTI_WIRE** layer and should all be the same grey colour.

Adding source and destination arrows

If your cable ends are next to each other and the bottom multi-layer wire is solid, then you are finished. If not then we need to add signal references.

In the **Schematic** tab of the ribbon use the **Source Arrow** command to add a source to the multilayer wire, as we did in chapter 8 for ordinary wires. We are going to number this cable as **cable 537** so use this as both the code and description for the source arrow.

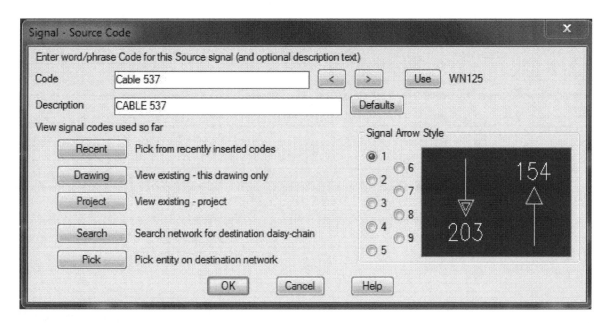

Add a corresponding destination to the other end of the cable.

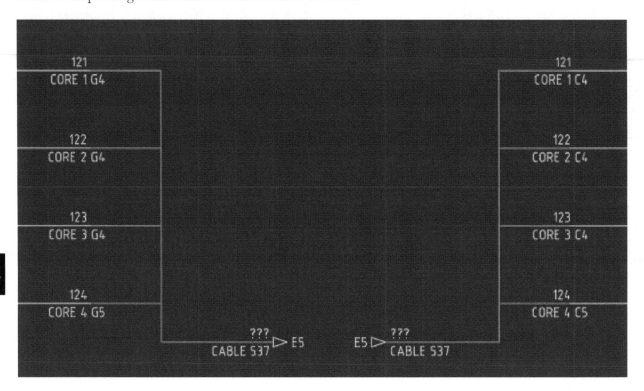

Since the **_MULTI_WIRE** layer cable does not have a wire number the symbol **???** is displayed next to the source and destination arrows.

To tidy this up, left click the source arrow to select it then right click to bring up a menu as shown below.

Select **Attributes** and then choose **Hide Attribute**. Click on the **???** for both the source and destination arrows. Press **<Esc>** to exit the command after hiding the attributes. You can also use the **Move Attribute** option to reposition any text if required.

When selecting attributes it is often easier if you turn off **snap to grid**.

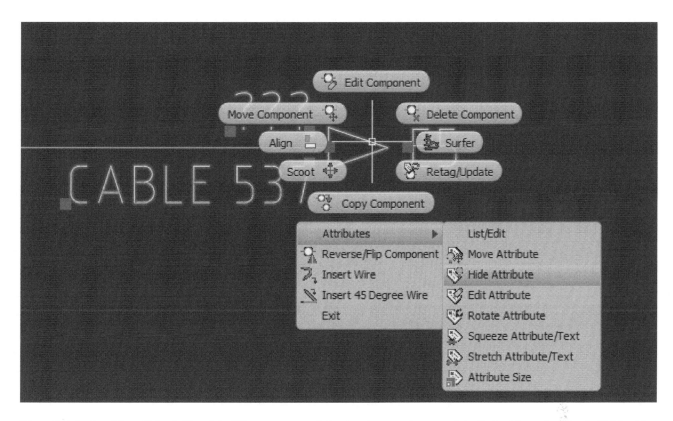

Your finished cable will look like this. The source and destination markers are labelled with each other's X-Y grid reference. In this screenshot they are drawn next to each other so they both have an X-Y reference of **E5**.

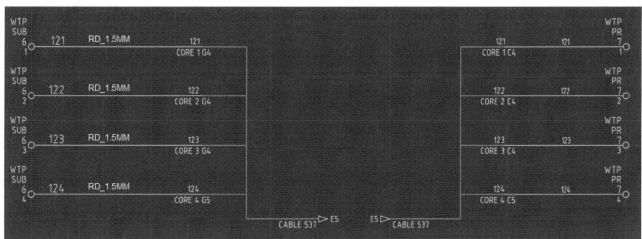

Older versions of AutoCAD might not let you add signal references to the multilayer wire. In this case add the signal references before you change these wires to the **_MULTI_WIRE** layer. Unfortunately this will limit your ability to automatically update them as the drawing changes.

14.4   Cable markers and Fan in / Fan Out

You can use the cable markers discussed earlier in this chapter in combination with the **Fan In / Fan Out** tool. There are two places you can position the markers, either before the **Fan In** or on the **_MULTI_WIRE** layer.

If you place the markers before the **Fan In** you should position them on the ordinary parts of the wires which are not on the **_MULTI_WIRE** layer. In this case everything works as it did when we looked at cables and reports earlier and is not affected by the **Fan In / Fan Out** operation.

Alternatively, you can add a single cable marker on the **_MULTI_WIRE** layer to represent all four cores. We will do this now to demonstrate the operation.

Add a cable marker to the combined wire by selecting the **Cable Marker** button from the **Schematic** tab and clicking the combined wire at the bottom of the drawing. When prompted, fill in the dialogue box as in the following image, using the **Lookup** button to pick the same four core cable from the catalogue that we used before. It is **LAPP** part **1120360**.

For the **Cable Tag** value use **cable 537**. Give the cable a description of **PUMP CONTROL**.

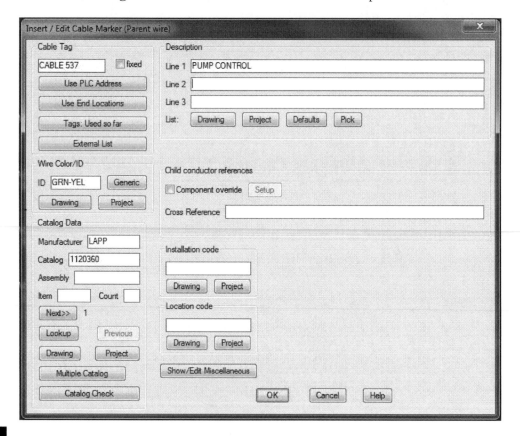

14 Click **OK**.

When prompted to insert child components click **Close** since we only need to insert the main parent cable marker.

The cable marker will now be added to the drawing as shown below. You will probably need to use the **Move Attribute** function to tidy it up.

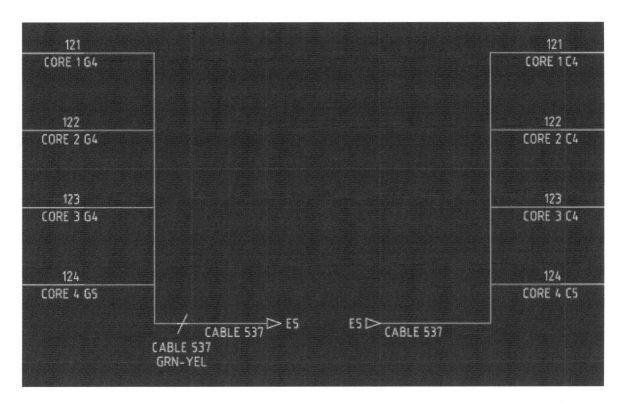

Core colours

You will see that the attribute **GRN-YEL** is shown. This is the core colour of the first core of the cable we picked from the catalogue.

To avoid this being shown you could delete the cable colour from the **Wire Color/ID** box, in the **Insert / Edit Cable Marker (Parent Wire)** dialogue box above, after selecting the cable from the catalogue.

You could also delete it after inserting the cable marker, by selecting the cable marker, right clicking next to it, and choosing **Edit Component**.

Core colours are handled differently depending on whether you add your cable markers to the separate cores or on the single line **_MULTI_WIRE** cable.

If you put them on the separate cores, the manufacturer's catalogue values are used for each core colour by default, as in the cable marker examples earlier in this chapter. You can still change them manually.

If you put the cable marker on the **_MULTI_WIRE** cable then the core colours for the cable reports are taken as the description values you entered in the **Fan In / Fan Out** command for each core. You may remember we set these to **core 1**, **core 2** etc. You will see this effect if we now do a **Cable From / To** report.

Cable report with Fan In / Fan Out

Save your drawings. Go to **sheet 4** and run a **Cable From/To** report for the whole project. Include wire numbers (**WIRENO** field) and core ID (**CBLWC** field) as columns using the **Change Report Format** button.

Put the report on your drawing. It will replace the previous report.

You should now see our new cable, **cable 537**, added to the report alongside the earlier **cable 536**.

You will see that the wire numbers and terminal numbers have been collected automatically. The descriptions (**CORE 1**, **CORE 2**, etc.) that we used for each **Fan In Source** of **cable 537** have been used in place of the catalogue defined wire colours.

Compare this to **cable 536** which shows the catalogue defined colours of **BLK1**, **BLK2**, **BLK3** and **GRN-YEL**.

Note that only some of the columns are shown here to avoid making the text too small.

CBL	WIRENO	CBLP1C2	DESC1CBL	DESC2CBL	CBLWC	INST1	LOC1	CMP:PIN1
Cable 537	121	1	PUMP CONTROL		CORE 1	WTP	SUB	6:1
Cable 537	122	1	PUMP CONTROL		CORE 2	WTP	SUB	6:2
Cable 537	123	1	PUMP CONTROL		CORE 3	WTP	SUB	6:3
Cable 537	124	1	PUMP CONTROL		CORE 4	WTP	SUB	6:4
cable 536	102	2	MOTOR 1 SUPPLY	4 CORE 4MM2 UNARMOURED	BLK1	WTP	SUB	1:2
cable 536	103	2	MOTOR 1 SUPPLY	4 CORE 4MM2 UNARMOURED	BLK2	WTP	SUB	1:3
cable 536	104	2	MOTOR 1 SUPPLY	4 CORE 4MM2 UNARMOURED	BLK3	WTP	SUB	1:4
cable 536	101	1	MOTOR 1 SUPPLY	4 CORE 4MM2 UNARMOURED	GRN-YEL	WTP	SUB	1:1

14.5   Final thoughts on cables

The AutoCAD Electrical software's method of recording cables can be awkward since it is based on the underlying system of a mechanical drawing with electrical symbols placed in layers.

It may appear that there are many steps to drawing cables followed by considerable manual intervention to tidy the drawing. With practice this process is faster than it might seem and it should allow you to display cables in the way you wish.

14

15. Catalogue data and BOM (1 hour)

Until now we have concentrated on producing a schematic drawing without worrying too much about component part numbers. Your drawings can be enhanced by assigning part details to each component. This allows you to produce an automated bill of material from the schematic.

The AutoCAD Electrical software is supplied with a catalogue of manufacturers' parts. You can add your own components to this. You can also attach useful information to the catalogue entries, for example data sheets and web links.

In this chapter we will add manufacturers' part numbers and other details to the components in our motor starter drawing. Using this information we will produce a **Bill of Material** (BOM) report. We will also create a **Missing Bill of Material** report which ensures components that have no manufacturers' data assigned do not get missed.

We will ignore terminals at first. Later in the chapter we will use the **Terminal Strip Editor** as a fast way to add catalogue information to multiple terminals and see how to incorporate terminals into our reports.

Topics covered:

- Assigning catalogue data to schematic components
- Entering components made up of several items
- Adding new components to the catalogue
- **Bill of Material** (BOM) report
- **Missing Bill of Material** report
- Inserting components directly from the **Catalog Browser**
- Using the **Terminal Strip Editor** to enter catalogue data
- Creating custom catalogues
- Using multiple catalogues with your project

15.1 Adding data from the AutoCAD catalogue

Ensure you have the manufacturers' data installed (see page 3) for **Telemecanique, Allen Bradley (AB), LAPP** and **WAGO**. We will use these manufacturers' components in the examples.

Open **sheet 2** of the **TestRig1** project.

Left click switch **S1** to select it. Right click to bring up the menu and select **Edit Component**. The **Insert / Edit Component** dialogue box will appear.

15

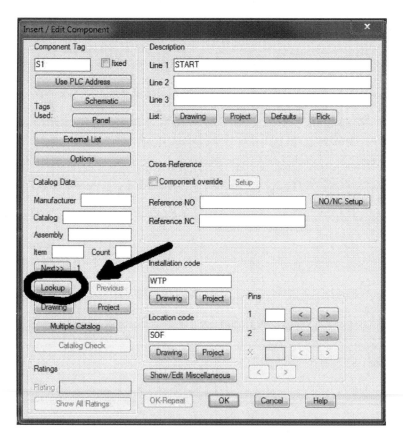

Click the button marked **Lookup** to open the component catalogue.

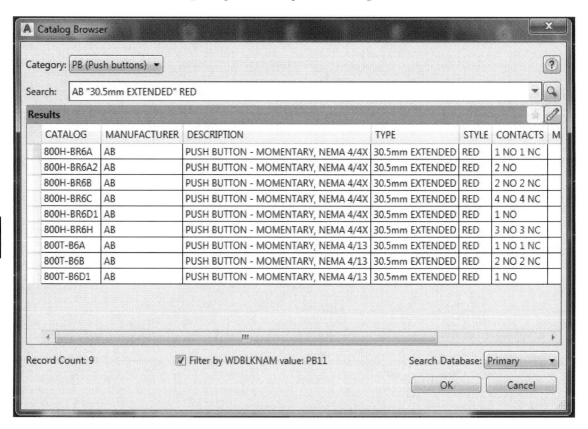

The **Category** drop down box allows you to select the type of component you wish to look for. Since component **S1** is a switch, AutoCAD has selected **PB (Pushbuttons)** but you can change this to look for other types of items in the catalogue if you want to.

AutoCAD has also entered **AB "30.5mm EXTENDED" RED** as a guess at the component you wish to search for. Delete this and enter a search term which will bring up the component you want.

For our example we are going to use a Telemecanique green pushbutton switch with normally open contacts, Telemecanique part number XB6AA31B.

Type **XB6AA31B** in the search box and either press **<Enter>** or click the magnifying glass symbol at the right of the search box.

AutoCAD will only find one item.

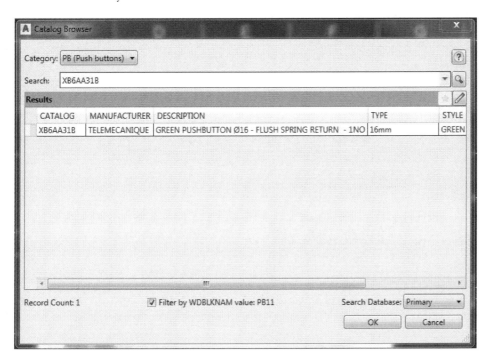

You could instead enter more general search terms, for example **GREEN TELEMEC**. This will return a list of items which contain those terms, in any order. You do not need whole words, any sequence of characters can be searched for.

Click the **XB6AA31B** entry in the list to select it. It will be highlighted. Then click **OK**. Do not click **OK** without first selecting the item, even if the search has only found one part.

You will return to the **Insert / Edit Component** box with the data for **Manufacturer** and **Catalog** filled in.

15

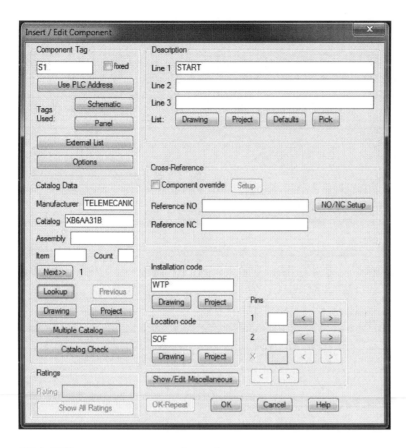

Click **OK** to return to your schematic.

Now repeat this process for switch **S2** and relay **K1**. For **K1** enter the information by selecting the coil, which is the parent component. You cannot assign the catalogue information directly to a child component.

Use the following part details. Note that the contactor we are going to use for **K1** is in the **Category** of **MS (Motor starters/contactors)** so you must select this family in the **Catalog Browser** window before entering your search text. By default AutoCAD will look in the **CR (Control relays)** category when you use **Lookup** for the coil of **K1**.

Component	Description	Manufacturer	Part Number
S2	Red NC pushbutton	Telemecanique	XB6AA42B
K1	24V contactor 3 pole	Telemecanique	LC1D09BD

You may be asked if you wish to change the default symbol for a catalogue entry. This symbol is used if you insert the component directly from the catalogue, rather than from the **Icon Menu**. We will discuss inserting components in this way later in this chapter.

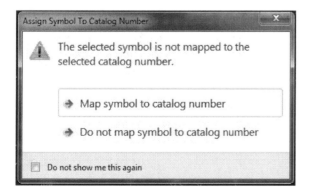

For now just click **Do not map symbol to catalog number**.

You will receive a warning that the pin list for the contactor may not match the schematic. This is because this particular contactor has its contacts identified with numbers. We have labelled them **L1**, **T1** etc. Do not worry about this as it is only an example. For a real panel you would enter the correct pin list.

You are also asked if you wish to update child components (the relay's contacts). Agree to this.

Save your drawing.

15.2   Multiple catalogue parts

Open **sheet 3** of your drawing.

We are now going to add details for switch **S3**. The switch we are going to use consists of a red mushroom head button plus separate contact blocks which clip on the back of it, allowing different contact arrangements to suit different projects.

The pushbutton head is **Telemecanique** part **ZA2BS14**, which is in the AutoCAD catalogue. The contact block is **Telemecanique** part **ZB2BE102**, which is not in the catalogue.

We start by clicking switch **S3**, right clicking, selecting **Edit Component** and assigning the pushbutton head, **ZA2BS14** as the catalogue entry using the **Lookup** button. On returning to the **Insert / Edit Component** dialogue box this information will be loaded as shown below.

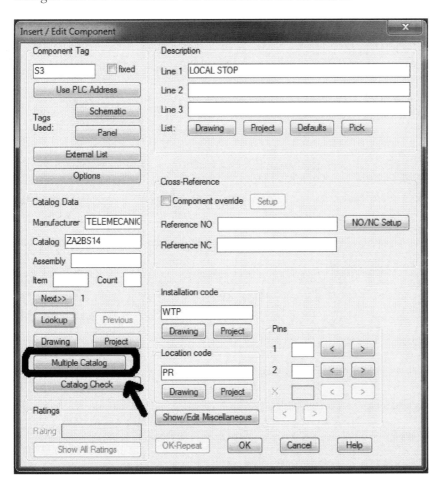

To add the contact block click the **Multiple Catalog** button. The **Multiple Bill of Material Information** dialogue box will open.

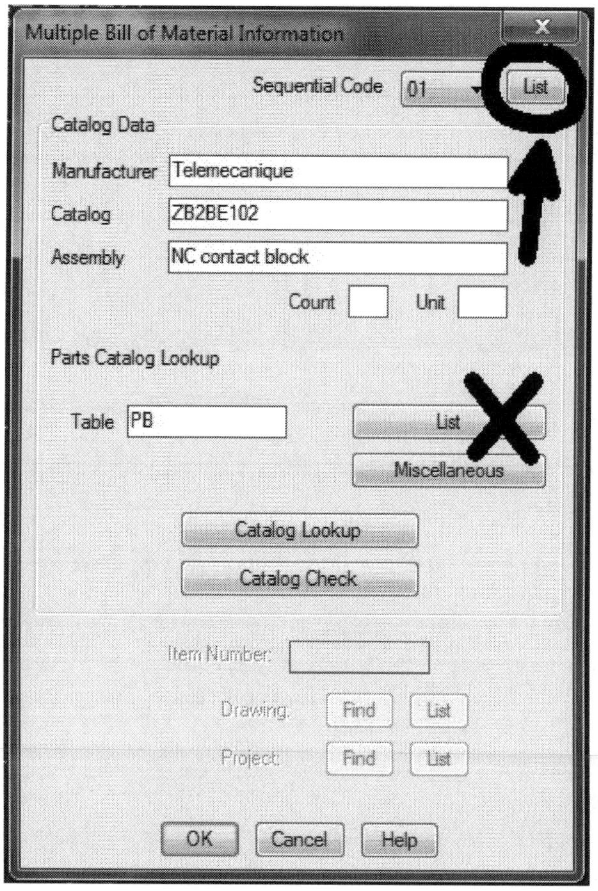

Type the values for **Manufacturer, Catalog** and **Assembly** as shown above. If this contact block was listed in the AutoCAD catalogue you could fill in its information by using the **Lookup** button instead of typing it manually.

You can have up to 99 parts added like this. For this item **Sequential Code** is set to **01**. If there was another item to add you would change **Sequential Code** to **02** to enter details for the second one.

Click **OK** to save the information you entered and return to the **Insert / Edit Component** screen.

Now click the **Multiple Catalog** button again to see the **Multiple Bill of Material Information** dialogue box.

Click the **List** button at the top right of the box (circled on the image above) to see a list of all additional items for this component. Do not click the other **List** button in the **Parts Catalog Lookup** part of the box.

Note that it was necessary to click **OK** to save the new items before looking at them with the **List** button.

15

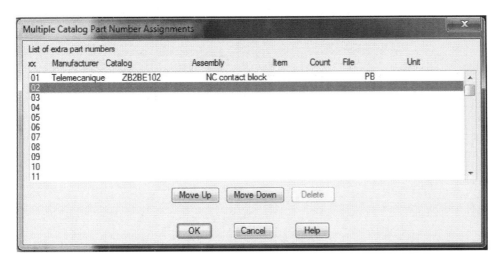

Click **OK** to return to the **Multiple Bill of Material Information** dialogue box.

In the **Multiple Bill of Material Information** dialogue box you can add a value to **Count** if there is more than one of an item. For example, you might have two identical contact blocks attached to the pushbutton head. If **Count** is blank, AutoCAD takes it as having the value **1**. **Unit** is optional, allowing you to include something like hose or busbar measured in metres.

Click **OK** to leave the **Multiple Bill of Material Information** dialogue box. On returning to the **Insert / Edit Component** screen you will now see a number **1** next to **Multiple Catalog**, indicating that there are extra components attached.

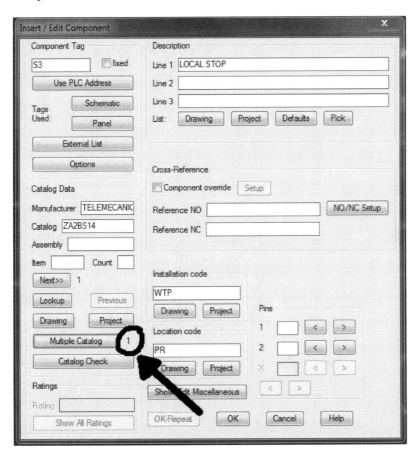

Click **OK** to return to your drawing. You will be asked if you want to assign this schematic symbol as a default for this catalogue item. Decline by clicking **Do not map symbol to catalog number**.

Save your drawing.

15.3   Adding new components to the catalogue

Open **sheet 2**.

Now we are going to assign information to our power supply. We will assume it is part **ABCD123** and is a **Special 15V Power Supply** made by the **Big PSU Company**.

You could just type these details directly into the **Insert / Edit Component Dialogue Box** and not bother with the catalogue for this item. The **Bill of Material** report would still work. Instead we will assume you use this part a lot and want it added to the catalogue.

Select your power supply, **PW1**. Right click and choose **Edit Component**. The **Insert / Edit Component** box will appear.

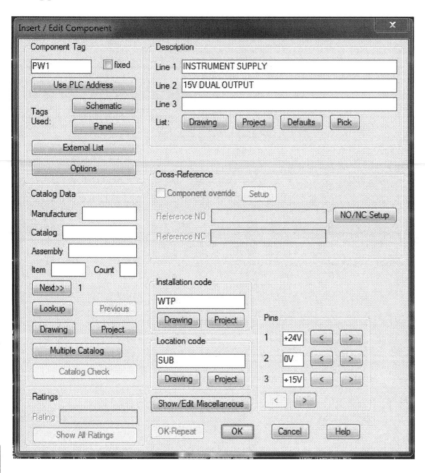

Click **Lookup.**

The **Catalog Browser** window will open.

Category **PW (Power Supplies)** will be selected by default because our custom power supply is assigned to this group. If the suggested **Category** value was not correct for your component type you could select a different one.

Clear the default search string and press **<Enter>**. You will see a list of all existing power supplies in the catalogue.

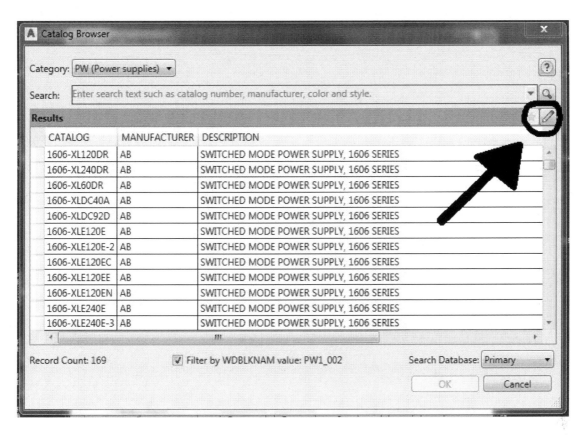

Click the pencil symbol below the search magnifying glass. This switches the catalogue into edit mode.

The whole list is highlighted in a yellow/cream colour and you can change the descriptions of existing components should you want to. Scroll right to the bottom of the list where you will find a blank line. Type your new component here.

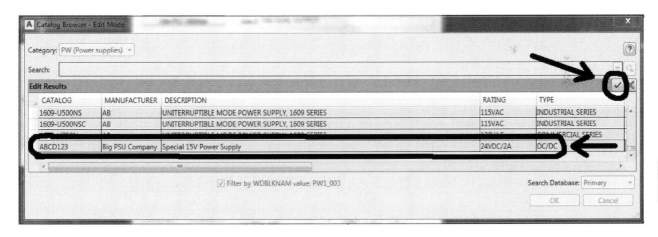

Enter the part number (**Catalog** column), **Manufacturer** and **Description** as shown. For a power supply it is also compulsory to add a rating (enter **24VDC/2A** and a type (enter **DC/DC**). There are other columns which you could complete to supply further information, including a web link to a manufacturer's website or datasheet.

After entering the data, click the tick symbol at the top right of the dialogue box as shown above. This will save the entered details and leave edit mode.

You might find that you can no-longer see your new part as it has been shuffled in with the other power supplies in the list.

Enter a distinctive piece of text, for example the part number, **ABCD123**, or the manufacturer, **Big PSU Company**, in the search bar and press **<Enter>**. Your new power supply will be displayed.

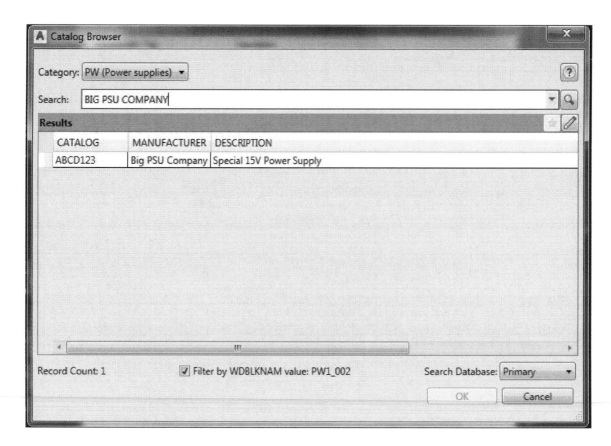

Click the power supply to select it. Then click **OK**. Since we have not defined a proper pin list in the catalogue data you will see the following prompt:

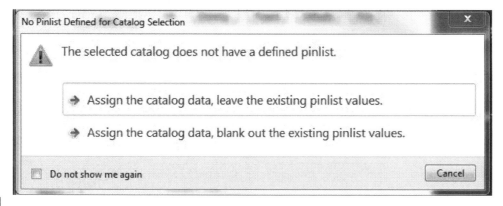

15 Select **Assign the catalog data, leave the existing pinlist values** to keep the pin list values (**+24V, 0V**, etc.) that we have already placed on the drawing in earlier chapters.

You will now return to the **Insert / Edit Component** dialogue box. The manufacturer and part number for your power supply will have been filled in.

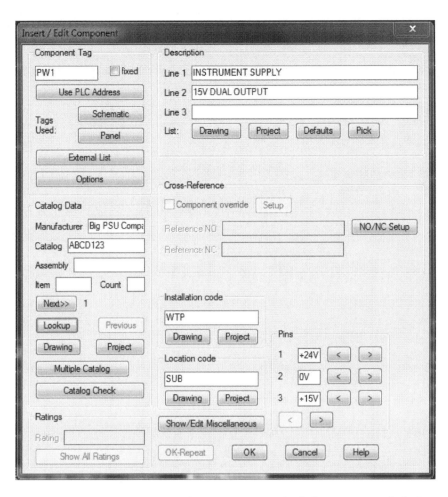

Click **OK** to exit back to your drawing. When asked if you want to link the power supply symbol you are using as the default for this catalogue entry, decline by selecting **Do not map symbol to catalog number**.

Save your drawing.

15.4   Bill of Material report

Create a new drawing to put your bill of material report on. The easiest method is to right click the **TestRig1** project in the **Project Manager** window and choose **New Drawing...** from the menu that appears.

Call it **sheet 5** and use the **first_template** as your template to create it. Enter "**Motor Starter**" for **Description 1** and "**Bill of Material**" for **Description 2**. You can enter these on the **Create New Drawing** screen as shown in the image below.

15

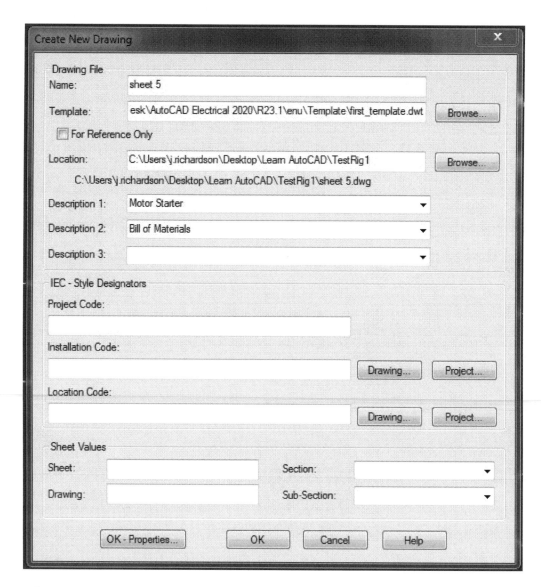

When prompted, apply the project defaults to the new drawing.

Go to the new **sheet 5** drawing.

Select the **Reports** button from the **Schematic** panel on the **Reports** tab of the ribbon. Do not click the other **Reports** button which is in the **Panel** part of the **Reports** tab.

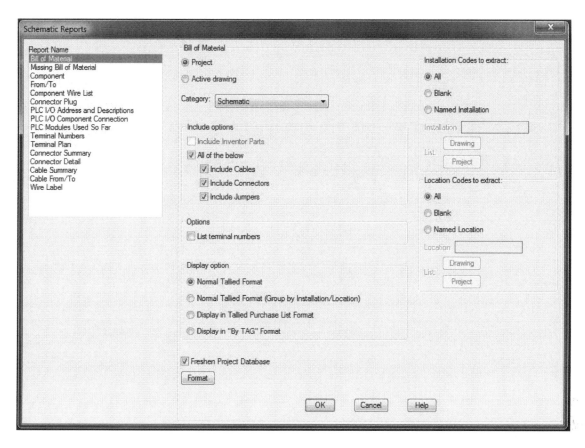

Select the **Bill of Material** report and ensure settings are as the screenshot above.

Choose whole **Project** rather than **Active drawing**. Set **Category** to **Schematic**. We are not going to include terminals yet so leave **List terminal numbers** unticked. Leave **Freshen Project Database** ticked.

Click **OK**. When asked which drawings to process, choose **Do All** and click **OK** again. Agree to **QSAVE** the drawing. A preview of the bill of material report is shown in a dialogue box.

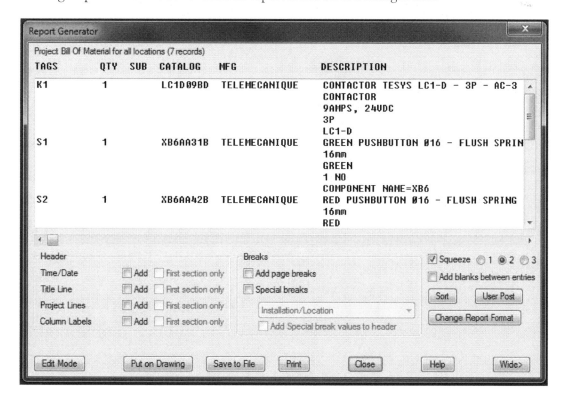

The **Change Report Format** allows you to change the way the report is produced by altering the fields used as column headings. This is similar to the way we modified the **Cable From / To** report in chapter 14.

The **Edit Mode** button allows you to modify the data within the report, overriding the values taken from your drawings and changing the order in which components are listed.

Click **Put on Drawing** to place the report on **sheet 5**. You will see the **Table Generation Setup** dialogue box.

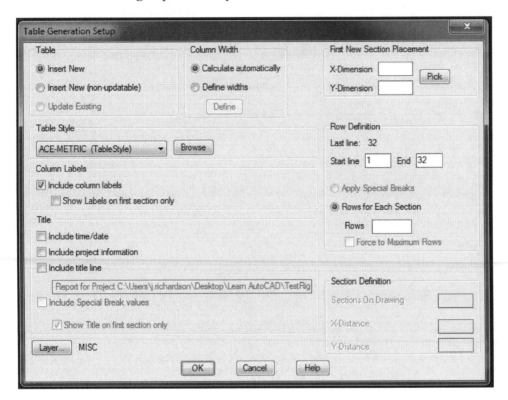

Ensure **Table Style** is set to **ACE-METRIC (TableStyle)** if you are using a metric drawing and click **OK**.

Place the outline of the table that appears on your drawing at the top left corner. This will leave space for us to add the **Missing Bill of Material** report later.

The **Report Generator** dialogue reappears. Click **Close**. You will now see your **Bill of Material** report.

TAGS	QTY	SUB	CATALOG	MFG	DESCRIPTION
K1	1		LC1D09BD	TELEMECANIQUE	CONTACTOR TESYS LC1-D - 3P - AC-3 440V 9A - COIL 24VDC CONTACTOR 9AMPS, 24VDC 3P LC1-D
S1	1		XB6AA31B	TELEMECANIQUE	GREEN PUSHBUTTON Ø16 - FLUSH SPRING RETURN - 1NO 16mm GREEN 1 NO COMPONENT NAME=XB6
S2	1		XB6AA42B	TELEMECANIQUE	RED PUSHBUTTON Ø16 - FLUSH SPRING RETURN - 1NC 16mm RED 1 NC COMPONENT NAME=XB6
S3	1	*1	ZA2BS14	TELEMECANIQUE	EMERGENCY STOP HEAD Ø40mm- KEY RELEASE - Ø22 - RED 22mm RED SHAPE OF HEAD=ROUND
		*1	ZB2BE102	Telemecanique	
PW1	1		ABCD 123	Big PSU Company	Special 15V Power Supply 24VDC/2A DC/DC
Cable 537	1		1120360	LAPP	UV RESISTANT CONTROL CABLE - OLFLEX CLASIC 110 BLACK CONTROL CABLE 12AWG 4 CONDUCTOR 600/1000V, BLACK PVC
cable 536	1	*50	1120360	LAPP	UV RESISTANT CONTROL CABLE - OLFLEX CLASIC 110 BLACK CONTROL CABLE 12AWG 4 CONDUCTOR 600/1000V, BLACK PVC

This report includes the components to which we added catalogue data. For **S3**, the contact block which we added as a multiple catalogue item has been included as an extra line below the main item.

You will also see the two cables we created in chapter 14 are shown. We did not add a count value to **cable 537**. For **cable 536** however, the count value which we set to 50 is shown. This could represent a requirement for 50 metres of cable.

Note that if you had not entered a **count** value for **cable 536**, both cables would be listed in the same box as a single entry because they use the same type of cable.

Items for which we have not entered catalogue data, such as the motor **M1**, are not included.

Components do not need to have entries in the AutoCAD main catalogue database itself to be picked up by the **Bill of Material** report. Just typing any text in the **Manufacturer** or **Catalog** fields of the **Insert / Edit Component** dialogue box is enough.

15.5   Missing Bill of Material report

Since the **Bill of Material** report only shows items with added catalogue data, items without this data might be missed. The **Missing Bill of Material** report lists items without catalogue data. This can highlight where missing information needs to be added or be used to ensure components without catalogue data are still ordered.

On **sheet 5**, click the **Reports** button in the **Schematic** panel of the **Reports** tab to open the **Schematic Reports** screen.

Click **Missing Bill of Material** to highlight it. Check selections are as below. As with the **Bill of Material** report we are not going to look at terminals yet so leave **Include Terminals** unticked.

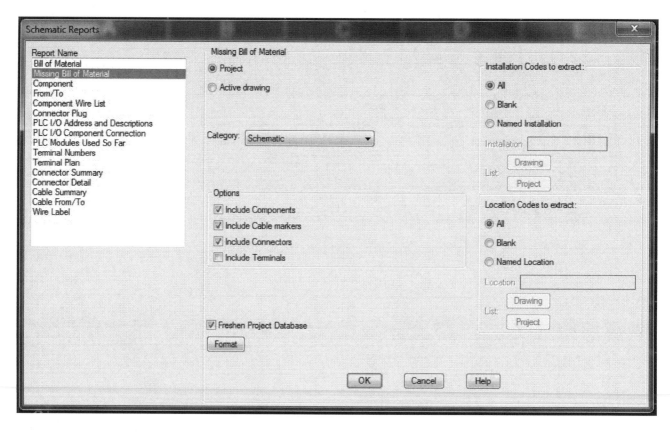

Click **OK** and select **Do All** when asked which drawings to process. The report preview will appear.

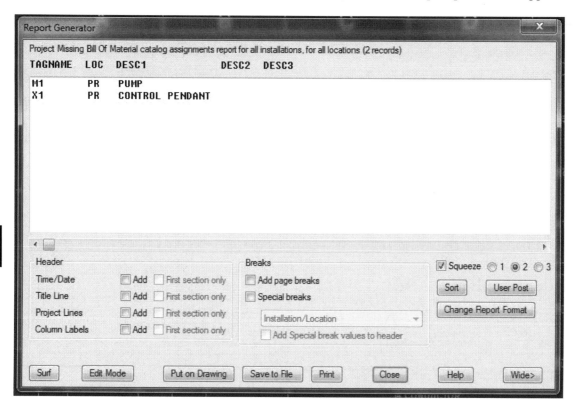

Click **Put on Drawing**. You will see the **Table Generation Setup** box.

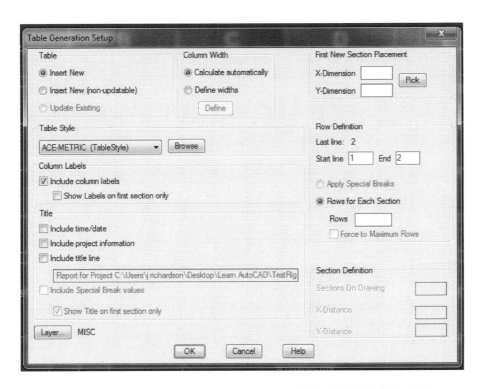

As with other reports, ensure you select **ACE-METRIC (TableStyle)** if you are using metric drawings. Click **OK** and place the report to the right of your **Bill of Material** report. Close the **Report Generator** box when it reappears.

You will now have the **Missing Bill of Material** report on your drawing.

TAGNAME	LOC	DESC1	DESC2	DESC3
M1	PR	PUMP		
X1	PR	CONTROL PENDANT		

This report shows the motor and connector on **sheet 3**. It highlights that these have no catalogue information assigned to them and ensures you do not forget to order them for your project.

Save your drawings.

Should you need to update the information in the **Bill of Material** or **Missing Bill of Material** reports, do this by creating the reports again. The old report will be replaced when you put the new version on your drawing. As with other reports, you can also save these reports as files.

15

15.6   Inserting components using the Catalog Browser

Until now we have inserted components using the **Icon Menu** and then assigned their catalogue information after choosing the symbol. An alternative method is to choose a component from the catalogue first and then insert it into the drawing, usually using whichever icon symbol has been tied to it.

To do this select the **Catalog Browser** button from the drop down menu below the **Icon Menu** button on the **Schematic** tab of the ribbon.

The **Catalog Browser** window will open. Select the category of component you wish to insert. For this example choose **PB (PUSHBUTTONS)**.

Next enter some text in the search box. For this example we will find the green pushbutton (Telemecanique part number XB6AA31B) we used earlier for switch **S1**.

Enter **XB6AA31B** in the search box and press **<Enter>** or click the magnifying glass search button. AutoCAD will list parts matching your search.

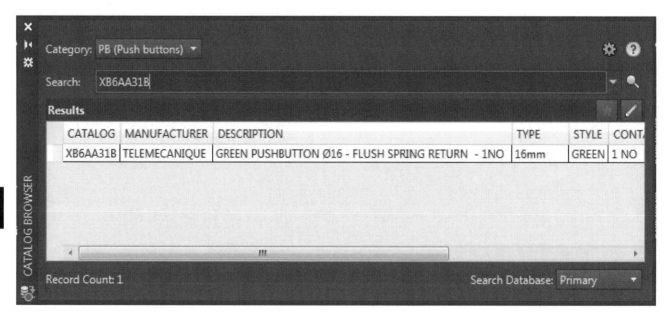

Click the line with the desired component to highlight it. A menu will appear next to it as shown below.

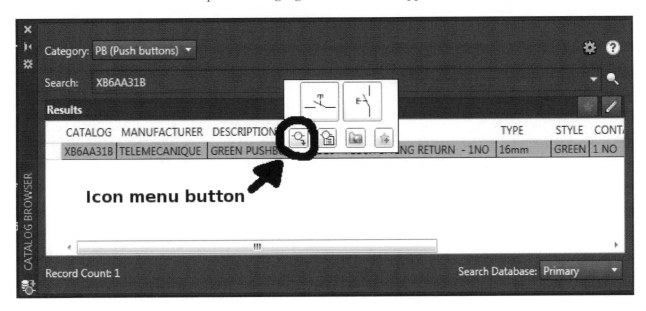

Icon menu button

The two switch symbols at the top of this menu are horizontal and vertical versions of the default schematic symbol for this catalogue component. To insert the component click on one of these. Then click on your drawing in the position where you want the component.

The **Catalog Browser** window does not close when you insert the component so it may cover part of your drawing. You can move it by left clicking its title bar (at the left of the image above) and dragging it out of the way. If you have two monitors it can be dragged to the other one. It does not need to stay within the bounds of the main AutoCAD window.

After clicking on your drawing to insert the component, the familiar **Insert / Edit Component** box appears but with the catalogue information already completed.

If you do not want to use the default schematic symbol for the component, click the **Icon Menu** button (shown on the image above) at the bottom left of the submenu. This opens the **Icon Menu** window to let you choose a different symbol.

Whenever you choose a different symbol to the default, AutoCAD asks if you wish to map the new symbol to the component's catalogue entry. This will then be included as an extra option, alongside the existing defaults, next time you insert this component from the **Catalog Browser**.

After experimenting with inserting from the catalogue, delete any extra symbols you have added. We do not need them for our example circuit. Close the **Catalog Browser** window.

15.7   Entering catalogue information for terminals

You can add terminal information by selecting terminals and looking up catalogue data as you would for any other component. This might be a tedious job if your project contains many terminals.

A faster way is to use the **Terminal Strip Editor** to assign terminal part numbers. In the early stages of your design you can add terminal symbols to your schematic without worrying about the exact part numbers. Later, when you finalise cable sizes and other connection details, you can add the manufacturers' part numbers quickly using the **Terminal Strip Editor**.

Open **sheet 3** of your drawing.

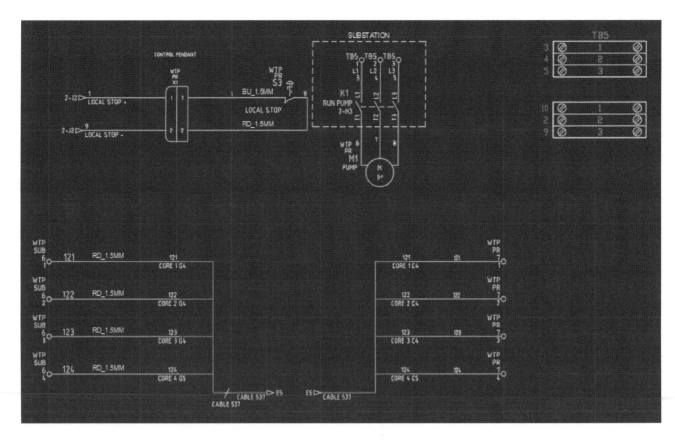

We will use the **Terminal Strip Editor** to set the terminals of terminal block **TB5** to WAGO 4 way 2.5mm² grey terminal blocks, WAGO part number 2002-1401.

In the **Terminal Footprints** panel on the **Panel** tab of the ribbon, click **Editor** to open the **Terminal Strip Editor**.

15   You may be asked to **QSAVE** the drawing. Agree to this. The **Terminal Strip Selection** window of the **Terminal Strip Editor** opens.

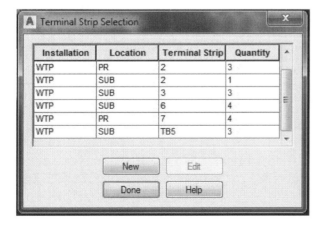

Scroll down to terminal strip **TB5**. Left click this line to highlight it. Then click **Edit**.

The **Terminal Strip Editor** will open for the **TB5** terminal strip.

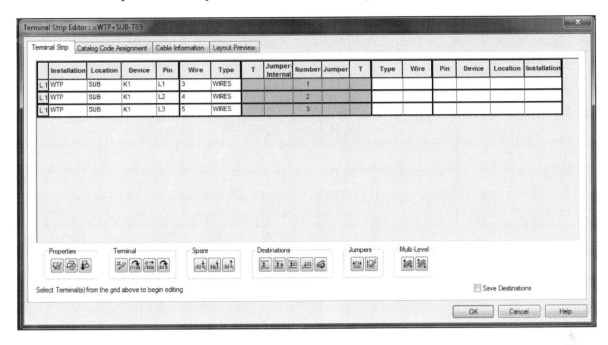

Click the **Catalog Code Assignment** tab.

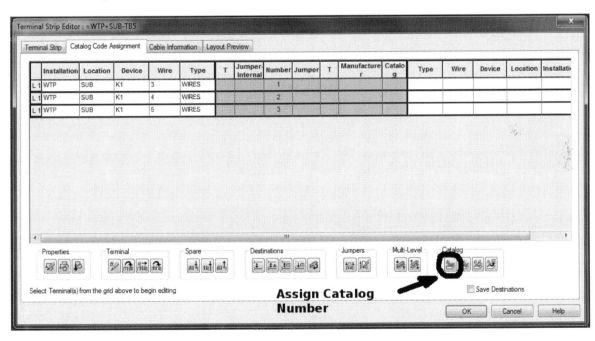

Click the first row (the row for terminal 1) to highlight it. Then click the **Assign Catalog Number** button shown above. The **Catalog Browser** window will open showing the AutoCAD library of terminal components.

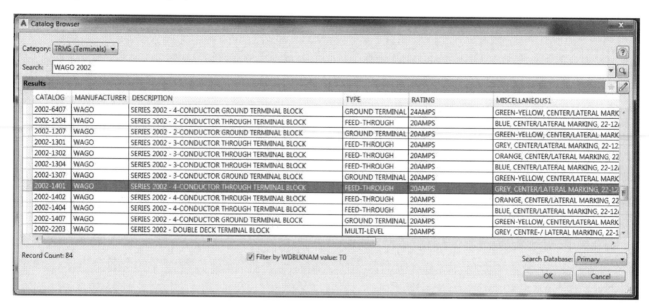

Type **WAGO 2002** in the **Search** box and click the magnifying glass button. All WAGO parts containing **2002** in their descriptions will be displayed.

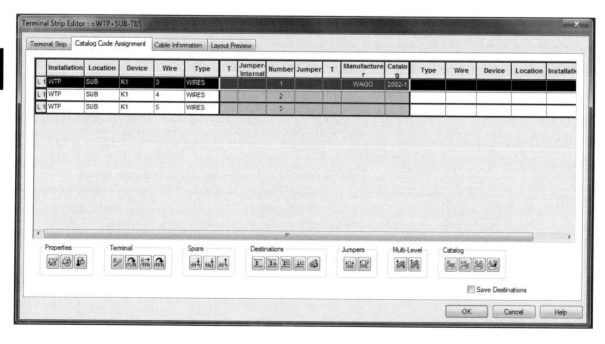

Scroll down the list of terminals to find part **2002-1401**, the 4 way grey terminal we want to use. Click this line to highlight it as shown. Then click **OK**. AutoCAD returns to the **Terminal Strip Editor** and you will see the catalogue details for the first terminal are now filled in.

Copying terminal catalogue details

We can now copy this catalogue number to other terminals. In a real project with hundreds of terminals this will save much time.

Ensure the first line, to which you have assigned the catalogue number, is selected. Right click on this line. From the menu that appears, move the mouse over **Catalog >** to see the submenu below. Select **Copy**.

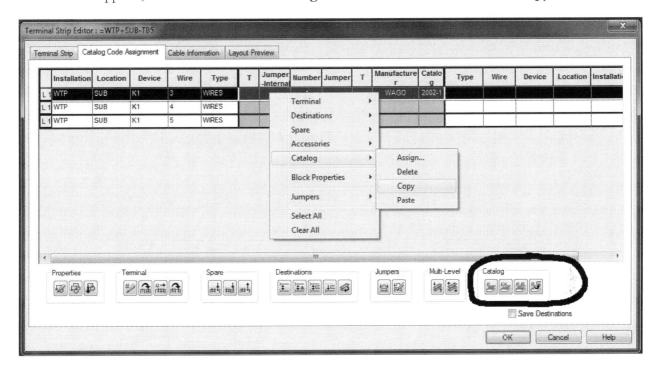

Now highlight the rows for terminals **2** and **3**. You can use **CTRL + Click** to select each one or **Shift + Click** to select a range of terminals, as in most Microsoft Windows programs.

Right click the highlighted rows and select **Paste** from the **Catalog** submenu. This will assign the copied catalogue number to the selected terminals. You can also copy, paste and delete catalogue numbers using the **Catalog** buttons circled in the image above.

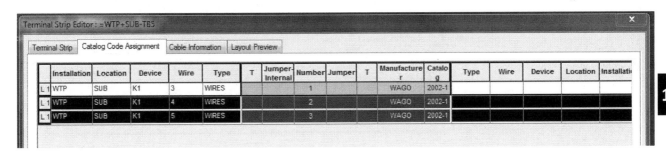

Note that, despite appearances, this table is not a spreadsheet. You can only select whole lines, not individual cells. Copying between them is via the submenu described or the buttons.

Click **OK** after assigning catalogue information to the terminals. You will be returned to the **Terminal Strip Selection** dialogue box.

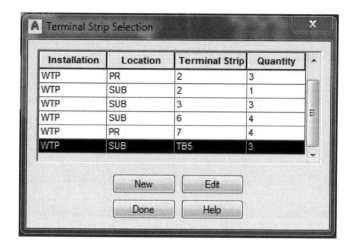

You can now select another terminal strip to edit or click **Done** to leave the **Terminal Strip Editor**. For our example click **Done**. We will assign components to terminal strip **3** in the next chapter.

Save your drawing.

Rerun the Bill of Material report

You can now go to **sheet 5** and re-create the **Bill of Material** report. This time ensure **List terminal numbers** is ticked.

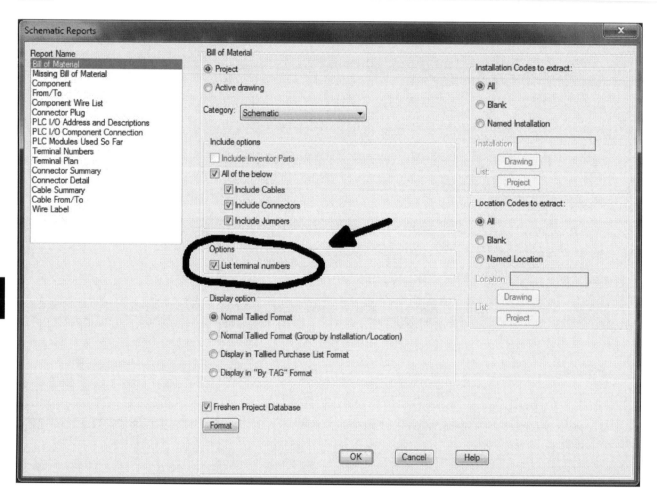

Put this on your drawing and the old **Bill of Material** report will be replaced with a new one which includes your terminals.

PW1	1	ABCD123	Big PSU Company	Special 15V Power Supply 24VDC/2A DC/DC
TB5:1 TB5:2 TB5:3	3	2002-1401	WAGO	SERIES 2002 - 4-CONDUCTOR T FEED-THROUGH 20AMPS GREY, CENTER/LATERAL MARK FRONT-ENTRY, CAGE CLAMP C
CABLE 537	1	1120360	LAPP	UV RESISTANT CONTROL CABL CONTROL CABLE

Similarly, you can redo the **Missing Bill of Material** report. This time tick the **Include Terminals** box to show any terminals which do not have catalogue numbers assigned to them.

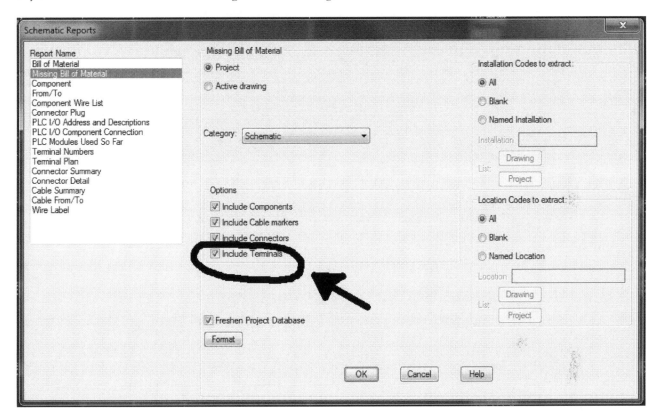

Terminals in this list are given a **Tagname** in the format:

Terminal strip : Terminal Number : Wire Number

For example, terminal strip **2**, terminal number **1**, connected to wire **101** is shown as **2:1:101**.

15

TAGNAME	LOC	DESC1	DESC2	DESC3
1:1:101	SUB			
1:2:102	SUB			
1:3:103	SUB			
1:4:104	SUB			
2:1:101	PR			
2:2:102	SUB			
2:3:103	PR			
2:4:104	PR			
3:1:10	SUB			
3:2:2	SUB			
3:3	SUB			
6:1:121	SUB			
6:2:122	SUB			
6:3:123	SUB			
6:4:124	SUB			
7:1:121	PR			
7:2:122	PR			
7:3:123	PR			
7:4:124	PR			
M1	PR	PUMP		
X1	PR	CONTROL PENDANT		

Save your drawings.

15.8   Manipulating component catalogues

Now that you understand how to create custom components and add components to the catalogue you can gradually build up a catalogue of items you frequently use. Rather than simply throw these in with thousands of default items supplied by AutoCAD you may wish to store them separately, exchange them with other AutoCAD users or even supply customers with a condensed catalogue containing only the items within their drawings.

The reader is advised to consult the AutoCAD help for further information on this topic. In this chapter we will explain where the catalogue files are located and cover some useful tools to get you started.

The component catalogue database file

15

The component catalogue we have used so far is contained in a Microsoft Access database file, **default_cat.mdb**.

This can be found in the folder:

C:\Users** *your windows username*\Documents\Acade 2020\AeData\en-US\Catalogs**

Name	Date modified	Type	Size
ace_electrical_standards.mdb	19/01/2014 15:34	Microsoft Access ...	1,076 KB
default_cat.ldb	07/10/2020 13:07	Microsoft Access ...	1 KB
default_cat.mdb	07/10/2020 12:07	Microsoft Access ...	271,856 KB
footprint_lookup.ldb	07/10/2020 13:05	Microsoft Access ...	0 KB
footprint_lookup.mdb	03/10/2020 13:06	Microsoft Access ...	61,320 KB
schematic_lookup.mdb	14/04/2010 11:09	Microsoft Access ...	392 KB
wd_lang1.mdb	10/12/2012 16:07	Microsoft Access ...	11,192 KB
wd_picklist.mdb	14/04/2010 11:09	Microsoft Access ...	132 KB
wddinrl.xls	14/04/2010 11:09	Microsoft Excel 97...	40 KB

Note that the **Documents** folder may appear as **My Documents** when using Microsoft Windows Explorer to find it. This folder also includes the footprint database which we will come across in later chapters. The files with extension **.ldb** are lock files which control access to the databases. They prevent them being corrupted if accessed by multiple users at the same time. If you close AutoCAD they disappear.

Extracting a project specific database

It is possible to create a new database containing only the items already used in your project. You could give this to a customer along with the project drawings. You could also use it as a way to create an almost empty database as a starting point for a custom catalogue containing only parts that you use regularly.

In the **Project** tab of the ribbon click the drop down menu beside **Other Tools**. Click the **Create Project-Specific Catalog Database** button shown below.

The **Create Project-Specific Catalog Database** dialogue box opens.

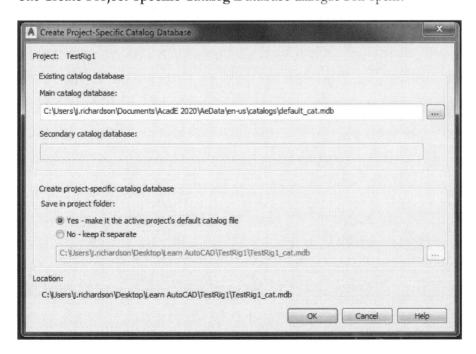

15

Select the option **Yes - make it the active project's default catalog file** as shown above and click **OK**.

If you now look in the **TestRig1** project file you will see a file called **TestRig1_cat.mdb**. This is a database containing only the components already used in your project. Your TestRig1 project is now using this as its primary component catalogue. If you have AutoCAD open you will also see the accompanying **.ldb** lock file.

Go to the **Schematic** tab of the ribbon and open the **Catalog Browser**. Look in the **PB (Push buttons)** category and click the magnifying glass search button with the search text blank. You will see that the only components present are the small number of buttons we have used in this book.

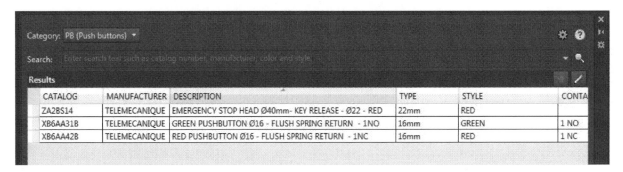

Adding a secondary catalogue

Sometimes you will want to use the full catalogue. At other times you may prefer to only search among items you use regularly. You can do this by adding a secondary catalogue.

Right click the **TestRig1** project in the **Project Manager** window. Select **Properties...** from the menu that appears and open the **Project Settings** tab.

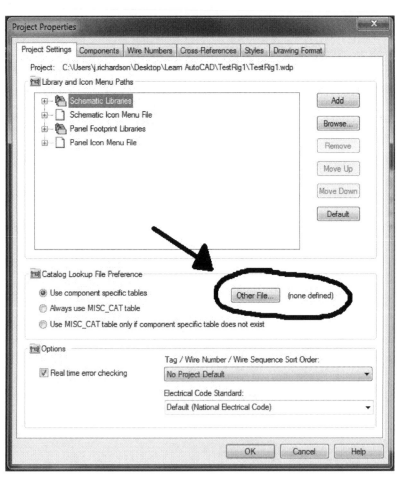

Click the **Other File...** button.

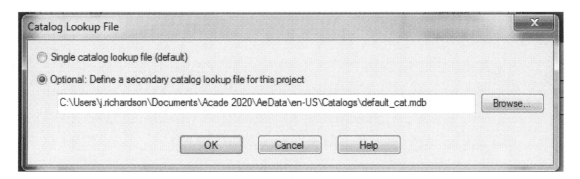

In the **Catalog Lookup File box**, select **Optional: Define a secondary catalog lookup file for this project** and use the **Browse** button to set the **default_cat.mdb** file we discussed earlier as the secondary catalogue.

Click **OK**.

If you now open the **Catalog Browser** you will see that you can switch easily between the **Primary** (custom) and **Secondary** (default) databases when selecting components by clicking the drop down menu at the bottom right of the **Catalog Browser** as shown below.

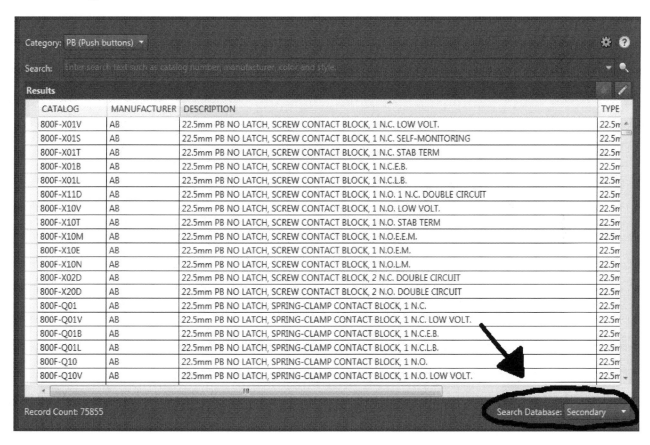

In this book it is only possible to give an introduction to these databases. Please see the AutoCAD help for more information on how you might use them

16. Panel layouts (1¼ hours)

In addition to a schematic drawing, you may wish to produce a physical panel layout. This could be a rough layout to guide the panel builders and estimate the size of enclosure needed. Alternatively, it could be a precise mechanical drawing.

The AutoCAD Electrical software facilitates this using scale drawings of each component, called footprints. These can be placed in a panel layout using a list extracted from the schematic drawing. This gives a fast way to lay out panels and ensures there are no discrepancies between the schematic and mechanical drawings.

In this chapter we will produce a scale drawing of a panel layout using manufacturers' component footprints from the supplied libraries. We will also learn how to create a new component footprint from scratch.

Terminal footprints are covered separately in chapter 17 which also includes some more advanced options for producing scale drawings.

Topics covered in this chapter:

- Changing the scale of the title block and layout drawings
- Placing component footprints
- Footprints for subassemblies
- Understanding the link between catalogue components and their footprints
- Custom footprints

16.1   Creating a drawing for the layout

Create a new sheet for your project called **sheet 6** using the **first_template.dwt** template. Give it the **Description 1** value of **Motor Starter** and the **Description 2** value of **Panel Layout**. Agree to apply the project default settings when asked.

This drawing, based on our template, will have a border sized for an A3 sheet of paper, 420 x 297mm. Obviously your panel is likely to be a different size. For our example we will assume our components are mounted on a backplate of 450mm x 450mm, a realistic backplate size for a 500mm square cabinet.

Use the rectangle function to draw a 450 x 450 square. (17.7 x 17.7 if you are using inches instead of mm)

Our drawing in model space will be full size so the square is 450mm x 450mm. For a real project you might use a manufacturer supplied backplate drawing rather than drawing a rectangle.

16

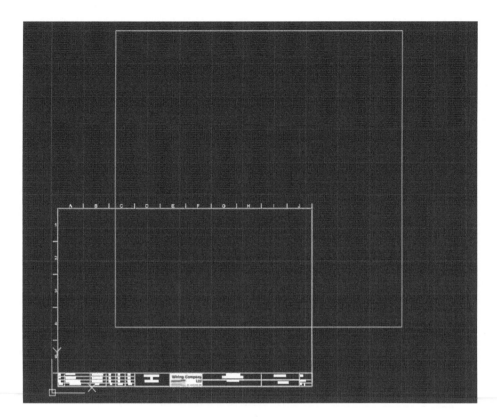

You will see that the square does not fit within our border. The solution is to increase the border size to accommodate it.

Drag the cursor over part of your drawing border to select it. Since it is an AutoCAD block it will be selected as a single object.

Ensure the 450 x 450 square for your backplate is not selected.

Type **SCALE** at the command prompt and press **<Enter>**.

Command: Specify opposite corner or [Fence/WPolygon/CPolygon]:
SCALE

You will be asked to specify a base point.

2 found
SCALE Specify base point:

Use the mouse to click the bottom left corner of your drawing frame to specify this as the base point. AutoCAD will then ask for a scale factor.

Specify base point:
SCALE Specify scale factor or [Copy Reference]: 2

Type **2** and press **<Enter>**.

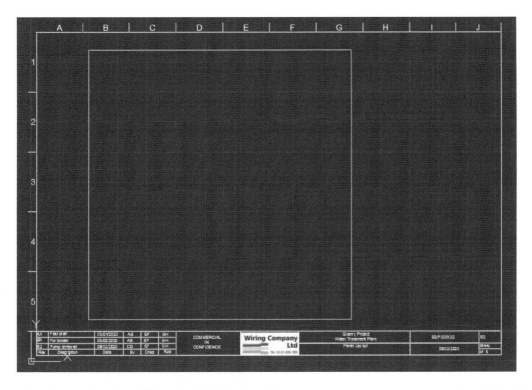

The drawing border will be doubled in size. If necessary, move your square to be within the new drawing frame area.

Note that you can specify any scale factor, including decimals like **2.5** or, if you want to make the border smaller, **0.5**. For your own drawings you would choose a value to fit the size of your panel design.

Save your drawing.

16.2   Paper layout

We still need to print our drawing onto A3 paper even though our drawing is over 500mm high. This scaling can easily be done in layout space.

Select the **Layout1** tab at the bottom of the drawing. This is still set up to print the viewport nicely onto your sheet of paper. Unfortunately the viewport only shows a quarter of the drawing.

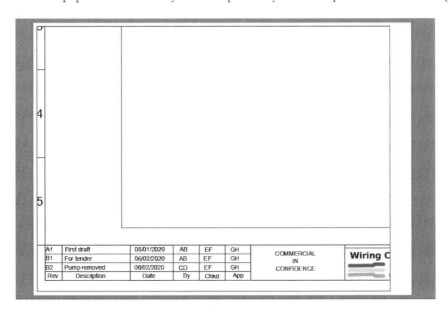

To correct this, double click in the centre of the layout with the left mouse button. The edge of the viewport will be highlighted in thick black lines.

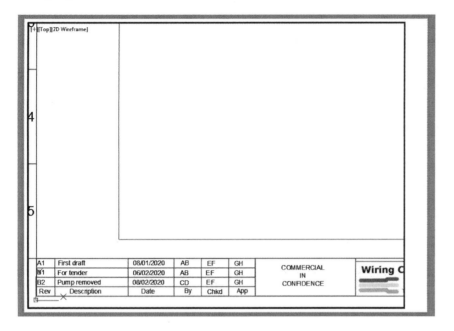

Double click the mouse wheel in the centre of the page. The viewport will auto-scale to include your whole border from model space.

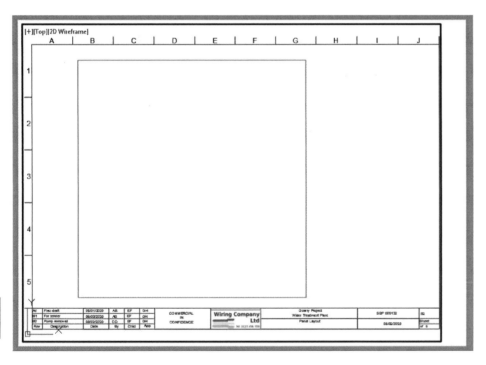

Double click outside of the viewport with the left mouse button. This will return the thick black lines around the viewport to normal and prevent you accidently changing the viewport scale or location again.

See chapter 5, page 86 for a more detailed explanation of the viewport.

Click the **Model** tab at the bottom of the screen to return to model space.

Save your drawing.

16.3   Drawing the panel layout

Now we will insert physical footprints onto our panel to produce a scale mechanical drawing of the backplate. AutoCAD will list each component in our schematic. Provided the catalogue information is all there we can select each in turn and insert a correctly scaled footprint drawing.

The footprint libraries are set in the **Project Properties**. Ensure you are using the **panel** footprint library for an imperial drawing scaled in inches and the **panel_mm** library if you have a metric drawing scaled in mm.

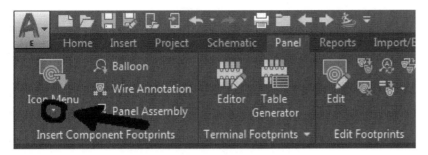

In the **Panel** tab of the ribbon go to the **Insert Component Footprints** panel and click the small drop down arrow as shown above. It will probably have **Icon Menu** on top as the displayed button.

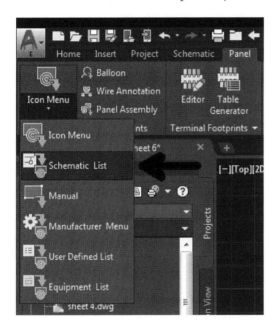

Select **Schematic List** from the drop down menu. If asked to insert an invisible block, **WD_PNLM**, into your drawing, click **OK**.

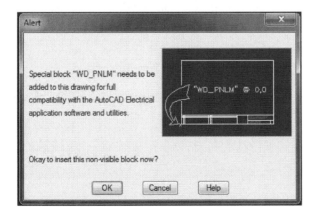

You are asked which of your schematic drawings you wish to search for panel components.

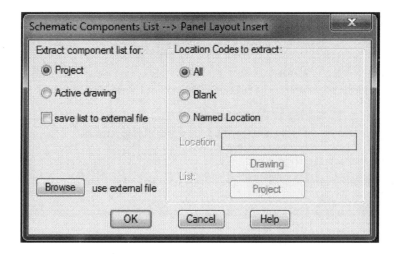

We will list all of our components so select **Project** and **All** location codes as shown above. Click **OK**. When asked which drawings to process, select **Do All** and click **OK**.

The **Schematic Components** window will be displayed. This lists each component extracted from your schematic drawings.

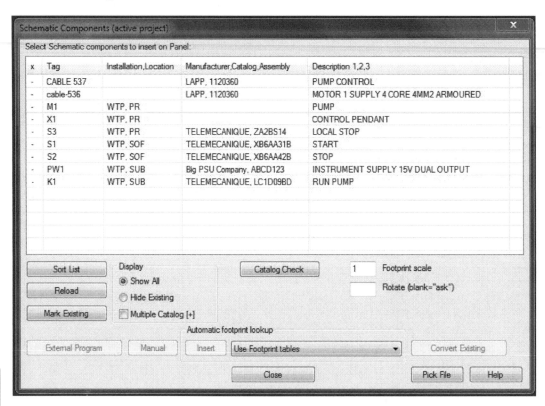

We are going to place a footprint for contactor **K1** on our layout diagram. To do this click the row in the dialogue box with **K1** to highlight it. Then click the **Insert** button at the bottom of the box.

The **Schematic Components** dialogue box will disappear and you will see your drawing with an outline of a rectangle at the cursor. This represents the outline of the contactor footprint. Left click once on your drawing to position the contactor.

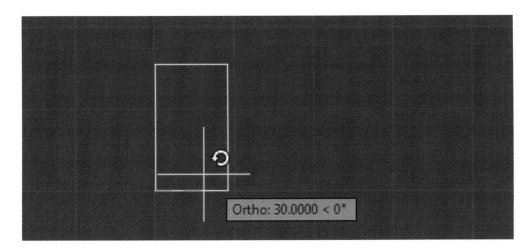

You can now move the mouse to determine whether the contactor is positioned vertically or horizontally. If you select the **Orthogonal** button at the bottom of your screen (beside **snap to grid**) then you are constrained to exactly horizontal or vertical. If you have **Orthogonal** mode switched off then you can position the contactor at any angle.

Left click again to fix the desired orientation. The **Panel Layout - Component Insert/Edit** dialogue appears:

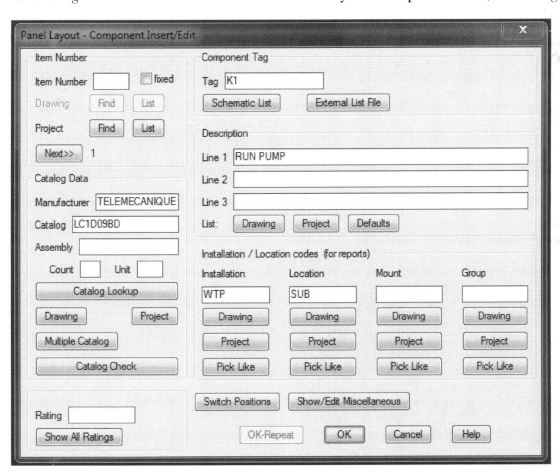

This box is already populated with information from the schematic so click **OK**. The **Schematic Components** window reappears.

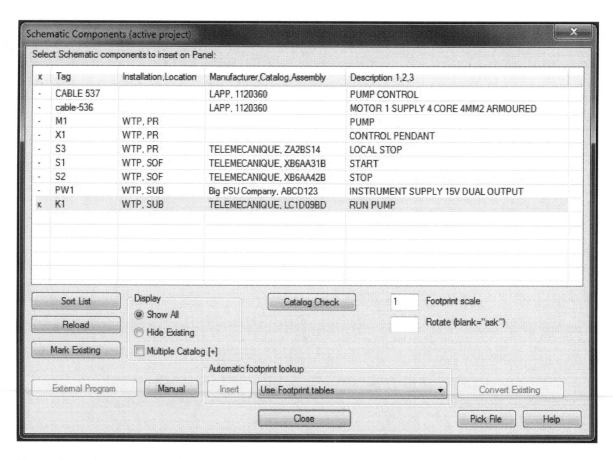

You will see there is now an **'x'** in the left hand column beside **K1**. This shows that the footprint for **K1** has been inserted. You can only insert one footprint for each item in the schematic drawing.

You could now select another line to insert another component. The **Reload** button searches the schematics to regenerate the list. Use this feature if you make a change to your schematic drawings, for example deleting a component. We are not going to place any more component footprints just yet so click **Close** to return to your drawing.

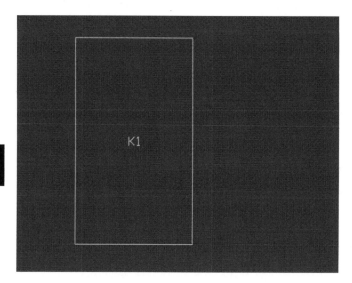

You will see the contactor footprint inserted on your drawing. It is a simple rectangle with the component tag attribute **K1**.

Save your drawing.

16

If you are using the **panel_mm** footprint library (metric) the footprint will be 77mm high and 44 mm wide. If you are using the **panel** footprint library (imperial) it will be 3.0315 inches by 1.7717 inches.

You can verify its size using the **Dimension** tool. If you select this tool and then click on the side of a rectangle or other shape, it will draw a dimension arrow and label it with the measurement. This is useful in mechanical drawings, particularly if they are not printed to a specified scale.

The **Linear** tool is similar but shows the dimension between any two selected points even if these are not part of a rectangle or similar shape. The **Dimension** and **Linear** tools are in the **Home** tab of the ribbon.

Although the rectangular footprint is very simple in this example, some footprints show a much more realistic picture of their associated component.

The important thing for now is the way that the footprint has been generated automatically and is linked to the bill of material and schematic drawing. If you were to go to **sheet 2** and change the contactor **K1** to a different catalogue item, the footprint in the panel layout would automatically update to a different image.

To remove a footprint you can simply erase it. If you then click **Reload** in the **Schematic Components** dialogue box, the 'x' in the left hand column will be removed, showing that it is no longer inserted.

Components with subassemblies

The schematic list only gives one entry for **S3**, our local stop button, even though it consists of two parts, the main stop button and the contact block subassembly. For this button the subassembly is insignificant so does not need its own footprint. For other devices, for example a contactor with extra contacts or terminal covers, the subassemblies might take up additional panel space.

If you need to add footprints for subassemblies then tick the **Multiple catalog [+]** box in the **Schematic Components** dialogue box. Subassembly items will then be shown, for example the **ZB2BE102** contact on **S3** in the example below.

16

Schematic Components (active project)

Select Schematic components to insert on Panel:

x	Tag	Installation,Location	Manufacturer,Catalog,Assembly	Description 1,2,3
-	CABLE 537		LAPP, 1120360	PUMP CONTROL
-	cable-536		LAPP, 1120360	MOTOR 1 SUPPLY 4 CORE 4MM2 ARMOURED
-	M1	WTP, PR		PUMP
-	X1	WTP, PR		CONTROL PENDANT
-	S3	WTP, PR	TELEMECANIQUE, ZA2BS14	LOCAL STOP
-	[+] S3	WTP, PR	Telemecanique, ZB2BE102, NC ...	
-	S1	WTP, SOF	TELEMECANIQUE, XB6AA31B	START
-	S2	WTP, SOF	TELEMECANIQUE, XB6AA42B	STOP
-	PW1	WTP, SUB	Big PSU Company, ABCD123	INSTRUMENT SUPPLY 15V DUAL OUTPUT
x	K1	WTP, SUB	TELEMECANIQUE, LC1D09BD	RUN PUMP

Sort List   Reload   Mark Existing

Display
- ◉ Show All
- ○ Hide Existing
- ☑ Multiple Catalog [+]

Catalog Check

Automatic footprint lookup

1   Footprint scale

Rotate (blank="ask")

External Program   Manual   Insert   Use Footprint tables   Convert Existing

Close   Pick File   Help

Potential issues

If you have followed the example exactly you have hopefully placed your first panel footprint.

Unfortunately there are many things that can go wrong. If you have used a different contactor, a different version of AutoCAD Electrical or loaded different manufacturers' data then it is possible you hit problems.

As you move to your own circuits you will often find the available footprint libraries incomplete. Even if you managed to place this footprint successfully it might seem a lot of work to draw a rectangle.

In the next sections we address these issues. The first step is to explain the file system behind the footprint libraries. Like many things in AutoCAD Electrical it is powerful and flexible but you cannot just switch it on and guess how it works.

We will explain how to create a custom footprint library with symbols for the components you use. This is a lot of work initially but you do not need to start using the full panel layout capability in your first week. Over time you can add to this until you have a powerful tool containing your most frequently used components.

16

16.4 The link between components and footprints

A table, the **Footprint Database**, links component catalogue entries to their footprints. You can view or edit this table using the **Footprint Database Editor**.

In the **Panel** tab of the ribbon, click the drop down arrow beside **Other Tools**.

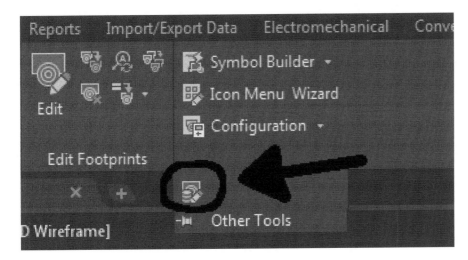

Click the **Footprint Database Editor** button shown above. You are asked if you wish to edit an existing table or create a new one.

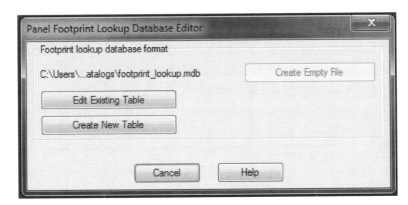

Click **Edit Existing Table**. The database has a table for each manufacturer and these are now shown.

Click on **TELEMECANIQUE** to highlight it then press **OK**. You will see the table which links each **Telemecanique** component in the catalogue to its matching footprint drawing.

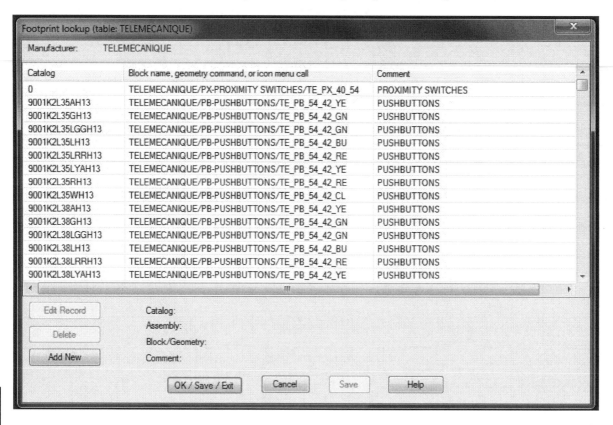

The left column in this table gives each component's catalogue number. The centre column gives the directory path and filename for a **.dwg** file containing the appropriate footprint. You can alter the width of the columns by hovering the mouse over the dividing line between cells in the title row of the table and pressing the left mouse button while you drag the dividing line left or right. Unfortunately you cannot make the window bigger.

The table is in alphabetical order by **Catalog** number. Scroll down to find the line for **Catalog** item **LC1D09B?**. Click to select this line as shown below.

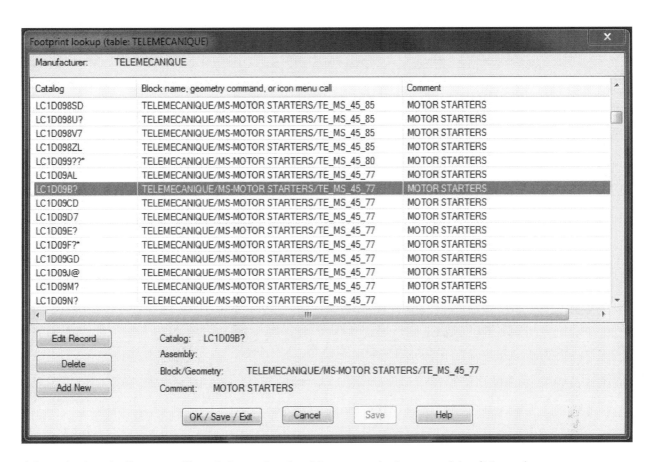

After selecting the line you will see information for this entry at the bottom of the dialogue box.

The **Catalog** value, **LC1D09B?** means that this line applies to all catalogue items with a **Catalog** number starting **LC1D09B**. The '**?**' is a wild card representing a single character. It allows the same footprint to cover contactors with the same frame size but different coil voltages, for example parts **LC1D09BD** and **LC1D09BL**.

Sometimes you will see **Catalog** values of, for example, **2002-140[124]**. The list of numbers in [ ] brackets is similar to a wild card. It means the line applies to **Catalog** values of 2002-140**1**, 2002-140**2** and 2002-140**4**.

The **Block/Geometry** value, **TELEMECANIQUE/MS-MOTOR STARTERS/TE_MS_45_77**, is the footprint file.

It tells AutoCAD to look in the assigned panel libraries for a file **TE_MS_45_77.dwg** which will be in folder **TELEMECANIQUE/MS-MOTOR STARTERS**.

With the **LC1D09B?** line selected, click **Edit Record**.

16

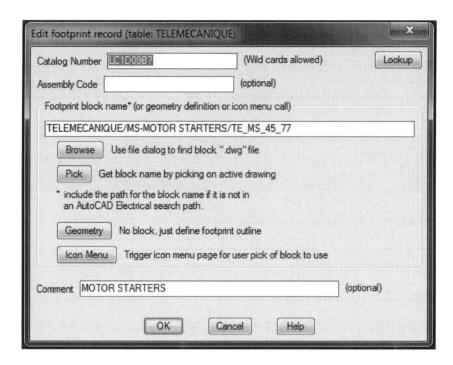

The **Edit footprint record** dialogue box opens. This allows you to change which footprint is assigned to a catalogue item. The **Lookup** button, at the top right, allows you to search for different catalogue items in the component catalogue. **Browse** allows you to look for a different footprint file to assign to the chosen catalogue item.

We are not going to alter anything at the moment so click **Cancel** to return to the previous dialogue box. Then click **Cancel** again to exit back to your drawing.

We are almost finished learning about the footprint database structure but, as a final experiment, have a look at the Microsoft Windows file structure.

The two panel libraries can be found at:

C:\Users\Public\Documents\Autodesk\Acade 2020\Libs\panel

and

C:\Users\Public\Documents\Autodesk\Acade 2020\Libs\panel_mm

Note that **Documents** may be labelled **Public Documents** when using Windows Explorer.

Using Windows Explorer, navigate to the **panel_mm** library and look inside. You will see folders for each manufacturer. There are also several **.dwg** files at the top level of the folder. These include special footprint files that are not connected to a manufacturer, for example the default terminal footprint, **wd_default_terminal.dwg**.

16

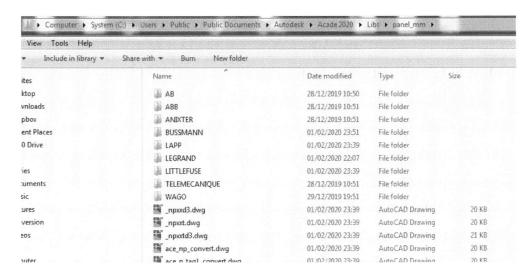

Open the **TELEMECANIQUE** folder. Inside this are subfolders for each component type.

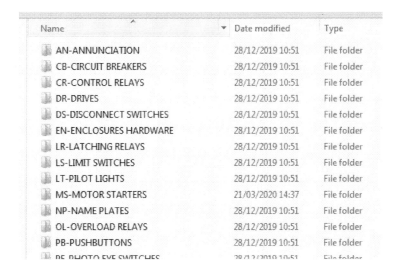

Open the **MS-MOTOR STARTERS** folder and you will see many **.dwg** files with a variety of naming formats.

These are the footprint templates for **MOTOR STARTER** type components made by **Telemecanique**. You can see the **TE_MS_45_77.dwg** footprint file that was tied to the contactor we used for **K1**. It is possible to open these **.dwg** files with AutoCAD to examine the shapes they contain.

Since we are looking in the **panel_mm** folder, this file is intended to be used in metric drawings. It therefore contains a 44 x 77 unit rectangle, which represents 44 x 77 millimetres.

If you were to look in the imperial **panel** library instead, you would find an identical structure and another footprint file with the same **TE_MS_45_77.dwg** name. This one is intended for imperial drawings scaled in inches. It therefore contains a rectangle of dimensions 1.77 x 3.03 units which represents 1.77 x 3.03 inches.

When you place a footprint, AutoCAD will use the **.dwg** file from whichever library you have selected. If you select both the **panel** and **panel_mm** libraries it will use the file from whichever library is listed first in the **Project Properties**. Only if it cannot find the filename it is looking for in the first library will it look at the second library listed.

If you try and insert a footprint and AutoCAD cannot find the file that is listed in the **Footprint Database** table you will get an error window as shown below. This example error message occurred when I tried to insert the footprint for an **AB** relay part **700-K31Z-ZJ** which should have footprint file **ABCRE150.dwg**.

In this example the footprint file **ABCRE150.dwg** was missing from the **panel_mm** library on my installation, even though it was present in the **panel** library.

By opening the **ABCRE150.dwg** file directly, I also discovered that the dimensions of the copy that was present were for a metric version, even though it was in the imperial measurement library.

Should you find any problems like this when using footprints then having an understanding of how AutoCAD and its footprint databases work will save you a lot of time and frustration.

Before continuing, close any footprint files you have opened, without saving them.

16.5 Making your own footprints

AutoCAD comes with data from many manufacturers. By default it is only recommended to install those you are likely to use. You may need to load more of the supplied manufacturer's data sets later as described on page 3.

It is likely that you will also need to add your own footprints, either using a drawing supplied directly by a manufacturer or by creating a footprint yourself from scratch.

In our schematic the fictitious custom power supply made by the Big PSU Company is one such item. Another is the fused WAGO terminal which (at least in my version of AutoCAD Electrical 2020) does not have a footprint symbol.

We will set up a custom footprint library and then create these new footprints in it.

Creating a new footprint library

You could put your custom footprints inside the **panel** or **panel_mm** library, placing them in the correct subfolders for manufacturer and component type. If you add a new manufacturer then you could create a new subfolder.

In this book we will make a new library. This has the advantage of keeping your custom footprints all together. We will call the library **panel_custom**. Inside we will create subfolders for each manufacturer. We will not bother creating sub-subfolders for different component types, as in the main library, but you could do this if you wanted to.

Using Windows Explorer, navigate to the library folder with the **panel** and **panel_mm** library folders. You will find them at:

C:\Users\Public\Documents\Autodesk\Acade 2020\Libs

Note that **Documents** will sometimes be shown as **Public Documents**. Create a new folder called **panel_custom**.

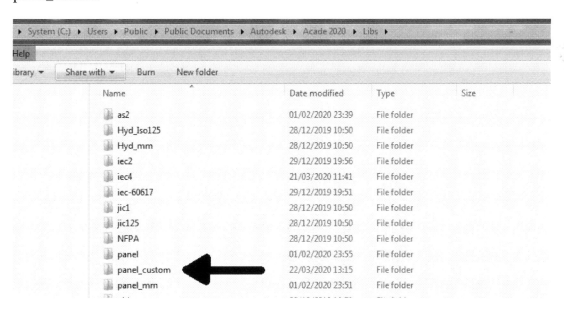

Inside your **panel_custom** folder create two subfolders called **Big PSU Company** and **WAGO**.

16

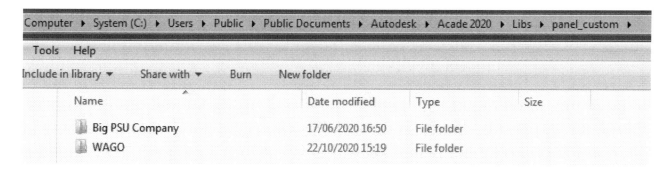

Name	Date modified	Type	Size
Big PSU Company	17/06/2020 16:50	File folder	
WAGO	22/10/2020 15:19	File folder	

In AutoCAD go to **Project Properties** for your **TestRig1** project. Select the **Project Settings** tab.

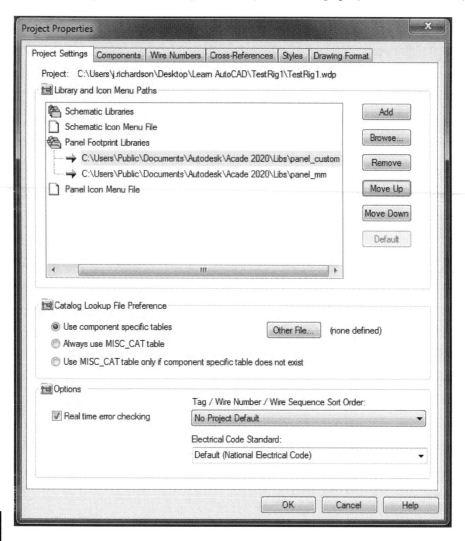

Click the heading **Panel Footprint Libraries** to highlight it. Then click **Add** to create a blank line for a new library name.

Click **Browse** to find your **panel_custom** library folder and select it.

On returning to the **Project Properties** window use the **Move Up** button to place the **panel_custom** library at the top.

The second library should be **panel_mm** for metric drawings and **panel** if you are using inches.

This way AutoCAD will look in your custom folder first. Any modified custom footprints will be used instead of AutoCAD supplied objects of the same name.

If you wish you can also add the unused library (the metric **panel_mm** library if you are using inches or the imperial **panel** library if you are using mm) as a third entry. This will not normally be used but occasionally a component's footprint only exists in one library, (sometimes in the incorrect library for their scaling) so this does not do any harm and may get you a few extra supplied footprints.

We have only created one custom footprint library on the assumption that all of your drawings use either metric or imperial measurements. If you use both, perhaps for different customers, you might want to create metric and imperial versions of your custom footprints and keep them in separate libraries.

Click **OK** to close the **Project Settings** window.

16.6   Creating a footprint symbol for the power supply

Custom panel footprints are created using the same **Symbol Builder** tool we used for custom schematic symbols.

Go to **sheet 6**.

In a spare part of the page draw the outline for the power supply. We will pretend it is 150mm x 80 mm with four 20mm square mounting lugs at each corner, each with a 10mm diameter hole. Draw this, or something similar, using the **Rectangle** and **Circle** commands.

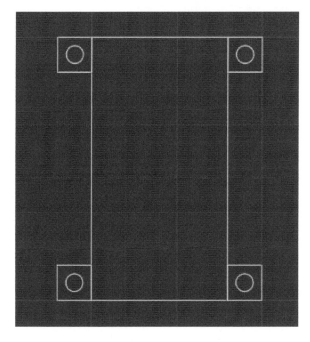

In the **Schematic** tab of the ribbon click the **Symbol Builder** button in the **Other Tools** panel. This may be on top, if not, click the drop down arrow to access the button as shown below. This tool is also in the **Panel** tab.

16

The **Select Symbol/Objects** dialogue box will appear.

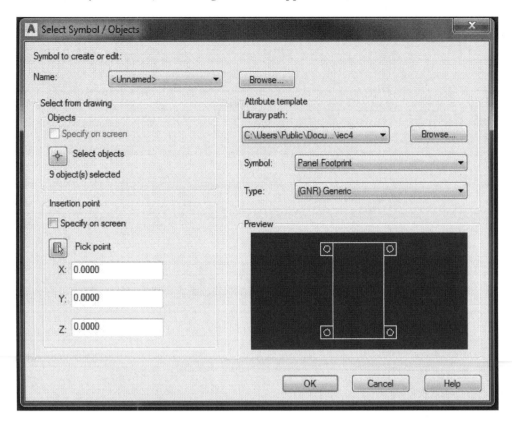

In this box click the **Select objects** button. You will be returned to your drawing. Select the power supply outline you drew. You can do this by dragging the mouse to select all items in an area. Press **<Enter>** to return to the **Select Symbol/Objects** dialogue box.

The **Preview** image will now show your footprint outline.

The **Library path** needs to point to one of your schematic symbol libraries, in the example shown it is pointing to the **iec4** library folder. **Symbol Builder** needs to access template files in these folders. AutoCAD will give you an error message and refuse to change the path if you try to set **Library path** to a folder without the correct templates.

Set **Symbol** to **Panel Footprint** and **Type** to **(GNR) Generic** which is your only choice for a footprint symbol.

Click **OK**.

16

The **Symbol Builder** will open, showing a large view of your selected symbol.

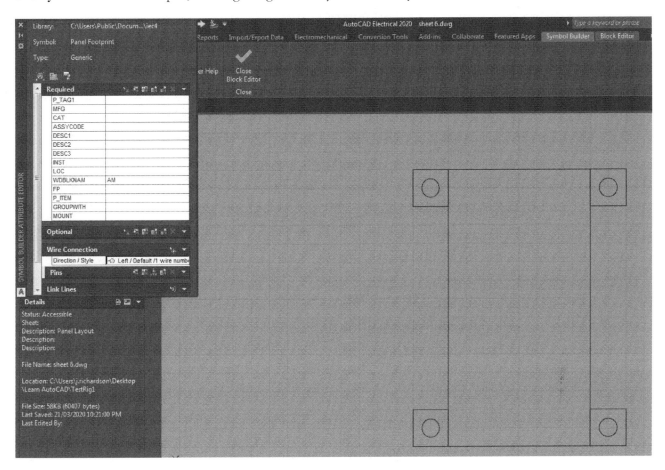

The **Symbol Builder** tool was covered in detail in chapter 10 when we created custom schematic components. For a footprint symbol there is less work required than for a schematic component since you probably do not need to add terminals.

It is compulsory to add the **P_TAG1** attribute. The other **"Required"** attributes are optional but it is recommended to add them so these pieces of information appear on your drawing.

For the purpose of this example place all of the **Required** attributes on the symbol.

You can highlight all of the **Required** attributes and insert them in one go by clicking the **Insert Attribute** button. After inserting them you can move them around and change the text size as you would any normal piece of text. You can also change the text size using the **Properties** button in the **Symbol Builder Attribute Editor** window.

For more detailed guidance on the **Symbol Builder** tool see chapter 10.

16

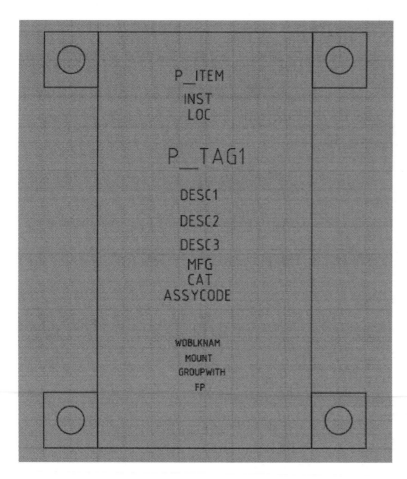

After inserting the attributes, close the **Symbol Builder Attribute Editor** window and then click **Done** on the ribbon. Do not click **Close Block Editor**.

The **Close Block Editor: Save Symbol** dialogue box opens.

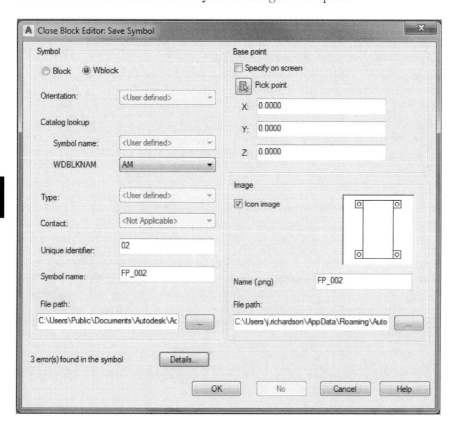

As in Chapter 10, select **Wblock** rather than **Block**. This will allow the symbol to be used in other drawings, not just this one.

Under **Base point**, click the **Pick point** button. You will be taken back to the picture of your symbol. Click a sensible insertion point, for example the top left corner of the symbol, and left click on it. You will return to the **Close Block Editor** screen with the coordinates of this point filled in. In future, when you insert the symbol, it will be placed on the drawing with this insertion point at the cursor.

Since the symbol is a footprint it is given a filename starting **FP_** by default. In the above screenshot it will be called **FP_002**. Unlike the schematic symbols in chapter 10 there are no rules that must be followed for the filename.

The **Icon image** tick box tells AutoCAD to create an image file. This is useful if you want to insert your footprint from the **Icon Menu**. If you are using this then leave its file path (at the right of the dialogue box) alone. For this example we do not need an icon image but if you create one it will do no harm.

Use the '**...**' button to change the **File path** value on the left to point to your new footprint library folder. It is the folder:

C:\Users\Public\Documents\Autodesk\Acade 2020\Libs\panel_custom\Big PSU Company

When you have completed the information click **OK**. You will be asked if you want to insert the symbol after closing the block editor.

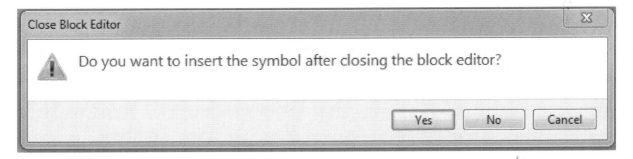

Click **No** because we are going to insert it with the **Schematic List** tool instead. You will be returned to your drawing.

The original rectangles and circles you drew as an outline of the power supply footprint are still on your drawing. They are no longer needed. Delete them.

Linking the power supply footprint to the catalogue

In the **Panel** tab of the ribbon, select the **Footprint Database Editor**. It is in the drop down menu at the bottom of the **Other Tools** panel.

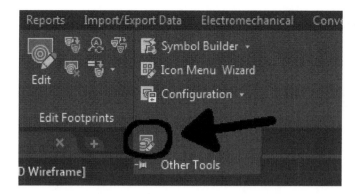

When prompted, choose **Create New Table**.

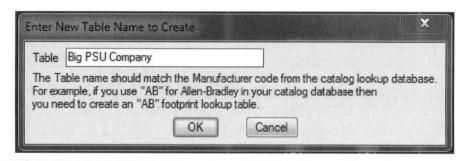

Create a table called **Big PSU Company** by typing this in the **Table** box and clicking **OK**. It is important that this name exactly matches the value you used for **Manufacturer** in the component catalogue on page 277.

The **Footprint lookup (table: BIG PSU COMPANY)** window will open.

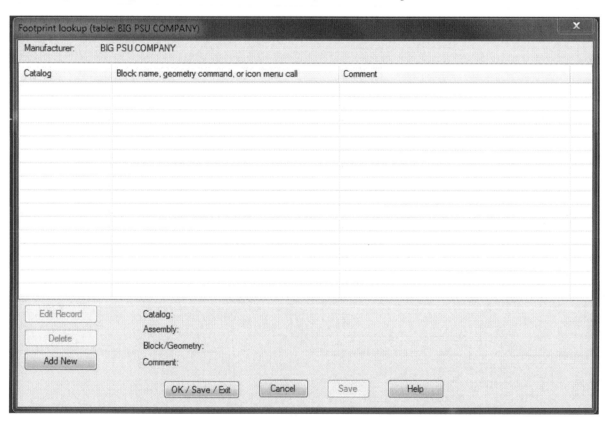

16

Click the **Add New** button. The **Add footprint record** box appears.

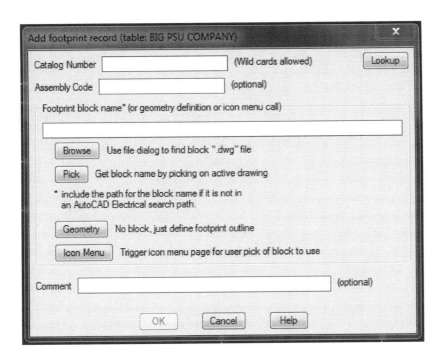

Click the **Lookup** button. The **Catalog Browser** window opens.

Change the **Category** at the top of this window to **PW (Power supplies)** otherwise we will not find our PSU component. Then type **BIG PSU** in the search box and click the magnifying glass symbol at the right of the search box or press **<Enter>**.

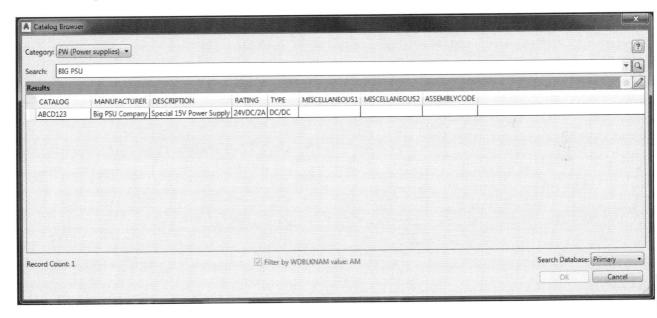

AutoCAD should show the record for our custom power supply as above. Click this line to highlight it. Then click **OK**. You will be returned to the **Add footprint record** window with the component **Catalog Number** filled in.

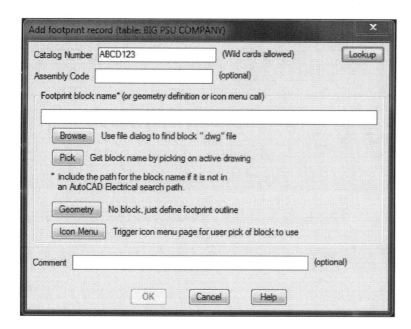

Now we must find our new footprint drawing to link to this catalogue item. Click the **Browse** button.

Navigate to the **Big PSU Company** folder within the **panel_custom** folder we created. Select the file you created earlier for the power supply footprint. In these screenshots it is **FP_002.dwg**. You can easily see the advantage of having separate folders for each manufacturer within your custom library and possibly thinking up a file naming convention to further identify your footprints.

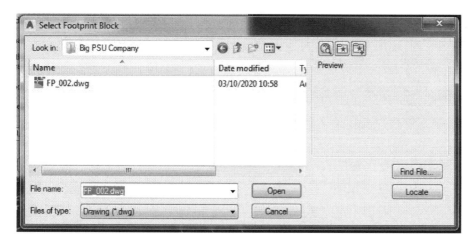

Click **Open** to select the footprint file and return to the **Add footprint record** window.

16

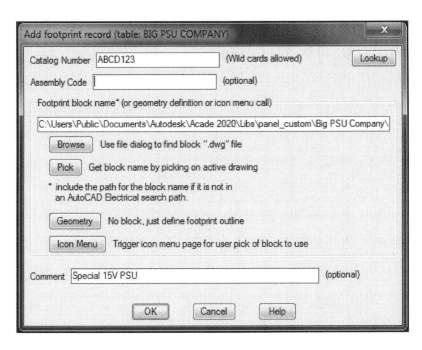

If you want you can add a comment. Click **OK** and AutoCAD will display the **Footprint lookup** table with the new entry added.

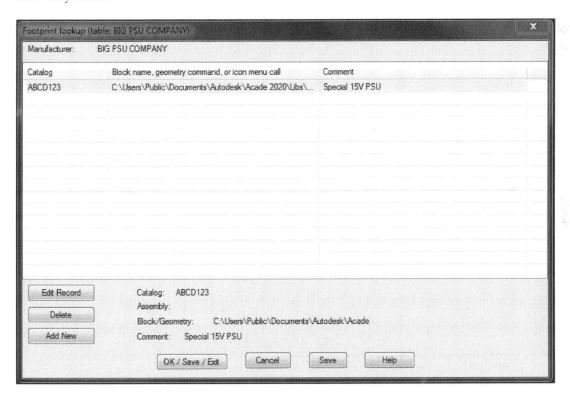

Click the **OK/Save/Exit** button to return to your drawing.

Inserting the new footprint

Open the **Schematic List** tool on the **Panel** tab of the ribbon as described earlier.

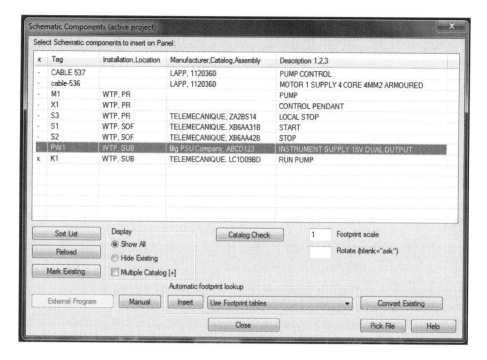

Contactor **K1** should still have an 'x' next to it to show it has been inserted. If not, click **Reload** to refresh the list.

Select the line for **PW1**, our custom 15V power supply. Click the **Insert** button.

You will be returned to the drawing with an image of the power supply at the cursor. Left click to position the footprint. Then click again to confirm its orientation.

The **Panel Layout - Component Insert/Edit** window will open. All information in this window will have already been filled in automatically. Click **OK** to close it.

You are returned to the **Schematic Components** dialogue box. There will now be an 'x' beside both **PW1** and **K1** to show they are inserted. Click **Close** to return to your drawing.

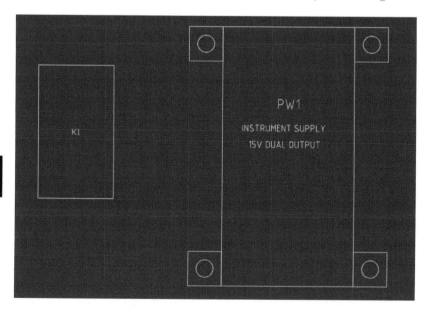

The footprint for **PW1** should now be inserted. It will also have been labelled with the attributes taken from the schematic drawing.

17. Terminals in panel layouts (2¼ hours)

In chapter 9 we used the **Terminal Strip Editor** to draw the physical arrangement of our terminals. This **Terminal Strip Editor** layout tool actually produces a scale mechanical drawing. If the terminals do not have any footprint data linked to them it uses a default terminal footprint which is a 50.8 mm x 6.35 mm (2 inch x 0.25 inch) rectangle.

Now that our terminals are linked to real catalogue parts we are going to use the **Terminal Strip Editor** to draw accurate footprints for them on our panel drawing. We will also assign a catalogue part to the fused terminal in terminal block **3** and learn how build a custom footprint for it.

Terminal footprints are a little more complicated to create than the power supply footprint in the last chapter. To make life easier we will produce ours by modifying the existing default terminal footprint.

We will then add DIN rail to our layout drawing, learn how to add footprints directly from the **Icon Menu** and see how to represent multi-level terminals using the AutoCAD Electrical software. Using **Terminal Strip Editor** we will add jumpers, end plates and other accessories to our terminal blocks.

Finally we will look at more advanced scale drawings. We will print drawings to exact scales and learn how to move the title block into the layout view which is a more flexible method for mechanical drawings.

Topics covered:

- Understanding the default terminal footprint
- Creating a terminal footprint by modifying an existing footprint
- Adding a **wipeout** to make a footprint symbol opaque
- Adding DIN rail
- Using the **Icon Menu** to add footprints
- Using multi-level terminals
- Adding jumpers, both within a multi-level terminal block and between terminals
- Adding terminal block accessories
- Creating a mechanical drawing which can be printed with a specified scale, for example 2:1
- Moving the title block into layout view

17.1 Understanding the default terminal footprint and scaling

Before creating our custom terminal it is worth understanding the default terminal footprint.

If no catalogue number is assigned to a single level terminal, **Terminal Strip Editor** uses a default footprint file called **wd_default_terminal.dwg**.

There are two versions of this file. The English (imperial) measurement version is stored in the **panel** folder:

C:/Users/Public/Documents/Autodesk/Acade 2020/Libs/panel

The metric version is stored in the **panel_mm** folder:

C:/Users/Public/Documents/Autodesk/Acade 2020/Libs/panel_mm

The metric version is based on a rectangle 50.8 units wide and 6.35 units high. In a metric drawing this will be a reasonable size for a typical terminal. The imperial version is 2 units wide and 0.25 units high, designed for drawings measured in inches.

If you use the metric footprint in an imperial drawing it will appear 50.8 inches wide, so large you may not even see it until you zoom out. Use the imperial footprint in a metric drawing and it will only be 2 mm wide by 0.25 mm high. So small you can hardly see it.

To avoid this problem, ensure you have set you drawing properties correctly to be metric or imperial. Then ensure you are using the **panel_mm** footprint library if you have a metric drawing and the **panel** library if your drawing is in inches.

When you insert terminals from the **Terminal Strip Editor** it is possible to change the **Scale on Insert** value shown below. A value of **25.4** will make imperial footprints fit a metric drawing and entering **0.03937** will shrink metric footprints to fit an imperial one. I do not recommend altering this value however.

It is better to use the correct footprint and drawing scale and leave the **Scale on Insert** at **1**. Fiddling the scaling can cause other problems, for example the blocks being the wrong distance apart or the text being an incorrect size.

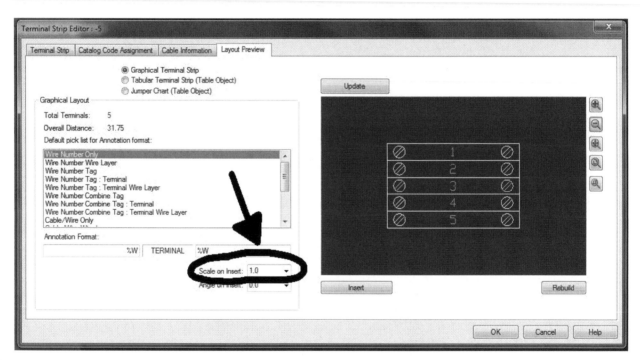

The **wd_default_terminal.dwg** default terminal footprint is only used for single level terminals.

Other files, **wd_default_02terminal.dwg**, **wd_default_03terminal.dwg** and **wd_default_04terminal.dwg** are used for two, three and four level terminals. These contain extra attributes for the additional wire numbers attached to multi-level terminals.

In this chapter we will create a new terminal footprint for our fused terminal based on the **wd_default_terminal.dwg** file. Although we will not alter this file it is worth making a back-up of it now in case you accidently press save while working on an altered version and change it by accident.

We will not be making a custom multi-level terminal footprint in this book but if you ever need to do this your starting point would be the multi-level default footprint with the appropriate number of levels.

17

17.2   Adding a fused terminal to the catalogue

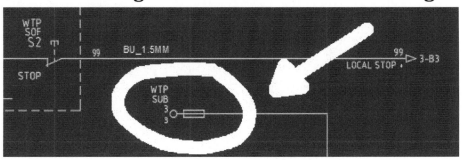

Go to **sheet 2**. Select terminal **3.3** (the fused terminal). Right click and choose **Edit Component** from the menu that appears.

In the **Insert / Edit Terminal Symbol** dialogue box click the **Catalog Lookup** button to open the catalogue. Select the category **TRMS (Terminals)**.

Click the pencil symbol to edit the catalogue. Scroll down to the empty line at the bottom of the table. On this line, add a new catalogue entry for a fused terminal part **2002-1611** from manufacturer **WAGO** as follows:

Catalog	2002-1611
Manufacturer	WAGO
Description	2 - conductor fuse terminal block for 5x20mm metric fuse
Type	Fuse block
Rating	6.3 Amp 250 V

Click the tick symbol to save your entry and leave edit mode. Your new component will be shuffled in with the other terminals. Search for **WAGO 2002-1611** to find it again.

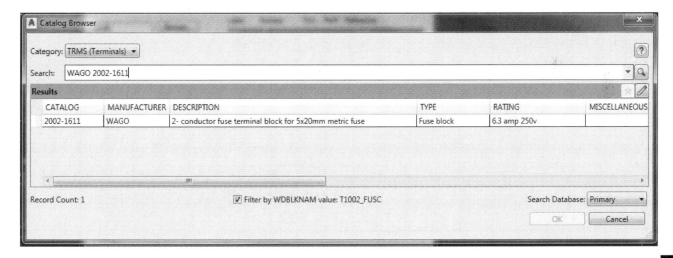

Select the item so that it is highlighted. Click **OK**.

You will return to the **Insert / Edit Terminal Symbol** dialogue box and find the manufacturer and part number for the terminal have been entered. Click **OK**.

You will be warned that the footprint for this catalogue item does not exist. Select "**Update the catalog on the footprint but leave the footprint symbol as is**". This option ignores the missing footprint. The other option will cancel your catalogue changes.

You are now asked if you always want to use this symbol for this catalogue number. Click "**Map symbol to catalog number**" which tells AutoCAD to always use this fused terminal symbol if you ever insert part **WAGO 2002-1611** directly from the catalogue.

17

Since we have already added a terminal layout for these terminals in chapter 9 you may be asked if you want to update these related components. Click **Skip** since we will be redrawing them later after we define a new terminal footprint.

You are returned to your drawing. Save it.

17.3   Create a terminal footprint

Now we will make a terminal footprint for our fused terminal. We will do this by opening the default terminal symbol in **Symbol Builder** and drawing a new shape but keeping the text attributes. We will then save the modified footprint in our custom footprint library.

Go to **sheet 6**.

In the **Panel** tab of the ribbon open **Symbol Builder**.

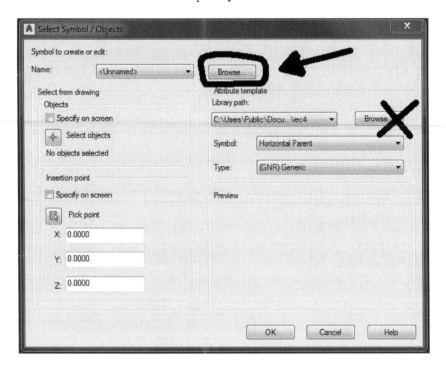

At the very top of the **Select Symbol / Objects** dialogue box click the **Browse** button to the right of **Name**. Do not click the **Library path** browse button which is slightly below this.

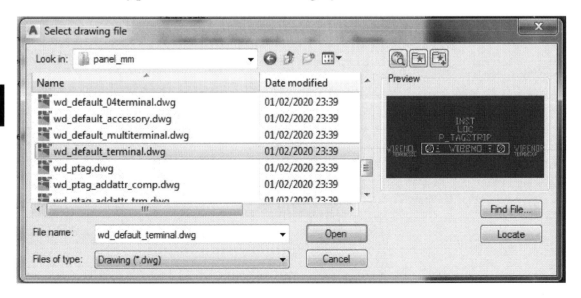

In the **Select drawing file** box which opens, navigate to the **panel_mm** folder for metric drawings. Choose the **panel** folder instead if your drawings are in inches. At the top level inside of this folder (not inside the manufacturers' folders) you will find the **wd_default_terminal.dwg** file. This is the AutoCAD default terminal footprint.

Select it as shown and click **Open**.

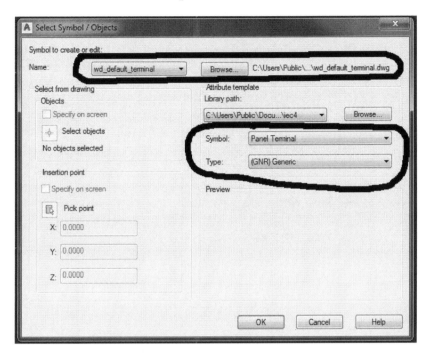

You are now returned to the **Select Symbol / Objects** dialogue box. Choose **Symbol** to be **Panel Terminal** and **Type** to be **(GNR) Generic** as shown above. Leave **Library path** pointing to your normal schematic symbol library, for example the **iec4** library folder. Click **OK**.

You will be presented with a rather cluttered **Symbol Builder** screen, including a copy of the default terminal symbol.

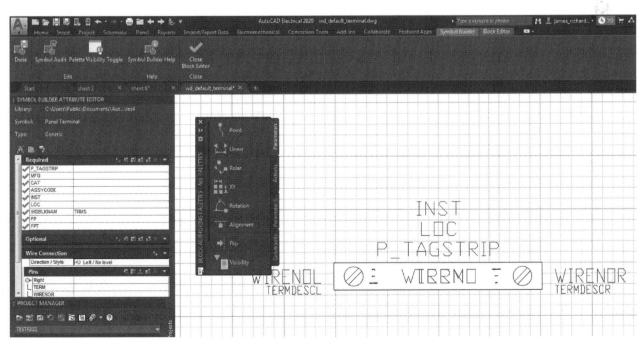

This may look intimidating but do not be frightened. It is just an AutoCAD drawing of the terminal with a different background colour, a few open windows and some extra tabs on the ribbon. Most of the ordinary AutoCAD features are still there and we will be using some of them in a moment.

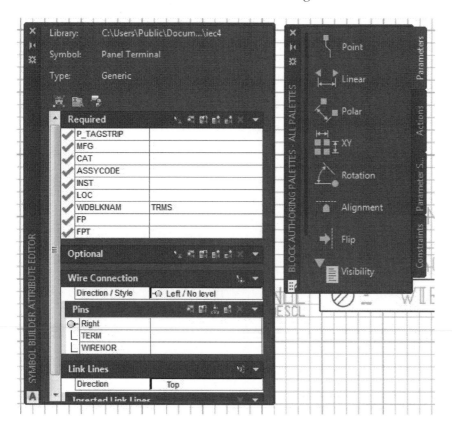

You will see the **Symbol Builder Attribute Editor** (which we used earlier for schematic symbols) and **Block Authoring Palettes** are open. We won't need these this time so feel free to close them.

With the clutter removed you can see the default terminal and its attributes as shown below.

17 Your ribbon will be open at the **Symbol Builder** tab but the other tabs are still accessible. Select the **Home** tab and choose the **Rectangle** drawing tool.

Draw a rectangle below the outline of the default terminal. Leave space above it for attributes. This rectangle should be a 66.1mm x 6.2mm rectangle (2.602 x 0.244 inches) which is the size of a WAGO 2002-1611 fused terminal.

Draw a fuse symbol and two small circles on top of it to make it look more like a fused terminal. Your drawing should now look like this:

Note that when creating terminal footprints you should always draw them with this horizontal orientation, as though they are clipped to a vertical piece of DIN rail. That is the way **Terminal Strip Editor** expects to find them. Ignore this rule and it will build your terminal strips from blocks placed end to end instead of side by side.

Next, select the attributes from the default terminal and move them to your new terminal. **WIRENOL** and **WIRENOR** are the attributes that allow **Terminal Strip Editor** to label your terminal blocks with wire numbers. The **Symbol Builder** template does not make it easy to add these when creating a blank symbol from scratch. That is why it is easier to modify an existing symbol.

After moving the attributes you should have this:

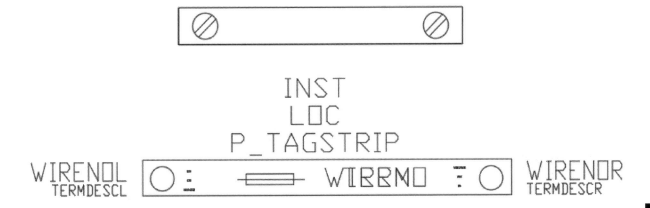

Select the old terminal outline and delete it.

17.4   Adding a wipeout

Terminal footprints usually contain an object called a **wipeout**. This is an opaque polygon which obscures any object behind it. It is especially useful for DIN rail mounted components since it prevents you seeing the DIN rail through the middle of the component.

In the **Home** tab of the ribbon click the small drop down arrow beside the word **Draw**.

17

In the menu that appears, click the **Wipeout** button. You can also run this tool by typing **wipeout** in the command line.

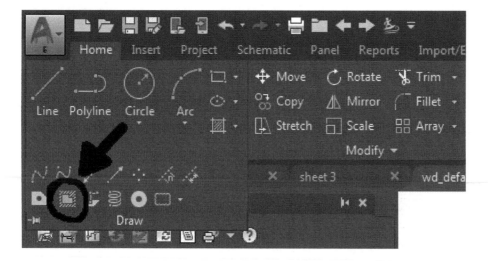

After clicking the **Wipeout** button, click to mark the four corners of a very rough rectangle below your terminal block. Do not worry about exact positions since we will be moving them in a minute. Press **<Enter>** to exit the **Wipeout** command. This joins the last two corners to create a polygon. If you have the grid turned on (It is turned off in some of this book's screenshots for clarity) you will see the wipeout shape obscures the gridlines.

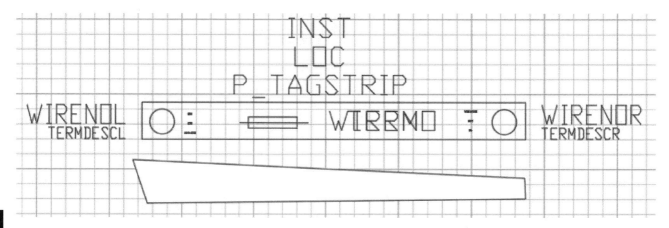

We need to send the wipeout shape behind our terminal block. The reason we drew it next to the terminal is to make selecting it for this process easier. Select your wipeout shape, ensuring nothing else is selected. Right click the mouse. Expand the **Draw Order** item in the menu that appears and choose **Send to Back**.

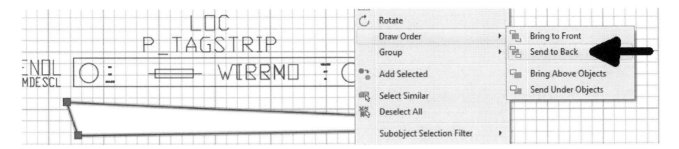

With the draw order set correctly we can now position the wipeout behind the terminal outline.

Drag the corners of the wipeout to be at the corners of the terminal block rectangle. The easiest way to do this is to select both the rectangle and the wipeout. That way you can drag the wipeout corners onto the highlighted corners of the rectangle forming the terminal block.

None of your terminal block shapes or attributes should be obscured because the wipeout is behind them. When you use the terminal in a drawing the wipeout will hide objects behind the terminal such as DIN rail. If you have the grid on you will see your terminal is now opaque and covers the grid lines.

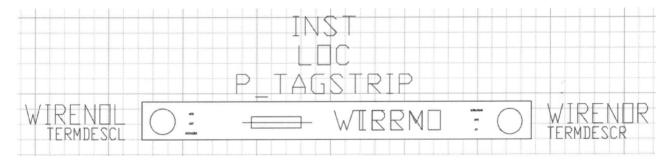

17.5   Saving the new footprint

Now we need to save our terminal as a new footprint. We must not save under the existing filename or we will destroy the default terminal file.

Go to the **Symbol Builder** tab on the ribbon. Click **Done**. Do not click **Close Block Editor.**

The **Close Block Editor: Save Symbol** screen appears.

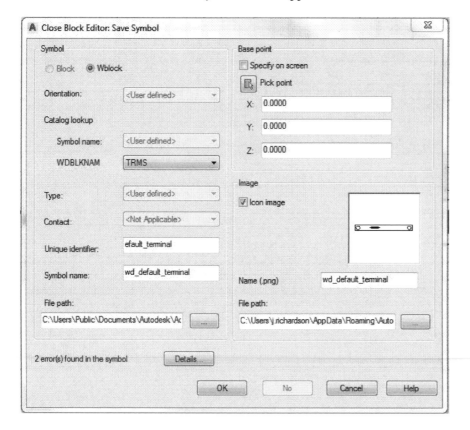

It is vital that you do not save this symbol on top of the default terminal block drawing so set up the **File path** at the left to point to the WAGO folder inside your **panel_custom** library.

Change the symbol name to **FP_fused terminal 2002-1611**.

If you want to create an icon image to allow you to add the new footprint to the panel **Icon Menu** then leave the **Icon image** box ticked. There is no need to change the file path at the right hand side of the box which controls where this image is stored.

At the top ensure you have selected **Wblock** so that your footprint is saved for use in other drawings, not just this one.

Under **Base point** at the top right, click the **Pick point** button. The dialogue box closes and you must click on your drawing to choose the insertion point.

For **Terminal Strip Editor** to work properly without overlapping or gaps between adjacent terminals, the **Base point** must be on the top edge of your block. Place it in the middle of this edge, where the centreline of the DIN rail would be for the type of terminal you are using.

17

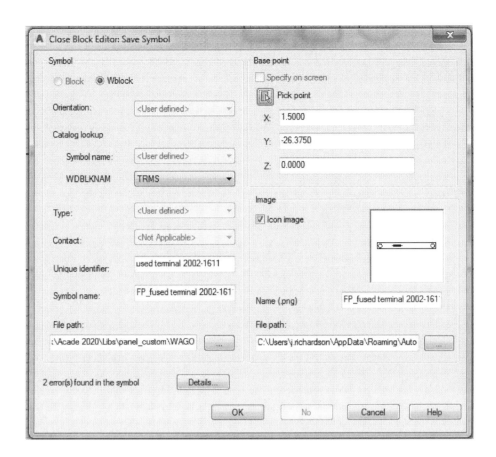

Click **OK** to save the symbol.

You will return to the drawing of the default terminal, **wd_default_terminal.dwg** which you used as a basis for your new symbol. Close this drawing (You can use the **X** on the tab at the top of the screen) and do not save changes to it when prompted.

17.6 Linking the footprint to the catalogue

In the **Panel** tab of the ribbon, open the **Footprint Database Editor** from the **Other Tools** drop down menu.

17

You are asked whether you want to create a new table or edit an existing one.

Choose **Edit Existing Table**.

In the list of manufacturers, select **WAGO**. You will see a list of all existing WAGO parts with footprints. Click the **Add New** button. The **Add footprint record** screen appears.

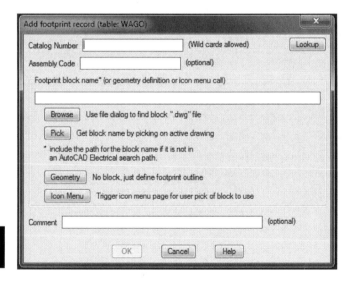

Click the **Lookup** button.

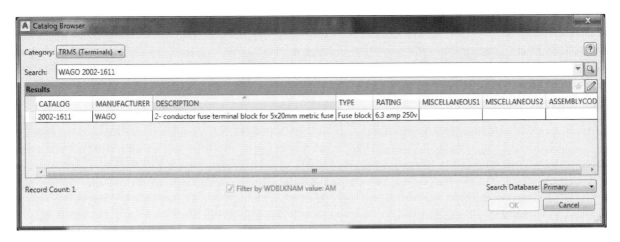

In the **Catalog Browser** window that appears, change the **Category** to **TRMS (Terminals)**. Your search will not find anything if this is set to the wrong type of component.

In the search box type **WAGO 2002-1611**. Click the magnifying glass search button or press **<Enter>**.

You should see the 2002-1611 fused terminal we placed in the catalogue earlier. Click this line to highlight it then press **OK**. Do not forget to highlight the line before pressing **OK** or it will not work. AutoCAD will return to the **Add footprint record** form. Catalog number **2002-1611** will be filled in.

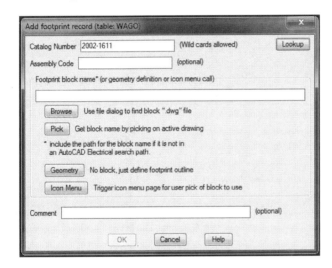

Now click the **Browse** button.

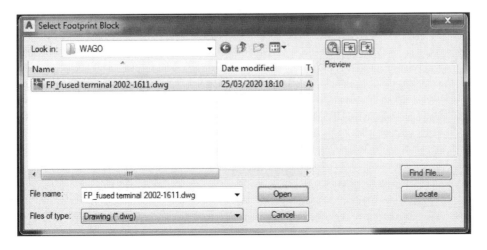

Navigate to the **WAGO** folder inside the **panel_custom** library folder which we created. You should see our terminal footprint file, **FP_fused terminal 2002-1611.dwg**

Select this file and click **Open**.

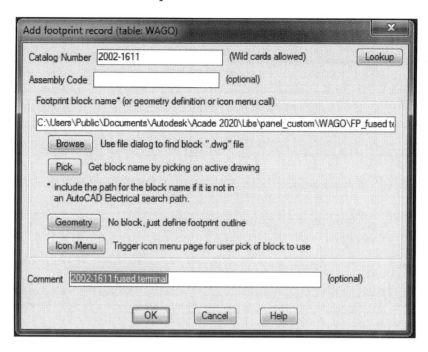

The **Add footprint record** form is now complete. You can add an optional comment. Click **OK**. You are returned to the **Footprint lookup** table editor.

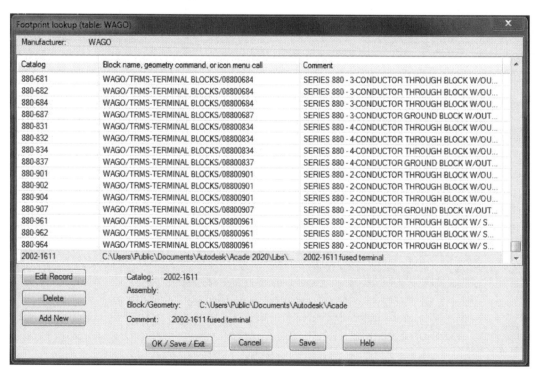

You should be able to see your new footprint as above. Click **OK / Save / Exit** to save your changes to the table.

17.7   Using the new footprint

Ensure you are on **sheet 6** of your drawing.

If you have been looking at the default terminal footprint or other footprint **.dwg** files then close them. You may have problems with **Terminal Strip Editor** if you use it while the footprint files it references are open.

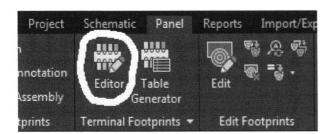

In the **Panel** tab of the ribbon click the **Editor** button to open the **Terminal Strip Editor**.

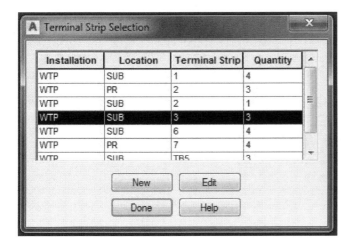

We are going to add the three terminals in terminal strip **3** to our panel layout. Select the row for **Terminal Strip 3** and click **Edit**.

The **Terminal Strip Editor** will open at the **Terminal Strip** tab.

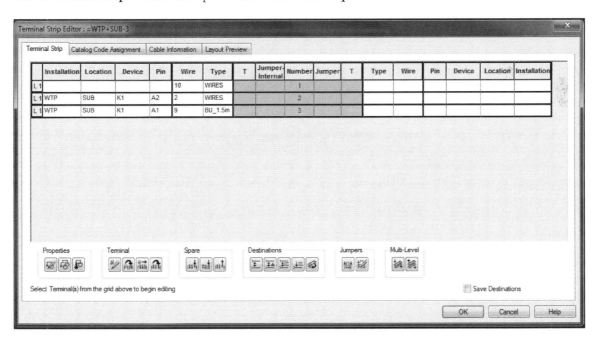

If necessary click the heading of the **Number** column to sort the terminals into numerical order. This is important since the table shows the order they will be in when placed on the panel layout.

Select the **Catalog Code Assignment** tab.

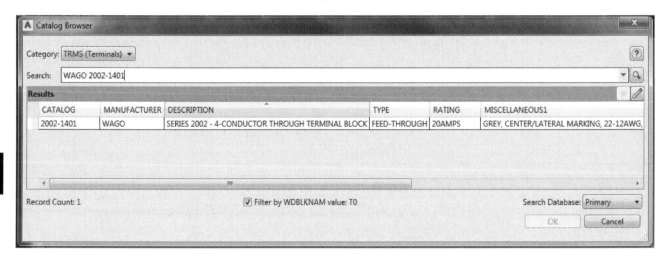

You will see that we have already set the catalogue part number for the fused terminal by editing it in the schematic. The other two terminals have not been assigned part numbers yet. Remember from chapter 15 that you can select multiple lines to add details to many terminals at once. Although this screen looks like a spreadsheet, you can only select lines, not individual cells. Copying, pasting and deleting catalogue details should be done using the buttons at the bottom right of the window under the word **"Catalog"** or by right clicking selected lines and choosing options from the sub-menu **Catalog** in the menu that appears.

For our example we will not assign a catalogue number to terminal **1**. It will therefore be displayed using the default terminal footprint.

For terminal **2** we will use a 4 hole, 2.5mm² straight through **WAGO** terminal block, part **2002-1401**. A footprint for this part is included in the libraries which are supplied with AutoCAD Electrical. Select the second line. Click the **Assign Catalog Number** button indicated with an arrow in the picture above. The **Catalog Browser** window will open.

Ensure **TRMS (Terminals)** is selected as the **Category** field at the top of the window. Search for **WAGO 2002-1401**.

When you find this item, click on the line to highlight it and click **OK**. You will return to the **Terminal Strip Editor** with the catalogue data added.

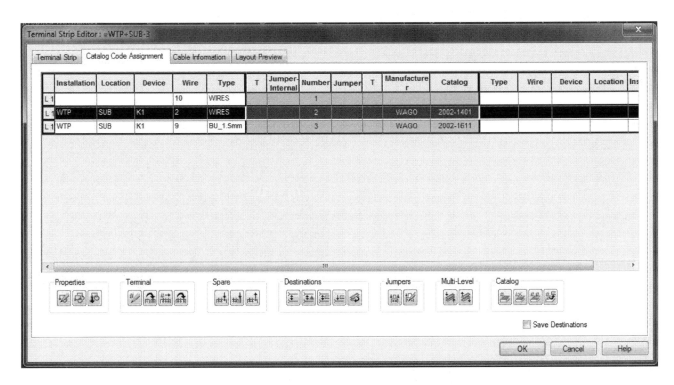

Click the **Layout Preview** tab.

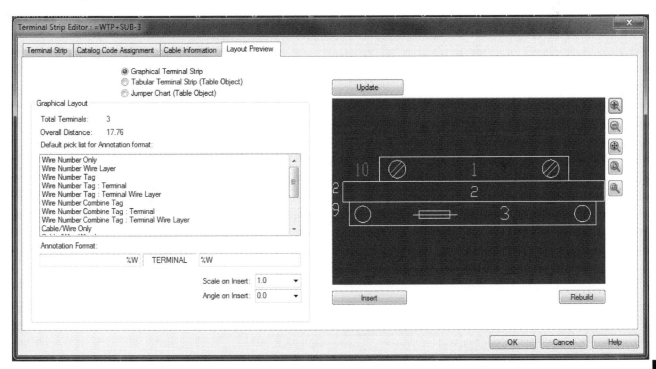

You should see the terminals as shown. Change **Angle on Insert** to **90** because we are going to use horizontal DIN rail. Click **Update**. The terminals are rotated.

17

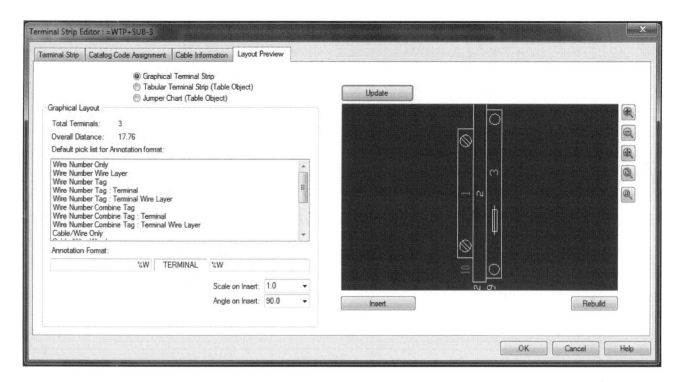

Now click **Insert** and put them on your drawing below the other components.

Click **OK** to exit back to the **Terminal Strip Selection** window. From this select **Done** to leave **Terminal Strip Editor** and go back to your drawing. It should look like this:

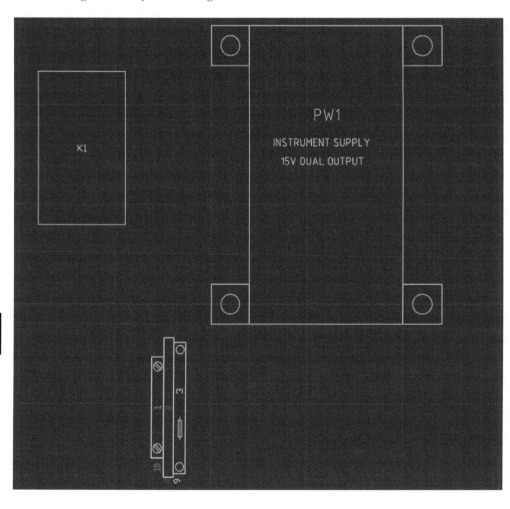

17

17.8 DIN rail

It is possible to add footprints directly from an **Icon Menu** in the same way that you can add component symbols to a schematic drawing. This **Icon Menu** contains a DIN rail tool which we will try now.

In the **Panel** tab of the ribbon, click the **Icon Menu** button. It is in the same stack of buttons as **Schematic List** so may not be on top.

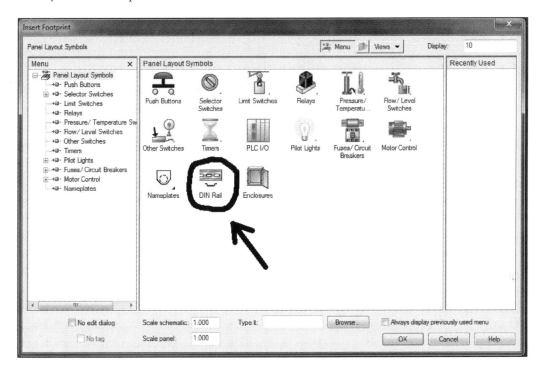

Select **DIN Rail** from the menu. The **DIN Rail** tool will open.

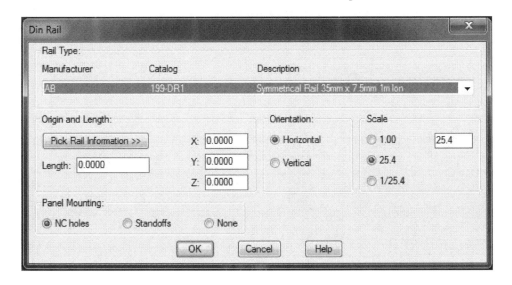

In this dialogue box select **AB part 199-DR1** as the type of DIN rail to insert. Do not worry that it is in nominal 1 metre lengths.

For a metric drawing you need to set **Scale** to **25.4**. For an imperial drawing leave it at **1**.

Choose whether you want horizontal or vertical rail. For this example choose **Horizontal**.

You can now specify the start and end of your rail. If you know the exact coordinates then it is possible to type this information. Alternatively, click the **Pick Rail Information >>** button. You will be taken to your drawing where you can click the start and end points of the rail.

If you know the length of rail to use but not the exact coordinates then you can use **Pick Rail Information >>** to define the start point and approximate end point. After doing this you can change the length to a typed value but leave the **X**, **Y** and **Z** values for the start point unchanged.

Try this tool now to install a 150mm long piece of DIN rail behind your terminals.

After inserting the DIN rail, a **Panel Layout - Component Insert/Edit** dialogue box opens. You can ignore this and just click **OK**, unless you wish to enter data to include DIN rail length and fixings in your bill of material.

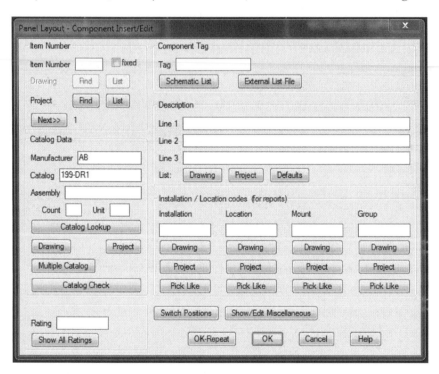

You drawing should now show your terminals and DIN rail.

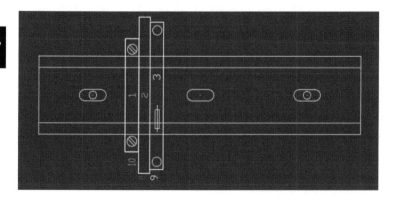

Since you placed the DIN rail last it may be in front of the terminals with the lines of the DIN rail going through them as shown above.

To fix this, select the DIN rail. In the **Home** tab of the ribbon click the small drop down arrow beside **Modify**. This will give another row of buttons. Click the drop down arrow beside the **Bring to Front** button as shown and select **Send to Back**.

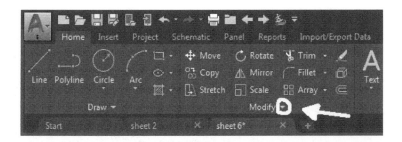

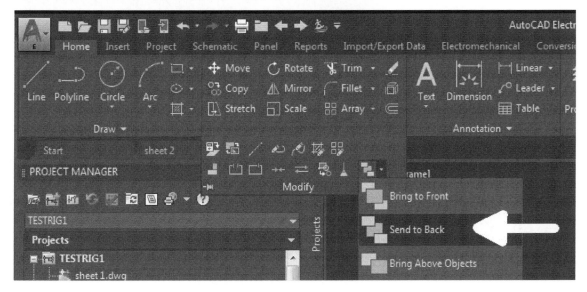

The wipeouts included in the footprints should now hide the DIN rail where it runs behind them.

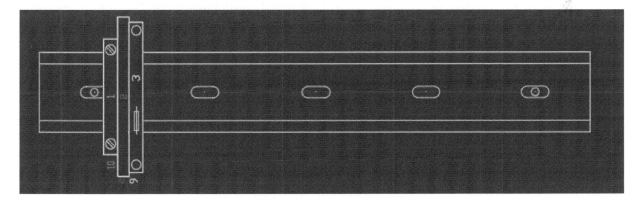

You will not need to send the DIN rail to the back if you add terminals after drawing the DIN rail.

The terminal footprint shapes (below) that we inserted in earlier chapters on **sheet 3** are not needed any more. You can delete them.

17

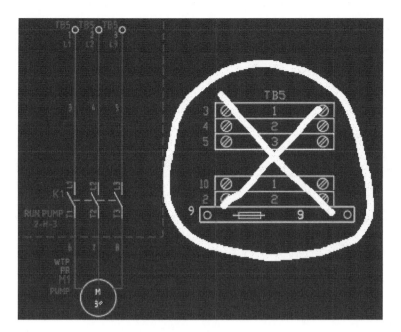

17.9   Purge command

Like component symbols, footprints are AutoCAD blocks. If you alter a footprint but the changes do not appear on your drawing, it may be that AutoCAD has remembered the old footprint.

In this case you might need to purge the old version of the block from your drawing. For details of the **Purge** command see page 205.

17.10   Multi-level terminals

Multi-level terminals are sometimes used to save space in electrical panels. They contain two or more electrically separate conductors within the same plastic terminal block.

On the schematic drawing these are represented by separate terminal symbols for each conductor. To produce the panel layout they must be combined into a single physical component. Joining them in this way is called **associating** terminals.

You can only associate terminals if they are in the same terminal strip.

Open **sheet 2**. Look at terminals **2.1** and **2.2**. We will use one double-decker terminal to provide both of these in our panel layout.

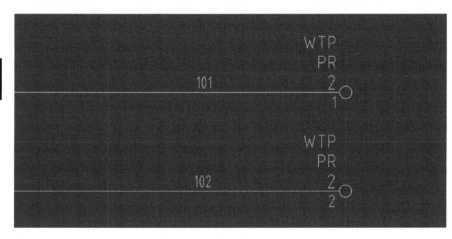

Select terminal **2.1**. Right click and choose **Edit Component** to bring up the **Insert / Edit Terminal Symbol** dialogue box. The top part of this box is shown below.

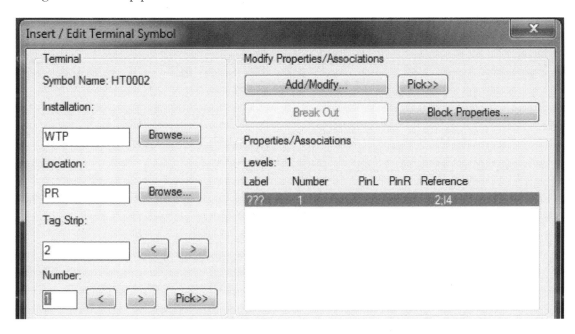

Notice that this terminal has a **Levels** value of **1**.

This single level has no special name, hence the **???** in the **Label** column. It is level number **1**. The **Reference** value of **2:I4** indicates that the terminal is on the schematic drawing **sheet 2** at grid reference **I4**.

Click the **Block Properties** button at the top right of the dialogue box.

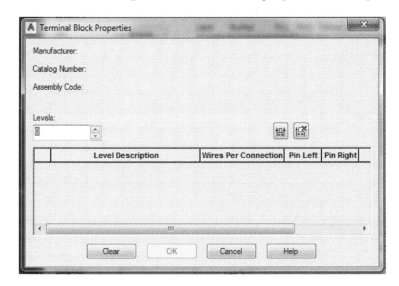

The default **Levels** value for a terminal is **0** levels. For a multi-layer terminal you can change this to **2** (for a double-decker terminal), **3** (for a 3 conductor terminal) and so on.

A single conductor terminal has a value of **0** levels, rather than the value of **1** which you might expect.

If you click the arrows beside the levels box you can increase the number of levels to two or more. When you do this, blank lines appear under **Level Description**. For each level you can type a name, for example **Top, Middle, Bottom**.

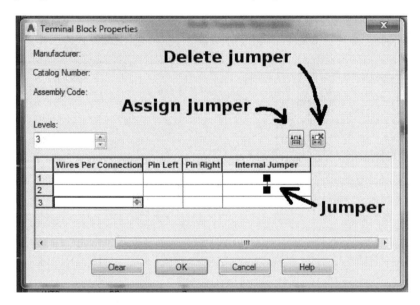

Some multi-layer terminals have the levels connected together inside of them to give many termination points for power supplies or earths. To represent this, highlight (using **CTRL + click** or **SHIFT + click**) the rows you wish to join. Then click the **Assign Jumper** button shown in the image below.

An internal jumper will be drawn between the rows. You can see it by using the scroll bar to show the columns at the right. You can also drag the corner of the **Terminal Block Properties** window to enlarge it. The **Delete Jumper** button can be used to remove the jumper.

This internal jumper (inside a terminal) is different to the external jumpers (between terminals) which we will add in the next section. It is a property of the terminal design, not a physical part that will appear in the bill of material.

17

The **Clear** button deletes all of the block information for the terminal, restoring it back to the default with a level value of **0**.

Instead of setting up a multilayer terminal ourselves we are going to load one from the catalogue. If you have been experimenting with levels in this **Block Properties** window, click the **Clear** button now to delete the information and return to the main **Insert / Edit Terminal** window. Otherwise just click **Cancel**.

You will return to the **Insert / Edit Terminal** dialogue box.

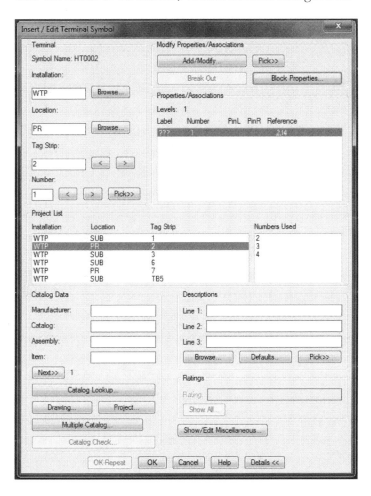

Click **Catalog Lookup...** to open the **Catalog Browser**.

Search for **WAGO 2002-2203**, a double decker terminal that is in the catalogue.

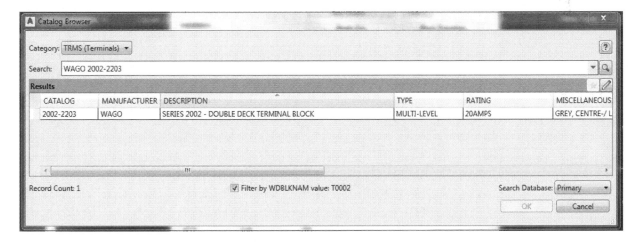

Click the row in the catalogue to highlight the **2002-2203** item. Then click **OK**.

The catalogue details are now completed in the **Insert / Edit Terminal Symbol** dialogue box. In the top half of this box you can see this terminal has two levels, **UPPER** and **LOWER**.

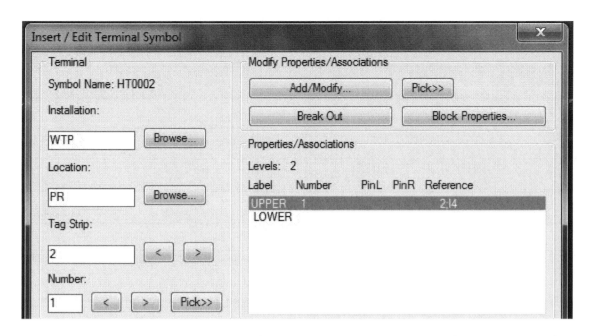

Click the **Block Properties** button. The **Terminal Block Properties** window opens. The details of the two levels are shown. You can drag the edge of this window to enlarge it so you can see all of the columns.

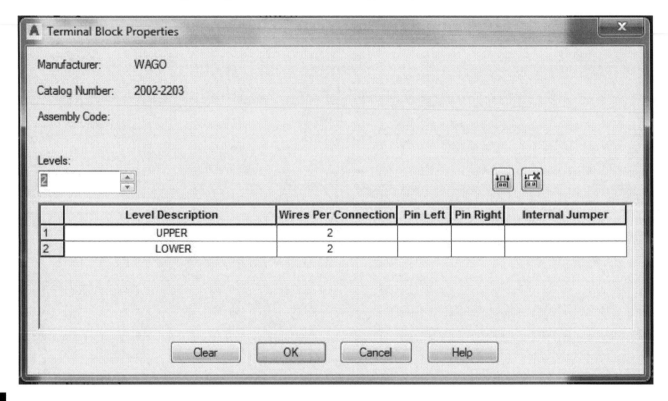

17 Click **OK** to close the window. Then click **OK** in the **Insert / Edit Terminal Symbol** window to save the assigned catalogue part and return to the drawing. When asked if you wish to link this symbol to the catalog number choose "**Do not map symbol to catalog number**".

Associate terminals using the ribbon

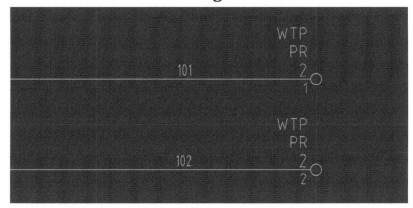

Now we need to link the terminals to tell AutoCAD they are part of a single multi-layer block. If they are on the same drawing it is easiest to use the **Associate Terminals** button. This is on the **Schematic** tab of the ribbon. Unfortunately it cannot be used to associate terminals which are on different drawings.

Click the drop down arrow beside **Edit Components** to see it.

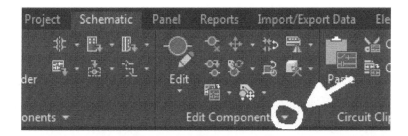

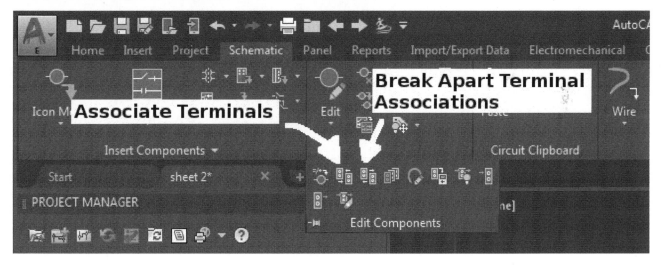

Click the **Associate Terminals** button. The cursor will become a small hollow square. If the command line window is open you will see it prompts you to select the **Master Terminal**. This will be terminal strip **2**, number **1**, the terminal that we added the multiple layers to.

Click terminal **2.1** to select it as the **Master Terminal**. It is easier to select terminals if you turn off **snap to grid.** Then click terminal **2.2** to select it as the terminal you wish to add to a level in the **Master Terminal**. Finally press **<Enter>**.

The drawing appears unchanged but the terminals have been combined.

Select terminal **2.2**, right click the drawing and choose **Edit Component** from the menu that appears. You will see terminal **2.2** is now a multi-layer terminal with the same catalogue number we assigned to terminal **2.1**. This is shown below.

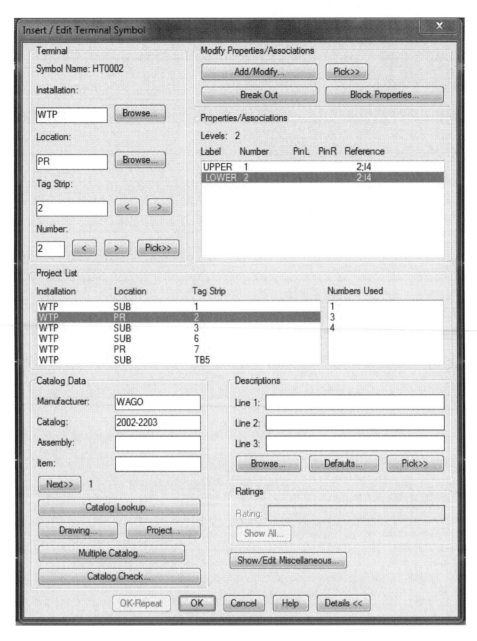

In the box under **Levels** you can see that terminal **1** is on the upper level and terminal number **2** is on the lower level.

If you were to click on terminal **2.1** you would see the same information, with terminal **2.2** now included on the previously blank level of terminal **2.1**.

Click the **Add/Modify...** button in the **Insert/Edit Terminal Symbol** dialogue box. This opens the **Add/Modify Association** window.

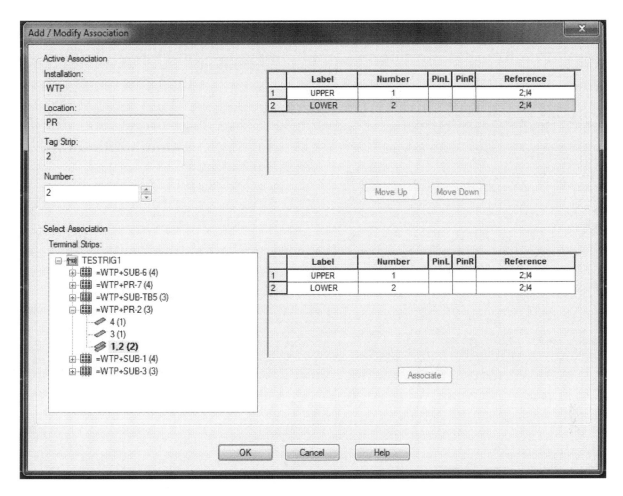

In the top part of this window you can highlight the schematic terminals assigned to levels in the physical terminal and use the **Move Up** and **Move Down** buttons to change which levels they are assigned to.

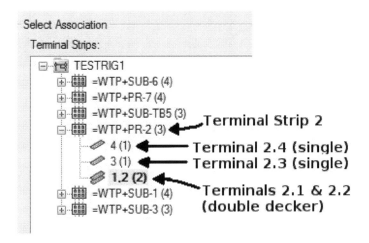

At the bottom left you can see a tree structure of all the terminals in the project. Terminal strip **2** has the location **WTP** and assembly code **PR**. It contains 3 physical terminals. These are **2.4** and **2.3** which are single terminals and **2.1** and **2.2** which are combined together in a double level terminal.

We are not going to use this box yet so click **Cancel** to return to the **Insert / Edit Terminal Symbol** window. Then click **Cancel** to return to your drawing.

Save your drawing.

17

Multi-level terminals in Terminal Strip Editor

In the **Panel** tab of the ribbon, click the **Editor** button to open the **Terminal Strip Editor**.

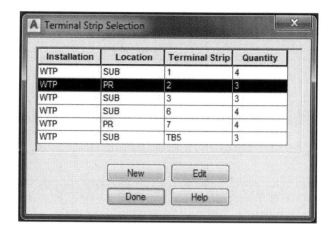

In the **Terminal Strip Selection** box, highlight **Terminal Strip 2** and click **Edit**.

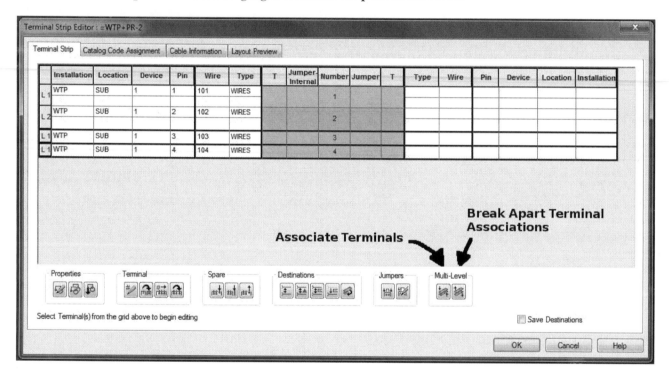

In the **Terminal Strip** tab of the **Terminal Strip Editor** you will see that terminals **1** and **2** are not separated by a thick black line, unlike the separate terminals, **3** and **4**. Notice also that there are buttons to allow you to associate and break apart terminals from within **Terminal Strip Editor**.

17 Select the **Catalog Code Assignment** tab.

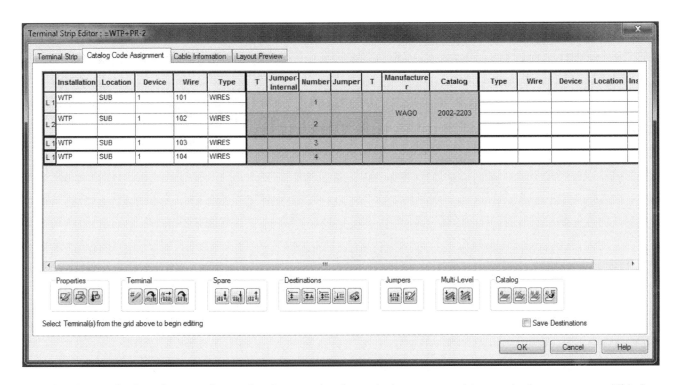

The **Catalog** and **Manufacturer** boxes for the associated terminals are merged into a single component. This is filled in with the item we assigned, WAGO part 2002-2203.

Now select the **Layout Preview** tab.

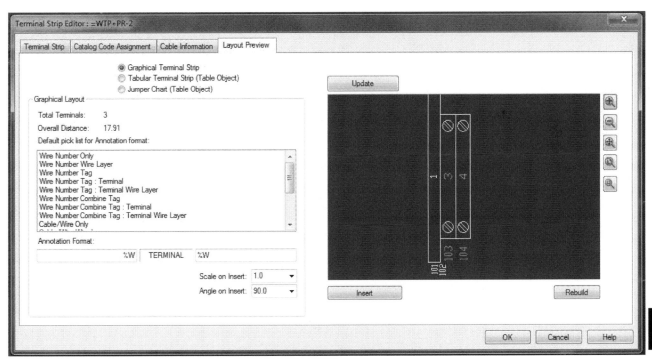

The **Layout Preview** now includes a single footprint to represent the combined terminals. This is numbered as terminal number **1**. The wire numbers (**101** and **102**) going to each level of this terminal are shown. The footprint block used by **Terminal Strip Editor** to display this is the default, two level footprint, **wd_default_02terminal.dwg**.

We will not bother placing this terminal layout on our drawing so exit **Terminal Strip Editor** by clicking **Cancel**, followed by **Done** in the **Terminal Strip Selection** window.

17.11   Associating terminals using the tree structure in the Add / Modify window

We will now associate terminals **2.3** and **2.4** using the **Add / Modify** dialogue box. This can be tricky to use but, unlike the **Associate Terminals** button on the ribbon, it can be used to link terminals on different drawings.

First select terminal **2.3**. Right click and choose **Edit Component** from the menu. In the **Insert / Edit Terminal Symbol** window click the **Catalog Lookup** button. Set the terminal to be **WAGO** part **2002-2203** (a double-decker terminal) as we did with terminal **2.1** earlier. Click **OK** to close the **Insert / Edit Terminal Symbol** window. Do not map the symbol to the catalogue number.

Terminal **2.3** will now be a multi-level terminal. The upper level is used for terminal **2.3**. We are going to add terminal **2.4** into the unused lower level.

The tricky part of this operation is that the correct order must be observed when combining the terminals. If not you will get an error.

We need to open Terminal **2.4** (the single layer terminal). Then, from within the **Insert / Edit** dialogue box for Terminal **2.4**, we choose the empty level in a multi-layer terminal (Terminal **2.3**) where we want it to go.

Select terminal **2.4**. Right click and choose **Edit Component**.

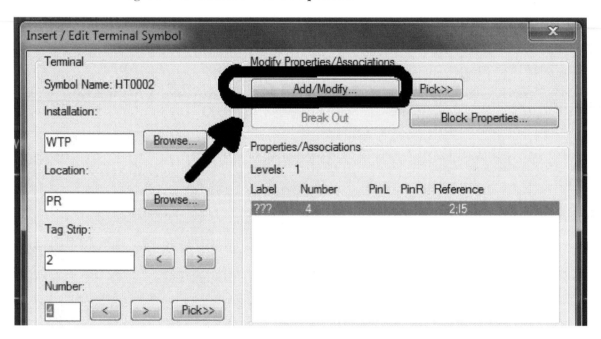

In the **Insert / Edit Terminal Symbol** window click the **Add / Modify** button.

17

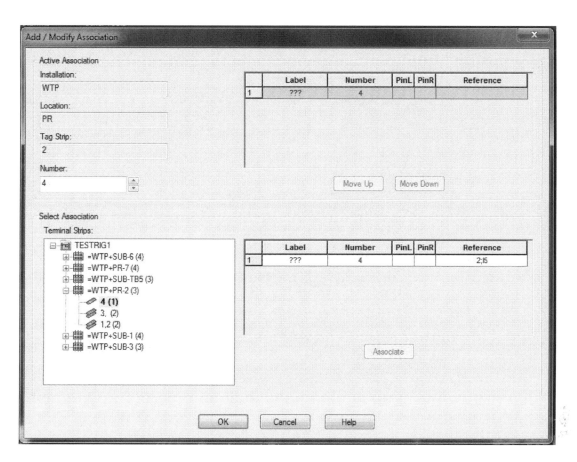

The top half of the **Add / Modify Association** screen shows terminal **2.4**. We need to choose the place it is going to in the bottom half of the window by selecting terminal **2.3**.

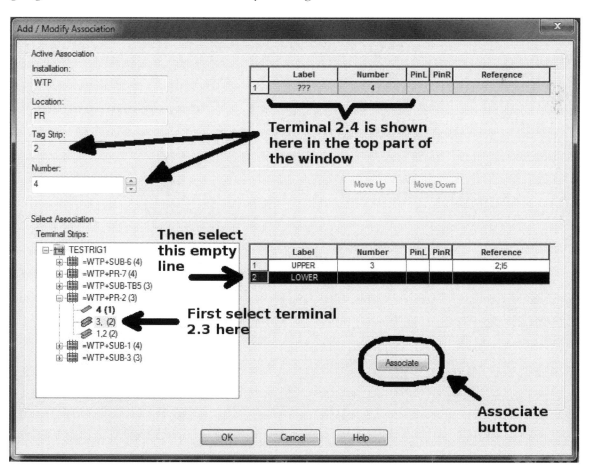

At the bottom left of the **Add / Modify Association** window click terminal **2.3** as indicated in the image above. The diagram at the bottom right will show a table with the two levels of this terminal. The **UPPER** level in this table already holds terminal **2.3** (its own number).

Click the empty **LOWER** line to highlight it. Then click the **Associate** button. This will move terminal **2.4** into the lower level of terminal block **2.3**.

You can see this change in the table at the top of the dialogue box shown below. The bottom part of the dialogue box does not update.

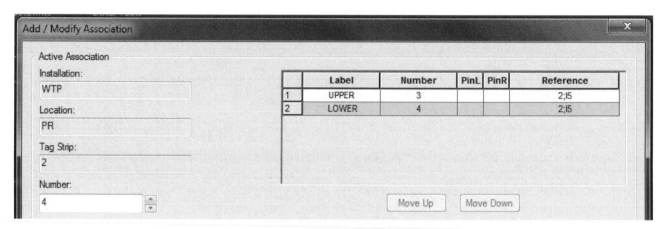

Click **OK**. You will return to the **Insert / Edit Terminal Symbol** window. This now shows both levels of the terminal in the **Properties/Associations** section.

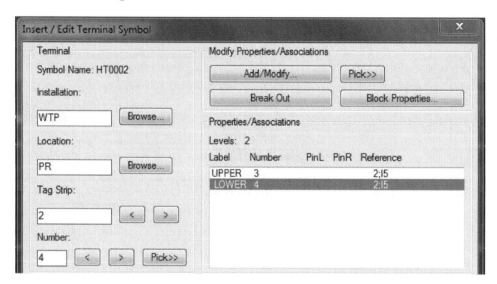

Click **OK** to save your changes. Select **Do not map symbol to catalog number** when prompted.

It is only after clicking **OK** in the **Insert / Edit Terminal Symbol** box to return to the drawing that the terminal tree structure updates. If you now edit terminal **2.4** and click the **Add / Modify Association** button you will finally see the updated tree structure.

17

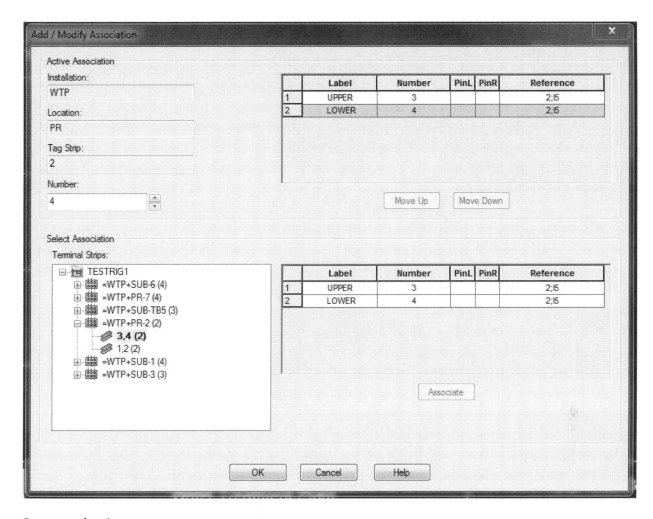

Save your drawings.

17.12 Jumpers

We saw earlier that you can add an internal jumper within a multi-layer terminal block to join the layers. This sort of jumper is a characteristic of the terminal itself and is not a separate catalogue part or entry on the bill of material.

Another sort of jumper is an external jumper. This is a physical link which joins two separate terminals. It does the same job as a short piece of wire but is neater and usually does not take up any of the wire connection points on the terminal.

AutoCAD Electrical allows you to add these jumpers but care is needed if they are to appear properly on the schematics.

To demonstrate the use of jumpers we will add an extra terminal, terminal **1.5**, next to terminal **1.4**. We will join the two terminals with a jumper, WAGO part 2202-402, which is in the catalogue.

First use the **Icon Menu** in the **Schematic** tab of the ribbon to add another terminal next to terminal **1.4**. Label it as **Tag Strip 1**, terminal **Number 5**. Give it an installation code of **WTP** and a location code of **SUB**. Draw a short length of wire to the right of this terminal as shown below.

17

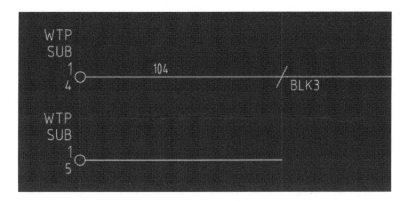

In the **Schematic** tab of the ribbon, click the small drop down arrow beside **Edit Components** to get further buttons. Click the **Edit Jumper** button.

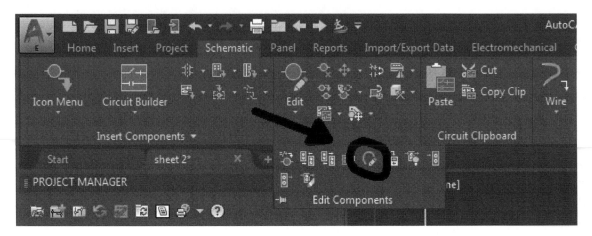

Despite the name, this tool both edits jumpers and inserts new ones.

After clicking the button, the cursor will turn into a small hollow square. Use this to click terminal **1.4** and then terminal **1.5**.

Next type **'e'** for edit and press **<Enter>**. If the command line is open it will prompt you to do this. Alternatively, you can just press **<Enter>** since edit should be the default option.

You will see the **Edit Terminal Jumpers** window.

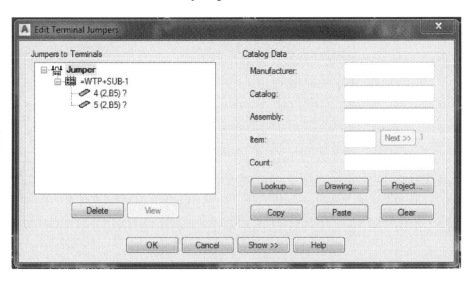

This window may look complicated but it is just showing you the terminals that you have chosen to link. You could just press **OK** to place the jumper but first we will add a catalogue part number for our jumper.

Click the **Lookup...** button. Search for **WAGO** part **2002-402** in the catalogue under **TRMS (terminals)**. Select it and click **OK**. You will return to the **Edit Terminal Jumpers** window with the catalogue details filled in.

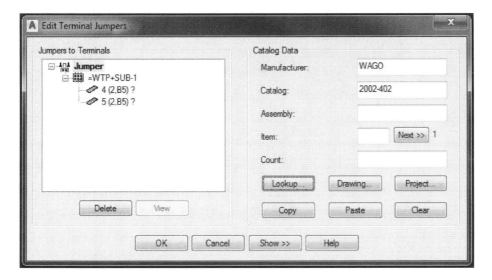

Click **OK** to go back to the drawing.

We have successfully added the jumper but our drawing does not look any different. The wire beside terminal **1.5** should now have the same wire number as wire **104** which is connected to terminal **1.4** but if you were to use the **Copy Wire Number** tool on it you would find it has no number.

To prove the link is there, click the **Edit Jumper** button again on the ribbon. Click terminal **1.4**. The command line will prompt you to press **'b'** for browse, **'s'** for show and **'e'** for edit if it is open.

Type **'s'** and press **<Enter>**

A line showing the jumper link will be drawn between terminals **1.4** and **1.5** as shown below. This line disappears if you zoom or do any other action. You cannot make it permanent.

Press **<Esc>** to exit the **Edit Jumper** command.

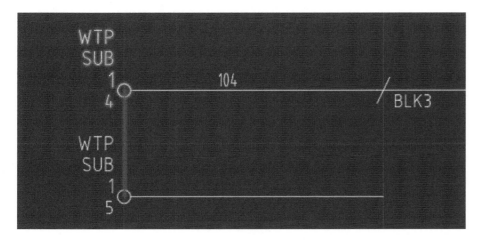

We will fix these problems with jumper visibility and wire numbers in a moment. First we will see how jumpers are handled by the **Terminal Strip Editor**.

Open the **Terminal Strip Editor** by clicking the **Editor** button in the **Panel** tab of the ribbon.

In the **Terminal Strip Selection** box choose terminal strip **1** and click **Edit**. The **Terminal Strip Editor** will open at the **Terminal Strip** tab as shown below:

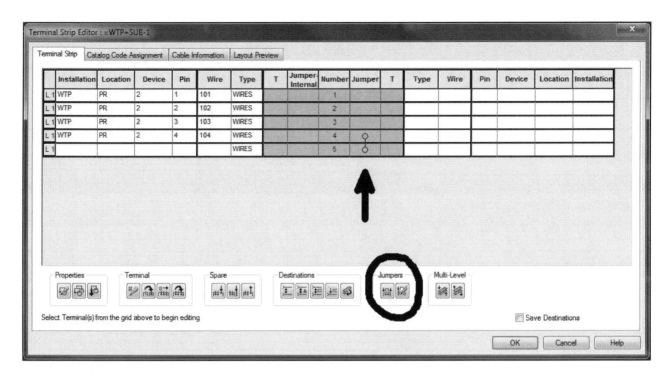

You can see the jumper drawn between terminals **4** and **5** in the **Jumper** column. You can also add and remove jumpers from within the **Terminal Strip Editor** using the **Jumpers** buttons on this tab.

If you go to the **Layout Preview** tab the jumper is not shown. You can, however, choose to insert a **Jumper Chart** on your drawing by selecting a radio button on the **Layout Tab**. This shows which terminals have jumpers.

We do not need to make any changes in **Terminal Strip Editor** so click **Cancel** then **Done** to exit back to your drawing.

Creating a wire layer for jumpers

It would be nice if AutoCAD drew the jumpers on the schematic drawing. There is a work-around for this which also fixes the problem with carrying wire numbers across.

Draw a wire between terminals **1.4** and **1.5** to represent the jumper. Create a new wire layer. This must include the word **"jumper"** as part of its layer name. Set the jumper wire to this wire type.

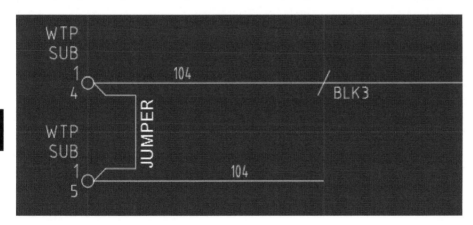

In the image above a link wire has been added with the wire layer named **"jumper"** (set colour to **"jumper"** and leave size blank in the **Create / Edit Wire Type** tool). A **wire color/gauge label** makes it clear what this link is.

Another advantage is that this wire transfers the wire numbers more reliably than the terminal jumper. You can prove this by adding a wire number copy to the wire attached to terminal **1.5**.

AutoCAD ignores any wire layers containing the word **"jumper"** in their layer name when creating the wiring **From / To** reports so the jumpers will not appear in those.

17.13   Terminal accessories

Blocks of DIN rail terminals often contain accessories which are not shown on the schematic. These include end plates, which insulate the conductors of the end terminal, end stops which prevent the terminals sliding along the rail, and various covers and labels. It is also common to include spare terminals to allow for future modifications.

Terminal Strip Editor allows you to add accessories and spare terminals. To demonstrate this we will add a **WAGO** part **2002-1491** grey 0.8mm thick plastic end plate to terminal **2** in terminal strip **3**.

Open **sheet 6** of the **TestRig1** project.

Open the **Terminal Strip Editor** by clicking the **Editor** button in the **Panel** tab of the ribbon. In the **Terminal Strip Selection** box choose terminal strip **3** and click **Edit**. The **Terminal Strip Editor** will open at the **Terminal Strip** tab.

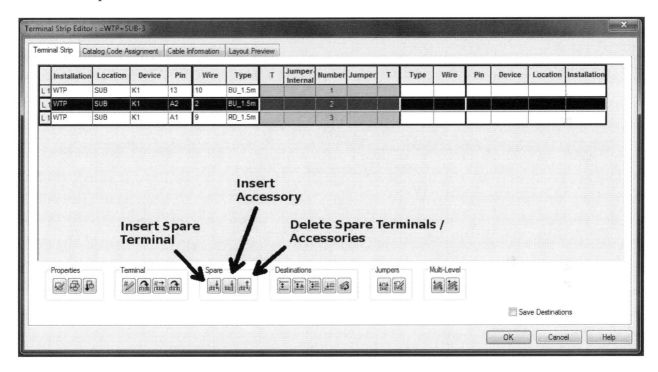

The three buttons under the heading **Spare** allow you to add accessories and spare terminals.

Click the row for terminal **2** to highlight it as shown above. Then click the **Insert Accessory** button. The **Insert Accessory** window will open.

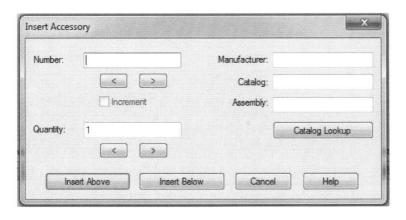

Click **Catalogue Lookup** and choose **WAGO** part **2002-1491**. This is a grey 0.8mm end plate which is meant to fit on the side of the **WAGO 2002-1401** terminal we are using for terminal **2**.

Enter **2** in the **Number** box and leave **Quantity** as **1**. This will insert a single end plate beside terminal **2**.

Click the **Insert Below** button. The end plate will be added as an extra line beneath terminal **2**. This line is also labelled as terminal number **2** in the **Number** column.

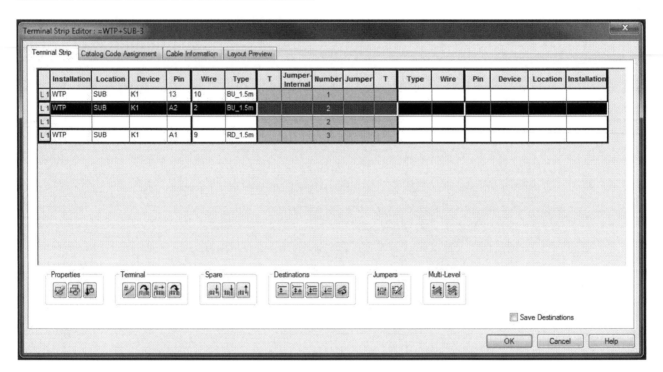

Select the **Catalog Code Assignment** tab. In this tab you can see the part number assigned to the accessory.

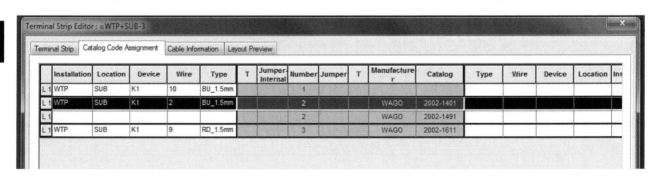

Finally select the **Layout Preview** tab. You will see the end plate as a block added between terminals **2** and **3**. If necessary click **Update** to refresh the image.

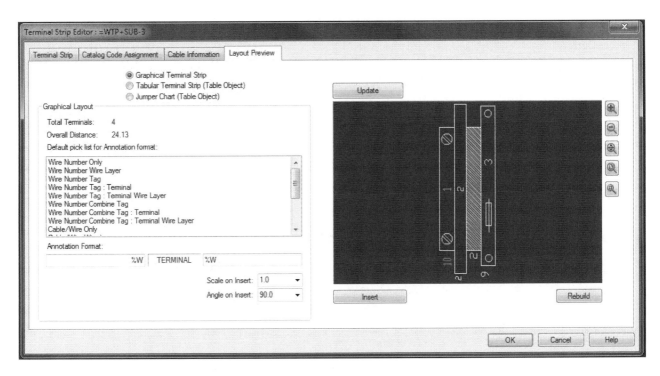

Click the **Rebuild button.** This will update the image on your drawing. Remember these changes are not visible until you leave the **Terminal Strip Editor.**

Click **OK** and when returned to the **Terminal Strip Selection** window click **Done.**

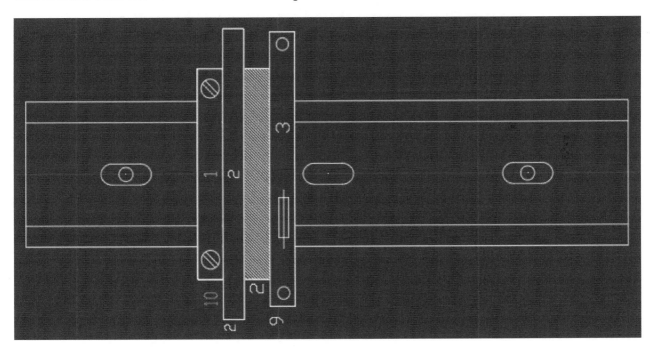

The modified terminal strip will be placed on your drawing as shown above.

If you are familiar with DIN rail terminals then the size and shape of the end plate we have inserted may not be what you were expecting. The correct footprint would be a thin, 0.8mm sheet of plastic which exactly matches the width of terminal **2.**

The reason for this discrepancy is that, at least in my version of AutoCAD Electrical 2020, there is no footprint for **WAGO** part **2002-1491** in the **panel_mm** footprint library.

Having failed to find a footprint, the **Terminal Strip Editor** uses a default footprint for the accessory in the same way it uses the default terminal footprint for undefined terminals.

The file it has used is **wd_default_accessory.dwg** which you can find in the top level of the **panel_mm** and **panel** libraries.

The number **2** displayed next to this default terminal footprint is the terminal number assigned to it. It is coincidence that this is the same as the wire number going to terminal **2** next to it.

If you wish you can create an accurate footprint for the WAGO end plate.

To do this, draw a 70.1 mm wide x 0.8 mm high rectangle as shown below.

Open **Symbol Builder** and select this rectangle using the **Select objects** button.

Since the end plate has no attributes we can start from this rectangle, rather than basing our symbol on the default footprint as we did with the fused terminal.

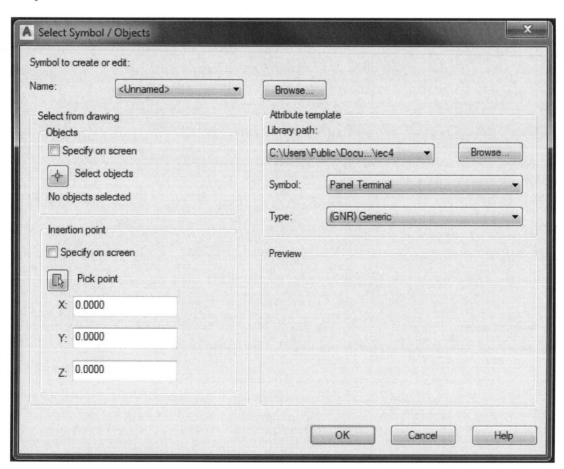

Set **Symbol** to be a **Panel Terminal** and type to be **(GNR) Generic**. Click **OK**.

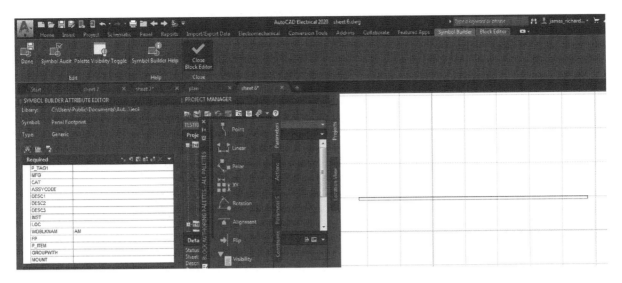

Inside **Symbol Builder**, do not add any attributes, just click **Done** on the **Symbol Builder** tab of the ribbon.

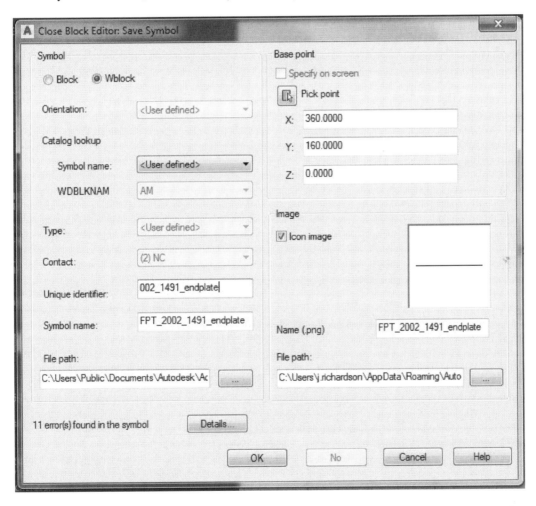

The **Close Block Editor** screen will appear. Click **Pick Point** and click on your rectangle to select the insertion point as the centre of the top edge.

Use the "**...**" button to set the **File path** on the left of the box to the WAGO folder inside your **panel_custom** library.

Set **Unique identifier** to be **2002_1491_endplate**, giving a filename of **FPT_2002_1491_endplate.dwg** for the footprint.

Click **OK** to return to your drawing. When asked if you want to insert the symbol now, click **No**. Delete your original rectangle.

In the **Panel** tab of the ribbon, click the drop down arrow beside **Other Tools**. Click the **Footprint Database Editor** button. You will be asked if you wish to create a new database or edit an existing one.

Click **Edit Existing Table**.

Select **WAGO** from the list of tables.

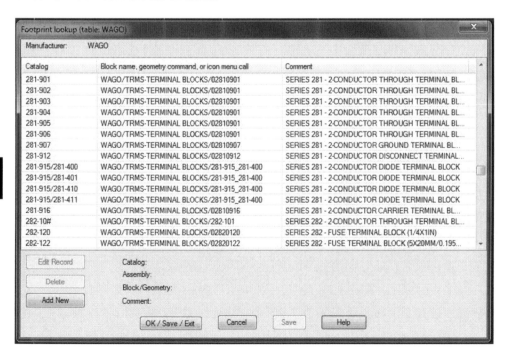

370

Click the **Add New** button. A blank **Add footprint record (table: WAGO)** dialogue box will appear.

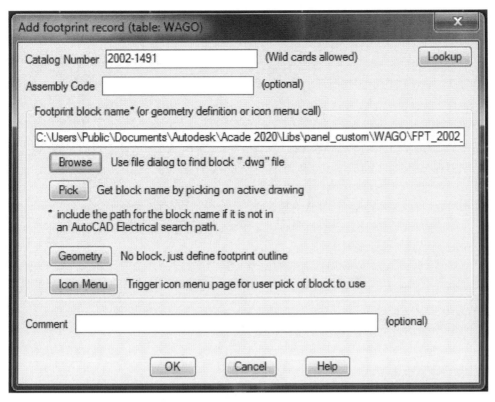

Use the **Lookup** button at the top right to find **WAGO** part **2002-1491** in the **TRMS (Terminals) Category** of the catalogue and select it.

Use the **Browse** button to find the **FPT_2002_1491_endplate.dwg** footprint file you saved in the **WAGO** folder of the **panel_custom** library and select it..

Click **OK** to return to the main **Footprint lookup (table: WAGO)** screen. Click **OK / Save / Exit** to return to your drawing. Save your drawing.

Open **Terminal Strip Editor** and go to the **Layout Preview** tab. You should see the modified endplate.

17

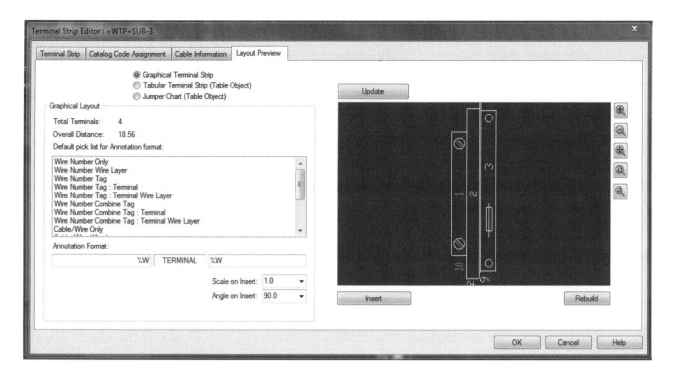

Click **Rebuild**, followed by **OK**.

Then click **Done** in the **Terminal Strip Selection** dialogue box. You should now see the updated terminal layout on your drawing.

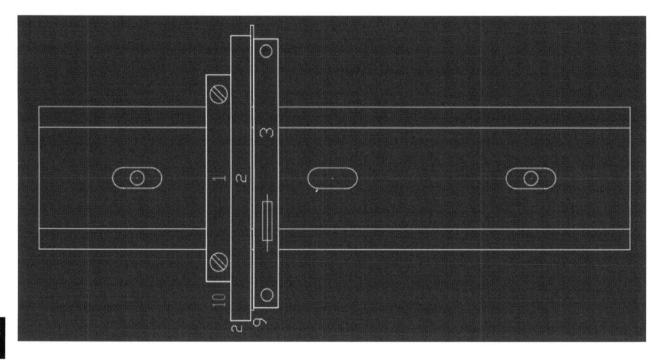

If you look carefully at the above illustration you will see two minor flaws in this new symbol. The first is that it is slightly misaligned with the terminal. That is because I have not selected exactly the midpoint of the DIN rail when I picked the insertion point. The other flaw is that you can see the lines of the DIN rail through the endplate.

For a neater footprint symbol you could add a **wipeout** to correct this.

17.14 Spare terminals

The **Terminal Strip Editor** also allows you to add spare terminals.

Open the **Terminal Strip Editor** and choose to edit terminal strip **3**. In the **Terminal Strip** tab, highlight the bottom row (terminal number **3**).

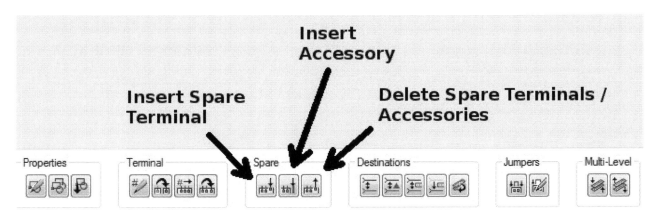

Click the **Insert Spare Terminal** button. The **Insert Spare Terminal** dialogue box will open.

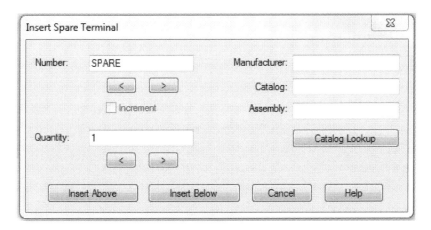

In this box enter the **Number** for the first spare terminal. You can also leave the default value and each terminal will be given the value **SPARE** as its terminal number.

The **Increment** tick box will number each terminal sequentially, starting with the **Number** value entered for the first terminal. It can only be selected if you are inserting more than one terminal.

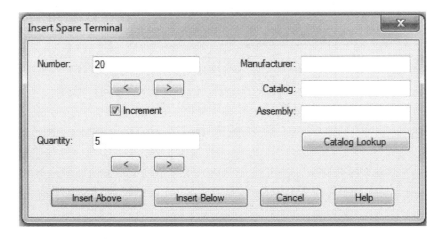

For our example, set **Number** to **20** and **Quantity** to **5** as shown above. Tick the **Increment** box.

Click **Insert Below** and the terminals will be added in the **Terminal Strip Editor** window.

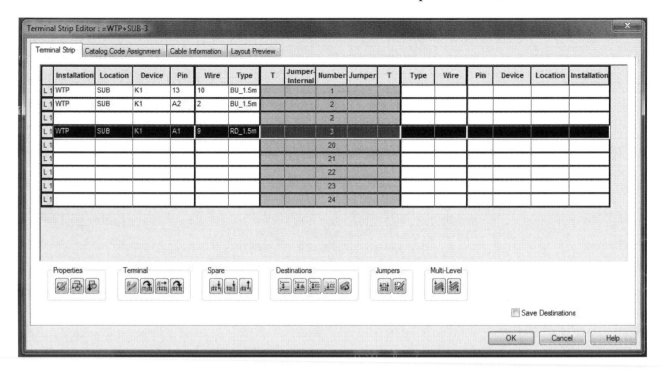

Select the **Layout Preview** tab and click **Rebuild**. Then exit from the **Terminal Strip Editor**. The extra terminals will now be added to your drawing as shown below.

Save your drawing.

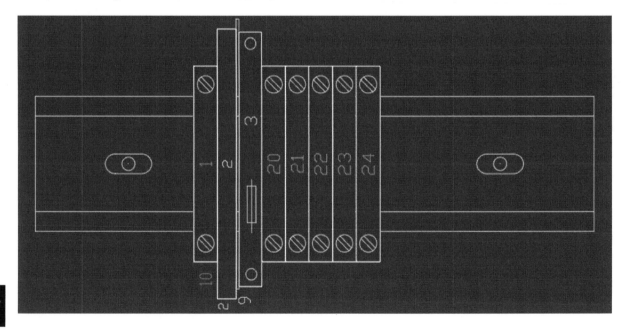

17.15 Scale drawings

Throughout this book we have concentrated on electrical schematics rather than mechanical drawings. Our title block has been in model space which makes it easy to see how the finished drawing will fit the page in the final printout. We used layout view to fit the drawing onto a sheet of paper, providing an easy way to print on different paper sizes.

In the previous chapter we produced mechanical panel layouts and scaled our title block to accommodate the size of a panel. This created a scale drawing in the sense that all objects were the correct relative size. It was not possible though to say what the absolute scale would be when printed or to set this scale to a chosen arbitrary ratio.

We finish this chapter by looking at refinements which allow you to do these things if needed.

Printing to an exact scale

Open **sheet 6** and go to **Layout1** view.

To make the border fit in this mechanical drawing we enlarged it in model space by a factor of 2. Since we made the title block itself the size of an A3 sheet of paper, this drawing will now be approximately **2 : 1** scale when printed on an A3 printer.

The ratio is only approximate because the size we drew the title block might not exactly match the printable area of the paper.

If you are printing it on A4 the scale will be approximately **2.82 : 1**. Remember that although A4 is half the area of A3, its linear dimensions are smaller by √2, which is approximately **1.41**.

Select **Print > Plot** from the **Application menu**. The **Plot - Layout1** dialogue box appears.

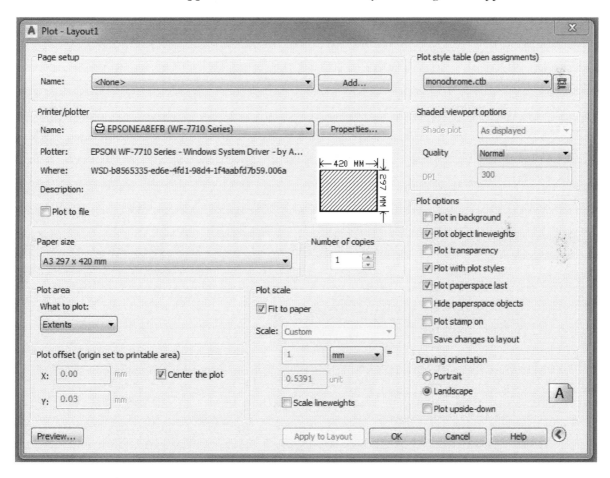

Currently the **Fit to paper** option is selected. If you used a smaller paper size than A3 for the printer your drawing would be scaled automatically to fit.

Untick the box labelled **Fit to paper**. Click the drop down box beside **Scale** and select **1:1** instead of **Custom**.

We do not want to print anything yet so click **Apply to Layout** to save these changes. Then click **Cancel** to return to the drawing without printing.

Previously there were two pieces of scaling:

- Model space to layout space - set by the viewport
- Layout space to printed paper - set in the plot dialogue box

Now that we have set the second of these to **1:1** you may find your layout viewport no longer fits the paper.

Correct this by selecting the viewport. Drag the corners to match the dotted printable area. Press **<Esc>** to deselect the viewport.

Double click inside the viewport, using the left mouse button, so that it is drawn with thick black borders. Then double click the mouse wheel inside the viewport. This will auto scale the viewport so that the drawing in model space fits it. Double click outside of the viewport or click the **MODEL** button (beside **snap to grid**, not to be confused with the **Model** tab) to leave **MODEL** view and get rid of the thick black lines.

Now select the viewport again.

17

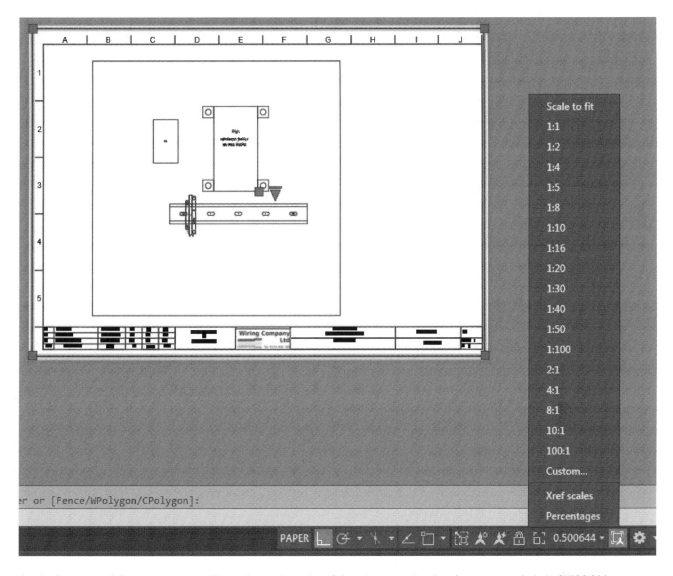

At the bottom of the screen you will see the scale ratio of the viewport. In the above example it is **0.500644**.

This scale value is the scale of the drawing with the model fully filling the viewport. A viewport scale value of **0.500644 : 1** is equivalent to a scale ratio of **1 : 1.9974**

It is desirable to have an integer so click the drop down arrow beside the scale value and select **1:2** (equivalent to a scale value of **0.5**).

If you are printing on A4 paper the scale of the above screenshot would be **0.354014 : 1** which is equivalent to a scale of **1 : 2.8248**. For A4 it is therefore desirable to set a scale of **1:3** for your drawing. This scale is not available as a preset option.

To create it, select **Custom...** from the bottom of the list and you will see the **Edit Drawing Scales** dialogue box.

17

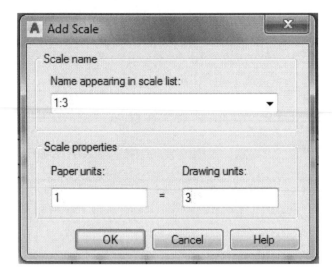

Click **Add...** and fill in the **Add Scale** box as below to create a new preset scale of **1:3**.

Click **OK** to close both the boxes.

Now select the viewport again and choose your new **1:3** scale. The drawing will be scaled to 1:3 which should be a good fit for A4 paper.

After setting your scale, print your drawing with these new layout settings and measure the DIN rail on the printout with a ruler. In model space it is **150mm** long. Our A3 drawing is scaled as **1:2** so it should be **75mm** on the printout.

If you are using an A4 printer with a **1:3** scale your printed DIN rail should be **50mm** long.

Moving the title block into layout view

17

The previous section is adequate to print the occasional mechanical drawing but requires a lot of manual work, first to scale the border in model space and again to scale the viewport in layout space.

If you are working with many mechanical drawings it is easier to move the title block itself into layout space.

Right click the **TestRig1** project in the **Project Manager** window. Choose **New Drawing...** and create a drawing called **sheet 7** using our template. Set **Description 1** to "**Mechanical Drawing**" and **Description 2** to "**Title Block in Layout View**".

Click **OK.** When prompted agree to apply the **Project Default Values** to the new drawing.

In model view, on the new **sheet 7**, select the border. Right click and select **Clipboard > Cut** from the menu that appears. The border will disappear.

Click on the **Layout1** tab.

Right click and choose **Paste** to paste the title block into the layout. Place its bottom left corner at the bottom left of the paper's printable area.

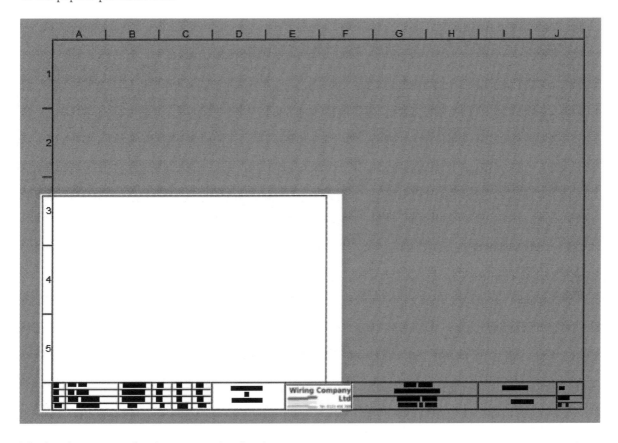

The border may not be the correct size for the paper.

If you are printing on A3 it should be close but not an exact fit. If you are printing on A4, as in the above image, it will be much too big.

Select **Print > Plot** from the **Application Button** menu. The **Plot - Layout1** dialogue box appears.

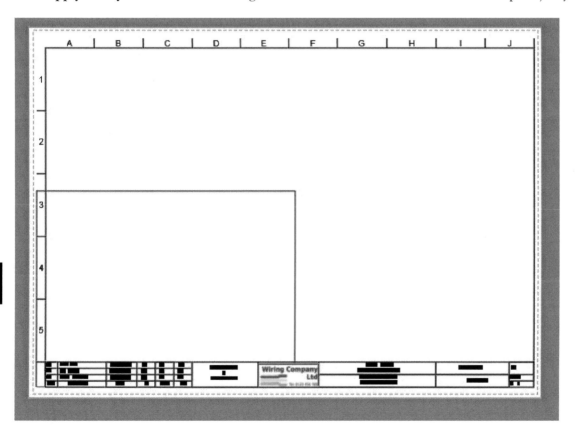

Choose your printer and set the correct paper size. Ensure **Fit to paper** is not ticked.
Set the **Scale** value to **1:1**.

Click **Apply to Layout** to save these settings. Then click **Cancel** since we do not want to print just yet.

You now need to position your border within the dotted lines showing the printable area.

Select the border. Right click to bring up a menu then use the **Move** command and if necessary **Scale** command to make it fit. When using the **Scale** command, after selecting the base point, you can scale by either entering a scale factor in the command line or by moving the mouse.

Since the border is designed for A3 you will need to scale it by approximately 0.71 if you want to print it on A4 paper. For A3 paper you will only need to scale it slightly, if at all. The exact amount of scaling is not critical since it only changes the size of the title block on the finished page. It will not affect the scale ratio used to print the model space objects within the drawing.

Next select the viewport. The corners will be highlighted. Previously we moved them to match the dotted line of the printable area. This time we want them to be inside the central area of the title block. Move the corners to correspond to the blank space inside of the title block frame. Then press **<Esc>** to deselect everything.

Now select only the viewport, without selecting the title block. You can do this by dragging the mouse from top right to bottom left in a way that fully includes the viewport but only includes part of the title block.

Select a scale for the viewport at the bottom of the screen. For our example choose **1:10**. Then press **<Esc>** to deselect the viewport.

Click the **Model** tab to switch to model space. Draw a rectangle which is 2000mm wide x 1500mm high close to the origin.

Return to the **Layout1** tab. You can hopefully see at least part of your rectangle. Double click the left mouse button inside the viewport. Then hold down the wheel and drag the mouse to position the rectangle in the centre of the viewport.

If you cannot find the rectangle then double click the wheel to centre the viewport on the rectangle. This will also change the scaling so you will need to select **1:10** scale for the viewport again afterwards.

Double click outside of the viewport to go back to **PAPER** view.

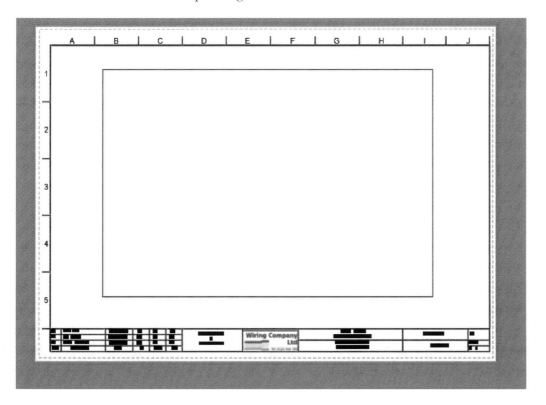

Save your drawing. If you now plot this layout you should find the rectangle is at 1:10 scale and measures exactly 200mm x 150mm on your sheet of paper.

If you produce many scaled drawings then you could create a new template with the title block on the **Layout** tab. You could then use this for your mechanical drawings while using the **first_template** we created in chapter 5 for electrical schematics.

17.16   Multiple viewports

For more complex drawings you can add several viewports to one sheet. To create a new viewport click the **Insert View** button in the **Layout Viewports** panel on the **Layout** tab of the ribbon.

When you click this button you will be taken to a view of your model space drawing. If you have followed the colour settings used in this book then this will be obvious because your screen will be dark grey. Navigate around your model to the part of the drawing you wish to display.

Left click to define one corner of the area of the model to be displayed in the viewport. Then left click again to define the opposite corner. If the command line is open you will be prompted to do this. If you are not happy with the selection, you can left click again to reselect the first corner.

When you have selected the area of the model to display, press **<Enter>** to confirm the viewport selection. You will be returned to the layout view with a rectangle at the cursor showing the size of your new viewport. Move the cursor to the place where you want the viewport to go and left click to position it.

The viewport will be placed and will initially be zoomed in on the part of the model you selected. The new viewport is locked by default so to alter it you will need to select it, right click, and choose **Display Locked > No** from the menu to unlock it (see page 33).

Once unlocked you can move the viewport, adjust its scale and change the part of the model it looks at in the same way as you could for the default viewport described elsewhere in this book. You might also wish to set its border to non-printable.

17

18. PLCs (1 hour)

Our drawings so far have been point to point schematics. These are general purpose drawings whose flexibility makes them suitable for systems with a wide range of component types.

An alternative style of schematic drawing is a ladder diagram. In this system two vertical bus wires, representing the power supply, run down the left and right of the drawing. Components are then added to horizontal "rungs" which join these supply rails.

Devices that output a signal, for example switches, sensors, relay contacts and programmable logic controller (PLC) outputs, are shown on the left.

Relay coils, PLC inputs, lamps and other devices which receive a signal are shown on the right.

This style is particularly suited to the large numbers of inputs and outputs in PLC systems. It is also common for pieces of older, pre-PLC era equipment which implement logic using large numbers of relays and contactors.

Ladder logic format may also be used to enter and document a PLC software program.

If you are drawing a system containing programmable logic controllers (PLCs) it will contain many input/output (I/O) cards, each with multiple channels. Rather than create these as custom schematic symbols, the AutoCAD Electrical software has a fast tool to generate PLC I/O cards. The PLC cards of many manufacturers are already pre-configured for you to use. If the PLC in your system is not included then you can easily add it. These PLC card symbols can be used in either ladder diagrams or point to point drawings.

Topics covered in this chapter:

- Using ladder diagrams in a drawing
- Using a pre-configured PLC card symbol
- Creating a custom PLC symbol

18.1   Using ladder logic in a drawing

Right click the **TestRig1** project heading in the **Project Manager** window. Choose **New Drawing...** and create a drawing called **sheet 8** using using the **first_template.dwt** template. Remember you must already have another drawing open for this command to work.

Set **Description 1** to **Motor Starter** and **Description 2** to **PLC drawings**. When prompted, agree to apply the **Project Default Values**.

Setting up the drawing properties

Open **Drawing Properties** for this drawing from the **Schematic** tab of the ribbon. Select the **Drawing Format** tab.

18

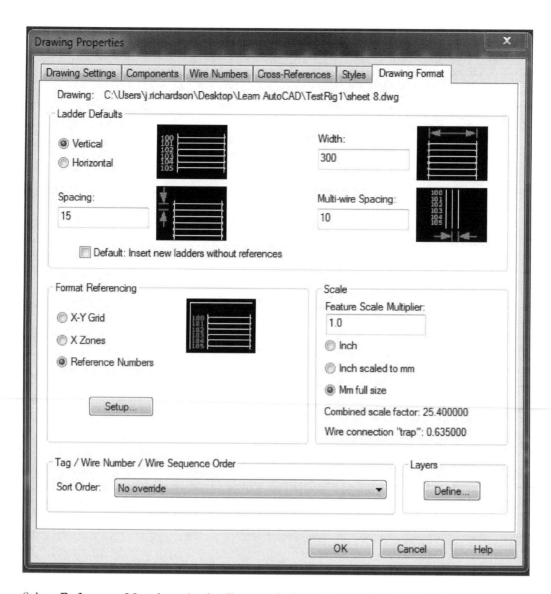

Select **Reference Numbers** in the **Format Referencing** section. This will number the ladder rungs and allow you to refer to parts of the drawing by rung number rather than using an **X-Y grid** as we did on our other schematics.

Selecting **Reference Numbers** does more than this. It forces AutoCAD to place wire rungs at discrete points down the ladder. If you do not select it, the rungs will not snap to defined positions. This makes it harder to produce a neat drawing.

Set **Spacing** to **15** for a metric drawing. This will give us enough rungs to fit in a PLC module without squeezing the blocks too close together. In an imperial scaled drawing you might choose **0.60** inches. Remember that any multi-pole components, for example circuit breakers, are spaced by this same setting (see page 47)

Width determines the distance between the supply rails forming the start and end of the ladder rungs. For our example, which is an A3 sized metric drawing scaled in mm, set it to **300** (use **12** for a drawing scaled in inches) so that the ladder rungs fill most of the page width.

For your own drawings you could choose a narrower ladder and have more than one column of rungs per page.

Click **OK** to return to your drawing.

Drawing a ladder

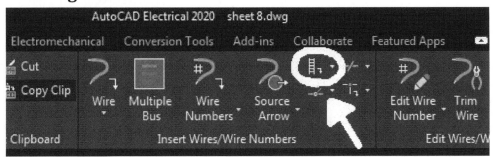

Click the **Insert Ladder** button in the **Schematic** tab of the ribbon. The **Insert Ladder** dialogue box will open.

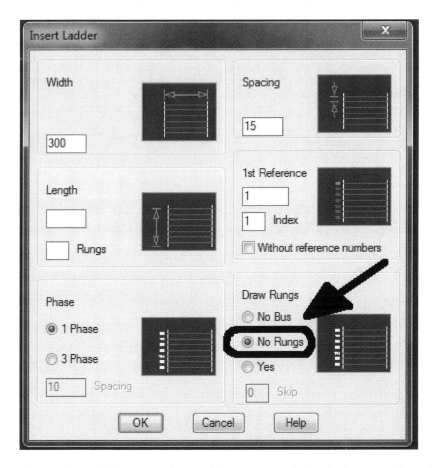

The **Width** and **Spacing** of the ladder are entered already from our **Drawing Properties** settings.

We will number the first rung as **1** and increment the number by **1** for each additional rung. These values should appear as defaults in the **1st Reference** and **Index** values. Change these values if you want a different numbering system, for example to number your rungs **10, 20, 30...**

The **Draw Rungs** section determines whether AutoCAD draws all of the ladder rungs in advance or lets you add them as needed. It also allows you to display rungs only, with the bus wires at each side hidden.

For our example select **No Rungs** as indicated with the arrow above. This allows us to add them later as required.

Click **OK**. You will be returned to your drawing with the cursor as a large cross-hair.

18

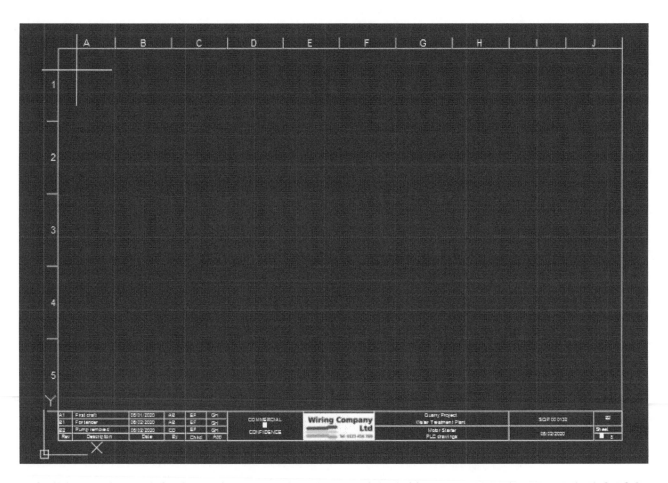

Left click near the top left of your drawing to place the top of the ladder. Leave enough space to the left of the ladder for the rung numbers.

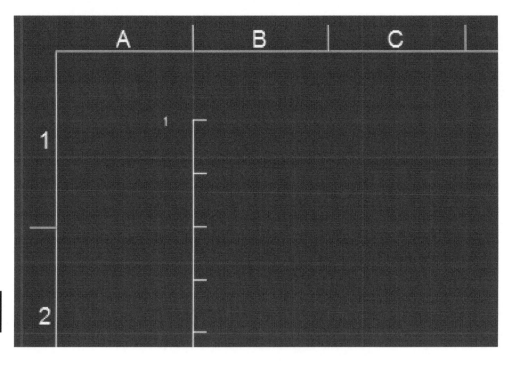

Now move the mouse downwards. A busbar will be drawn at the left of your drawing with small stubs (shown above) indicating the position of each ladder rung.

Move the mouse down close to the bottom of the drawing. You should be able to fit at least 15 rungs into the height of the page. Left click again to confirm the bottom of the ladder.

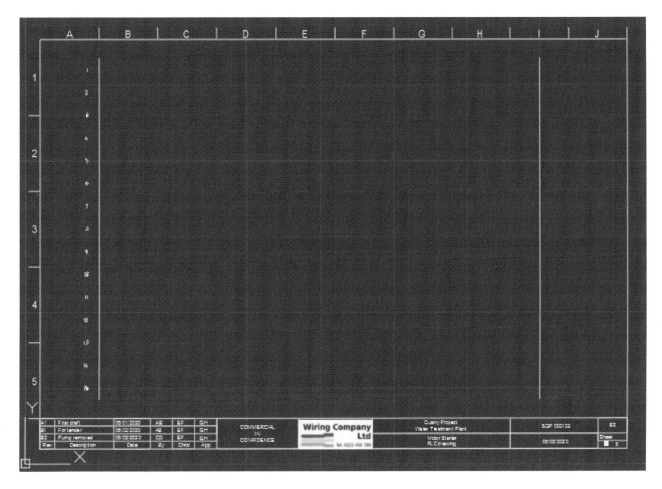

You will now have two vertical bus wires at opposite sides of the drawing.

The one on the left usually represents live in an ac system or positive in a dc system. The one on the right represents neutral or 0 volts. It is also possible to choose **3 Phase**, rather than **1 Phase**, in the **Insert Ladder** dialogue box. This would give you a three phase bus system which you could use to draw three phase circuits.

Each rung position is marked by a reference number on the left but the rungs themselves are not drawn yet because we selected **No Rungs**.

Adding a rung

Click the **Add Rung** button in the **Schematic** tab of the ribbon.

18

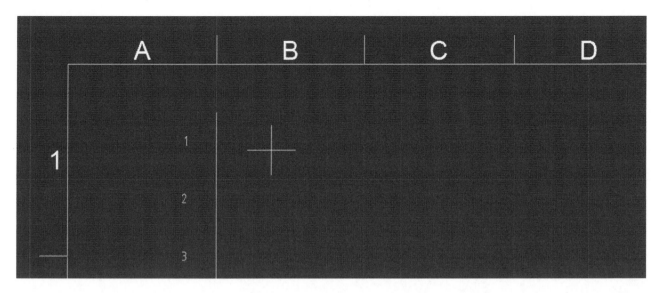

Click on your drawing near the number **1** marking the first rung. A rung will be drawn between the supply bus wires.

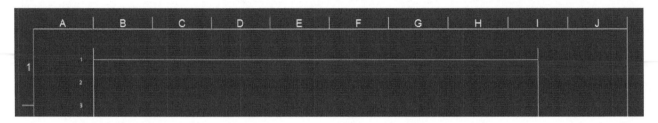

This rung will snap to the closest defined rung position to the point where you click. If you had left **X-Y grid** selected in **Drawing Properties**, rather than choosing **Reference Numbers**, then the rung would be inserted at the cursor instead of at a predefined rung position.

The bus wires at the left and right represent the power supply to the circuit. Devices which produce a signal, for example switches, sensors and PLC output cards, are placed on the left part of the rung. Devices which are controlled by or receive a signal, for example lights, relay coils and PLC input cards, are placed at the right of the rung. The rungs are just wires so you can add or modify them using the ordinary **Wire** command.

As an example, use the **Icon Menu** in the **Schematic** tab of the ribbon to insert a push button and a relay coil as shown below.

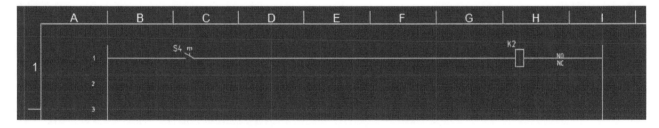

18

Now add a second rung using the **Add Rung** button. Join this to the first by drawing a vertical wire with the normal **Wire** tool which we used elsewhere in this book.

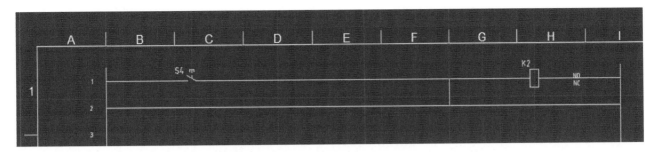

In the **Schematic** tab of the ribbon click the **Trim Wire** tool.

The cursor becomes a small hollow square. Click on the left part of rung **2** in the drawing. The left part of this rung will be removed. Press **<Esc>** to exit the **Trim Wire** command.

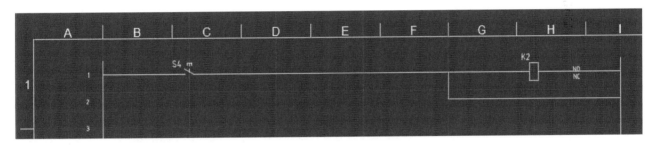

We can now add a light in parallel with the relay coil using the **Icon Menu** button in the **Schematic** tab of the ribbon. The example light shown is found in the **Pilot Lights** folder of the **IEC4 Icon Menu**.

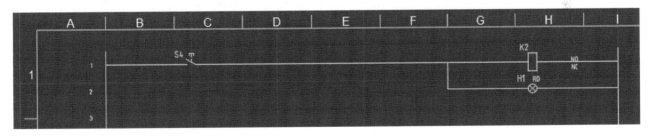

Save your drawings.

18.2   Inserting pre-configured PLC cards from the library

We will now insert an Allen Bradley 1746-OB8 digital output card. This is one of the card definitions that is supplied with AutoCAD Electrical.

First use the **Add Rung** command to add a rung for rung **3**. We will insert our PLC card onto this rung. This will make it easier to line up the card connection points with the rung positions.

18

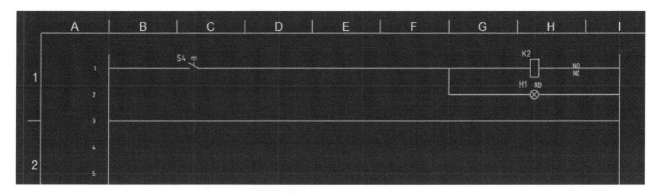

From the **Schematic** tab, click the **Insert PLC (Parametric)** button

The **PLC Parametric Selection** dialogue box is displayed.

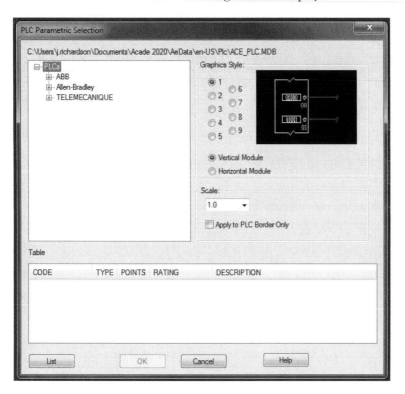

Click on the **+** symbol beside **Allen-Bradley** in the list of manufacturers. Expand the subheadings as follows:

18

Allen-Bradley > 1746 > Discrete Output

Under the heading **Discrete Output**, click the name of the IO card, **1746-OB8** to highlight it.

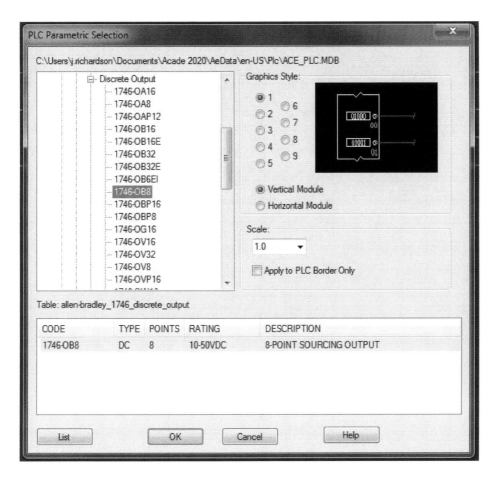

Details of this card will then be displayed (see the above image) in the section at the bottom of the dialogue box.

Leave graphics style as **1** unless you want to modify the card's appearance. **Vertical Module** should be selected unless you want your PLC symbol to be drawn horizontally across the page.

Leave scale set to **1.0**.

The box **Apply to PLC Border Only** is used if you wish to insert the PLC connections at normal scale but enlarge the border around them. For our example leave it unticked.

Click **OK**. The dialogue box closes to show your drawing and a dotted shape will appear at the cursor.

18

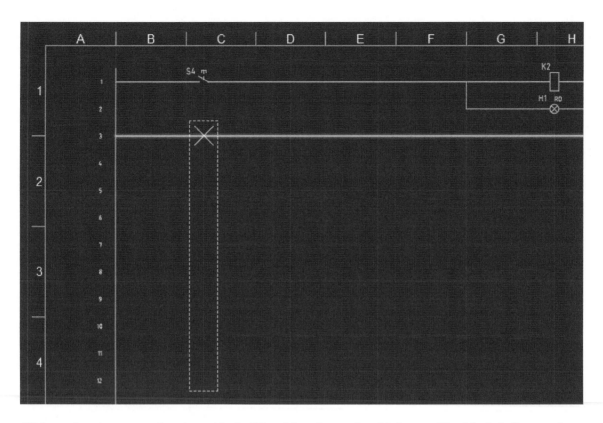

Click to place it on your drawing with the **X** positioned over the third rung. The **Module Layout** box appears.

Leave spacing at **15** to match the spacing of your rungs. Click **OK**. The **I/O Point** dialogue box will ask which PLC rack the card is in and its slot position within the rack. In our example we will enter it as **Rack 2, Slot 5**.

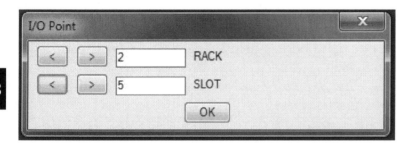

Press **OK** and you will be asked for the IO address of the first IO point on the card. We will enter this as **O:050**.

Click **OK** again and the symbol will be inserted.

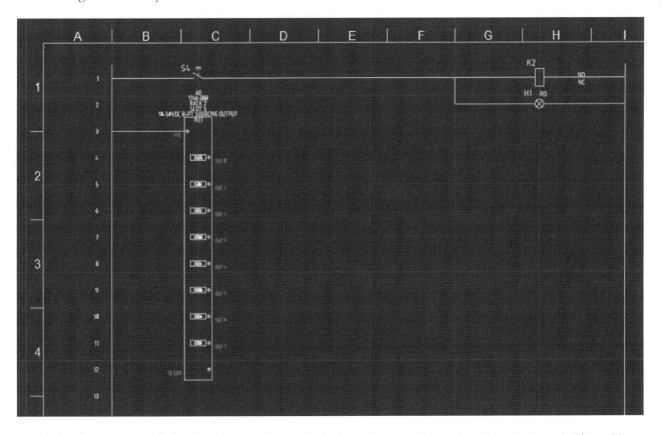

Look closely at the card (in the close-up image below) and you will see the Slot, Rack and I/O address information have been added. The I/O addresses are incremented automatically based on the starting address of **O:050** which you entered.

18

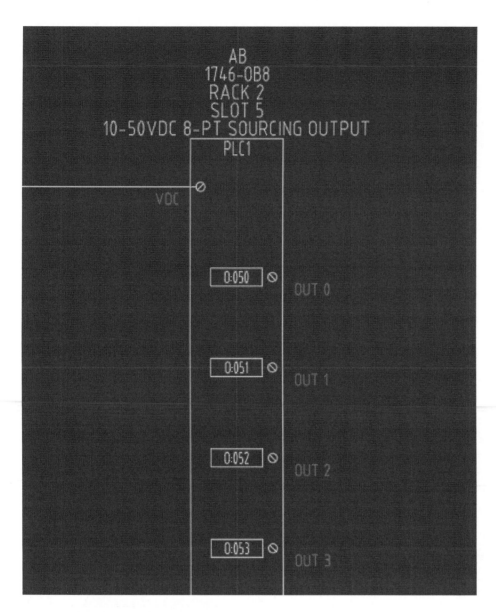

Completing the drawing

Since we added the module on top of a rung, its power supply (**VDC**) terminal is already connected to the positive supply rail. Use **Add Rung** to connect the 0V supply (**DC COM**) to the 0V supply rail.

Add some rungs to the outputs and place loads for the PLC to drive, for example lights or relay coils, on these rungs. You can use the **Wire** command, instead of **Add Rung**, if you wish.

When inserting multiple rungs you only need to click the **Add Rung** button once. Each time you click the drawing, another rung will be added without the need to click the button again. Press **<Esc>** or choose a different command to exit the **Add Rung** tool.

It is not compulsory to connect a rung to unused outputs.

18

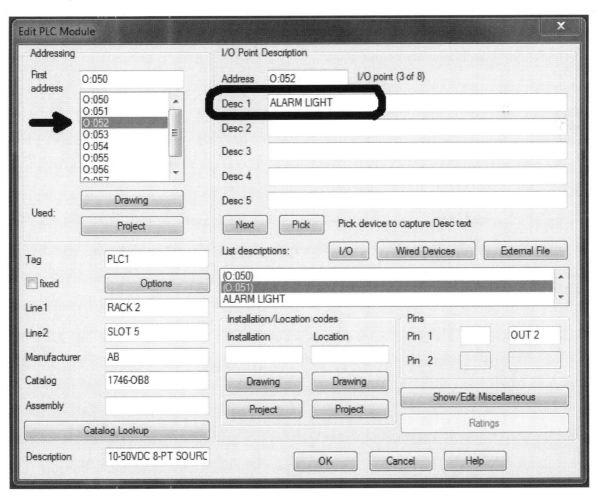

You may wish to add text labels to the PLC signals. To do this select the PLC module, right click and choose **Edit Component** from the menu that appears. The **Edit PLC Module** dialogue box opens.

To add a description, select the IO point from the list in the top left of this box. Then complete the description fields for that point. In the above example the third output, **O:052** has been selected and the description **ALARM LIGHT** added. There are five lines of description for each address point.

These descriptions will be displayed in capitals if you have the **"Description text upper case"** box ticked (see page 43) in the **Components** tab of the **Project Properties** for your project.

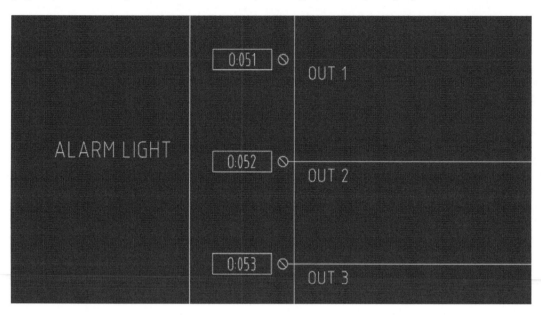

Save your drawing.

Breaks and spacers

When inserting a card, you can select **Allow Spacers/Breaks** in the **Module Layout** dialogue box that appears at the start of the process. You will then be asked to confirm the insertion of each terminal by the following dialogue box.

After each terminal you can add a spacer if required or break the card and continue it elsewhere on the drawing. After a break you must choose the place on your drawing to continue the card. You will also be asked many of the formatting and IO address questions again.

18

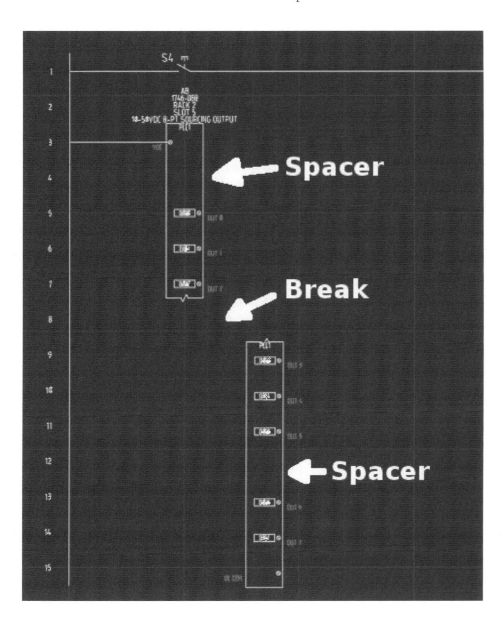

18.3 Creating your own PLC card symbols

If the PLC card you are using is not in the AutoCAD library it is simple to create a new PLC symbol and add it.

The PLC card definitions are stored in the database file **ACE_PLC.mdb**

You will find it in the folder:

C:\Users** *your windows username*\Documents\Acade 2020\AeData\en-US\Plc**

Note that the **Documents** folder may appear as **My Documents** when using Microsoft Windows Explorer to find it.

When you modify the PLC database by adding or deleting new PLC cards, the modified list of cards is available to all projects you work with using your installation of AutoCAD. To back up the PLC card definitions or copy between machines, copy the **ACE_PLC.mdb** file.

In the following example we will add a symbol for a 2 input, 3 wire temperature module, part **X20 AT2222** from the manufacturer **B & R Automation**, to the standard AutoCAD database.

Create a new drawing

Right click the **TestRig1** project heading in the **Project Manager** window. Choose **New Drawing...** and create a drawing called **sheet 9** using using the **first_template.dwt** template.

Set **Description 1** to **Motor Starter** and **Description 2** to **Temperature Inputs**. When prompted, agree to apply the **Project Default Values**.

Open **Drawing Properties** for this drawing from the **Schematic** tab of the ribbon. Select the **Drawing Format** tab.

Select the **Reference Numbers** option in the **Format Referencing** section. Set **Spacing** to **15** (or **0.6** inches for an imperial scaled drawing) and **Width** to **300** (or **12** if your drawing is in inches).

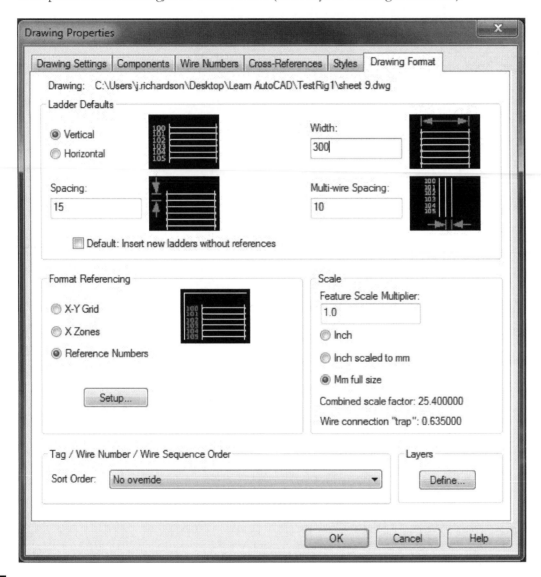

Click **OK** to return to your drawing.

Click the **Insert Ladder** button in the **Schematic** tab of the ribbon. The **Insert Ladder** dialogue box will open.

18

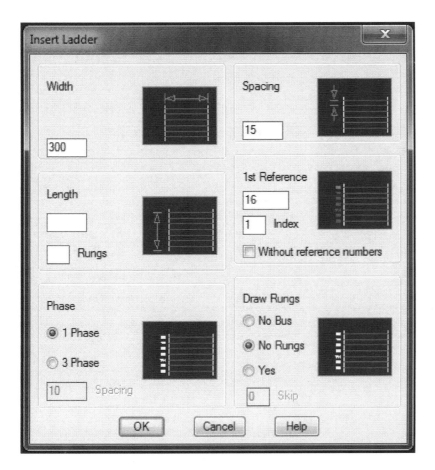

For **Width** and **Spacing** keep the default values which we set in **Drawing Properties** of **Width** = **300** and **Spacing** = **15**. (These will be set to **12** and **0.6** if you are creating a drawing scaled in inches.)

Select the **No Rungs** option so we can add rungs only where needed.

The first rung value (**1st Reference**) will be filled in automatically with the next number to continue from the previous ladder. In this screenshot this is **16**.

Click **OK**.

You will be returned to your drawing with the cursor as a large cross-hair. Left click near the top left of your drawing to place the top of the ladder.

Move the mouse downwards and click near the bottom of the drawing to draw the ladder.

18

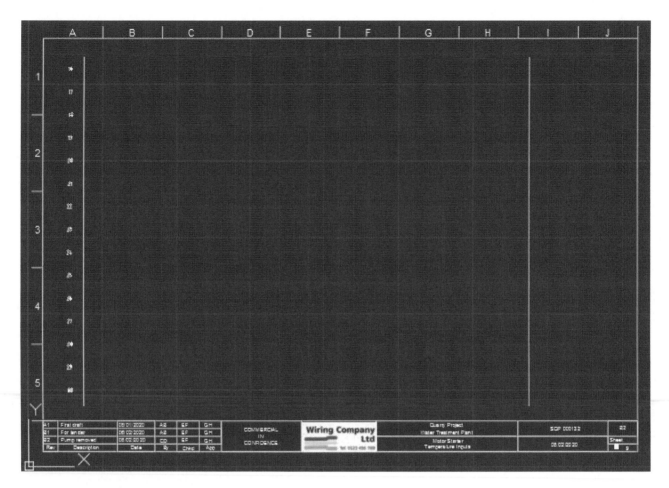

Create the PLC symbol

At the far right of the **Schematic** tab click the drop down arrow beside **Other Tools**.

You should see the **PLC Database File Editor** button shown below.

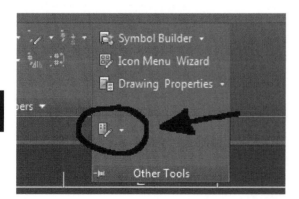

There is a drop down menu beside this button so expand this if the **PLC Database File Editor** button is not on top.

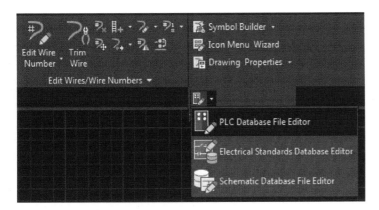

Click the **PLC Database File Editor** button.

You will see the **PLC Database File Editor** window. Since we recently used an Allen Bradley part the window has opened at this point in the library.

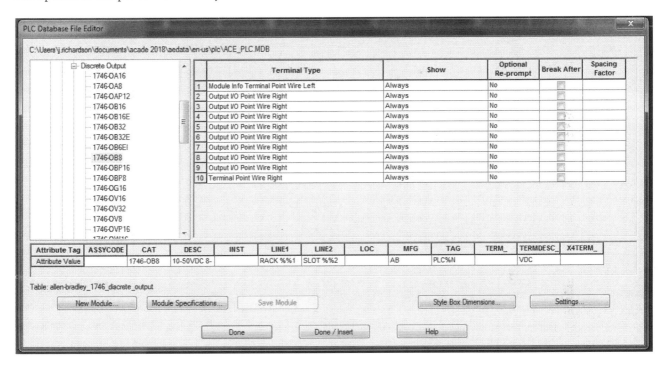

We are going to create a new manufacturer. We do not want our new card to be created under Allen Bradley output modules so we must navigate to the top of the PLC database file structure.

Use the scroll bar and '-' buttons in the box on the left to navigate to the top of the file structure. Click on the **PLCs** heading at the top of the tree to highlight it as shown below.

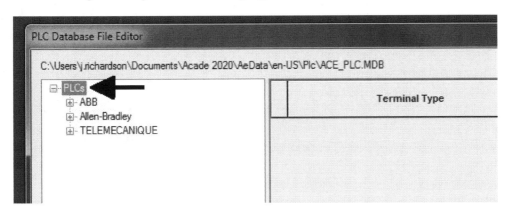

Now click the **New Module** button.

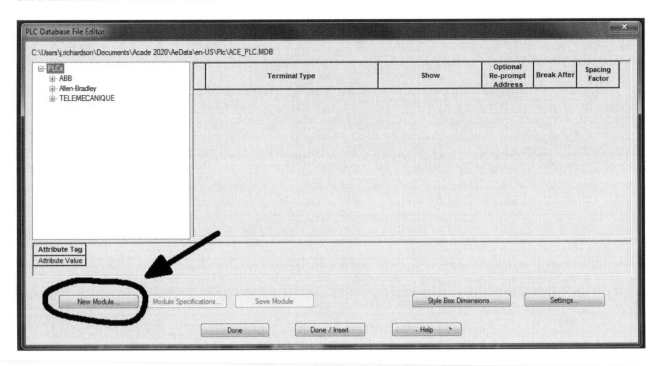

A dialogue box with blank fields will be presented.

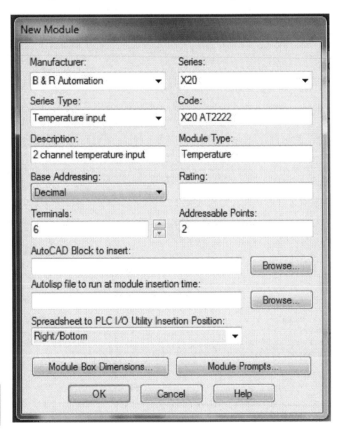

18

Fill in the **Manufacturer, Series, Series Type, Code, Description** and **Module Type** as above. If required you can also add a **Rating** value.

For our example set **Terminals** to **6, Addressable Points** to **2** and **Base Addressing** to **Decimal**.

Terminals defines the number of wire connections to the module. **Addressable Points** defines the number of IO channels.

The **AT2222** card used in this example has two temperature sensor inputs. Each sensor creates one signal value requiring a PLC channel **Addressable Point**. The sensors are connected with three wires per sensor so there are a total of six **Terminals**.

The **Base Addressing** box tells AutoCAD how to increment the IO addresses between channels. You can select decimal, octal or hexadecimal. If you choose "**prompt**" then you will be asked to choose a system each time you use the module.

"**AutoCAD Block to insert**" lets you add an extra block to the bottom of your PLC module. This is used to show configuration instructions or DIP switches for the module. You can leave it blank.

Click **OK** and you will see the correct number of terminals for your new module listed in the **PLC Database File Editor**.

B & R Automation has also been added to the list of manufacturers at the left with **Series** and **Module Type** forming subfolders below this in the tree.

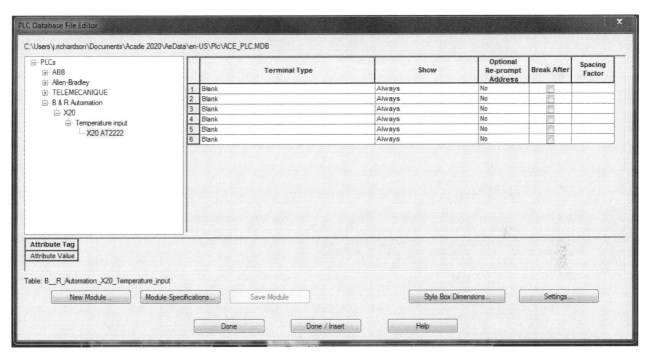

We must now configure each terminal. The first terminal will be designated as the header of the module. This means it will carry values covering details of the whole unit, for example **Rack** and **Slot** numbers.

There are two addressable channels since the PLC is measuring two temperatures. Addressable channels will be assigned to terminals **1** and **4** to carry this information with terminal **1** also being the header.

Finally, pins **2**, **3**, **5** and **6** are just plain wire connections. They do not carry any address information but are required because the temperature sensors have three connections each.

Right click in the **Terminal Type** column for pin **1**. A menu appears as below. Do not left click or you get a drop down arrow giving you options for the terminal instead.

18

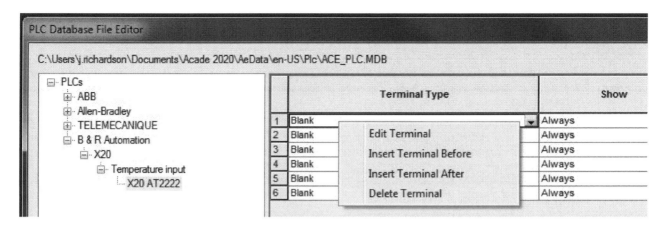

Select **Edit Terminal** and the **Select Terminal Information** box will open.

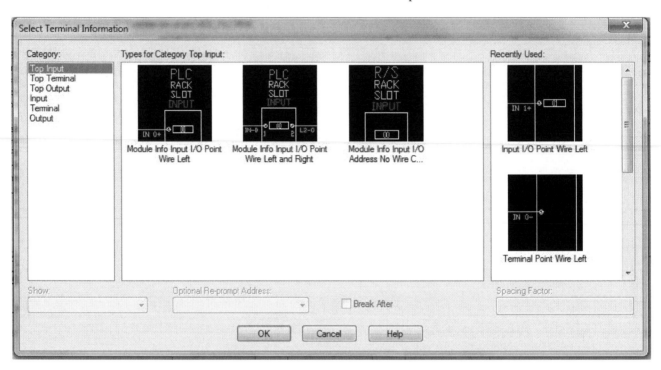

The **Category** box at the left gives the possible terminal functions.

Input and **Output** are terminals that carry a PLC IO address. **Terminal** is a terminal which is required for wiring but does not have an address allocated to it. The prefix **Top** means that a terminal is the first in the module so is required to carry header information such as part number and slot number as well as the terminal details.

Click on **Top Input** in the **Category** box.

You will be given three possible drawings for the wire connection as shown above.

Left click **Module Info I/O Point Wire Left** to highlight it then click **OK**. The convention with ladder logic is that inputs usually enter from the left and outputs leave to the right. These symbols follow this rule.

You will return to the **PLC Database File Editor** window. Terminal **1** will now have its **Terminal Type** assigned.

18

	Terminal Type	Show	Optio Re-pro
1	Module Info Input I/O Point Wire Left ▼	Always	No
2	Blank	Always	No
3	Blank	Always	No
4	Blank	Always	No
5	Blank	Always	No
6	Blank	Always	No

Now right click beside terminal **4** in the **Terminal Type** column and select **Edit Terminal**.

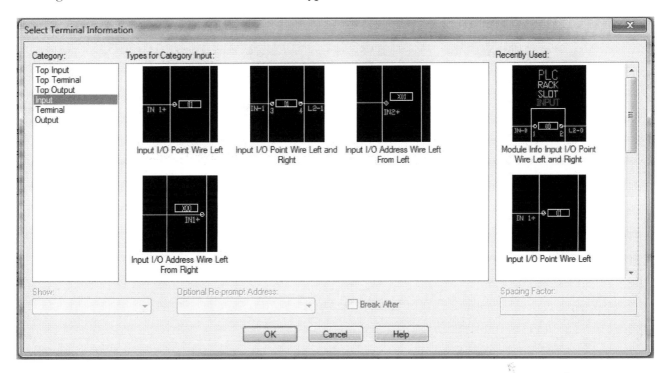

Choose **Input** from the **Category** list to get the options shown above. Select **Input I/O Point Wire Left** then click **OK**. This sets the terminal to be an ordinary addressed input which is not the first one in the module.

	Terminal Type	Show
1	Module Info Input I/O Point Wire Left	Always
2	Blank	Always
3	Blank	Always
4	Input I/O Point Wire Left ▼	Always
5	Blank	Always
6	Blank	Always

Finally we need to configure the other terminals as wire connection points with no PLC address. Use **CTRL + left click** to select the **Terminal Type** box for pins **2**, **3**, **5** and **6**. Right click the selected boxes and select **Edit Terminal**.

18

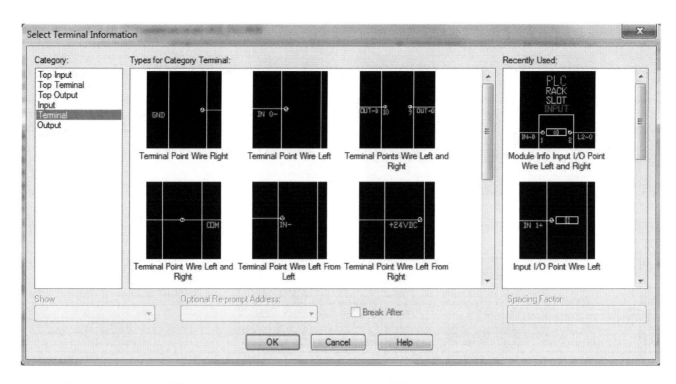

In the **Category** list select **Terminal**. Then choose the symbol for **Terminal Point Wire Left**. Click **OK** and all terminals will now have a type.

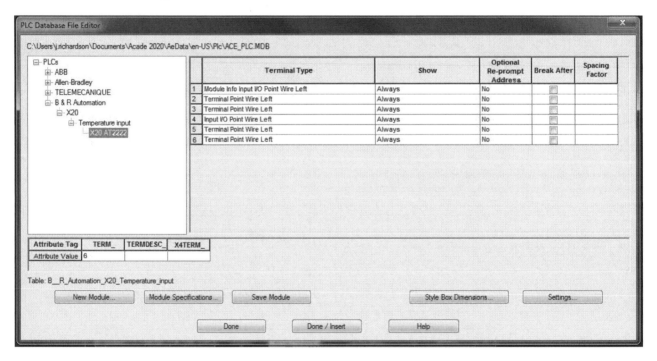

The **Show** column is set to **Always** by default. By changing this column it is possible to hide unused terminals.

The **Optional Re-prompt Address** column is set to **No** by default. With this setting AutoCAD will number the IO addresses by incrementing the first address supplied. If you have a module containing a mixture of inputs and outputs, these could have different address sequences. In this case you would set this column to **Input** or **Output** (a drop down menu with these options appears if you click in the column) for the first terminal of each block of inputs or outputs. This will make AutoCAD ask for an address at the start of each new address sequence.

Break After forces a break in the PLC module at this point when it is inserted. **Spacing Factor** gives an optional multiplier for the normal spacing between terminals, for example a value of 2 would give a double sized space.

18

Pin labelling

You may wish to label the pins of you PLC with non-sequential numbers to match those used by the manufacturer. You might also want to add a short descriptive label to each pin, for example "**GND**".

To label a pin, select the line for that terminal in the **PLC Database File Editor** box and alter the values of **TERM_** (the pin number) and **TERMDESC_** (the descriptive label) for that pin.

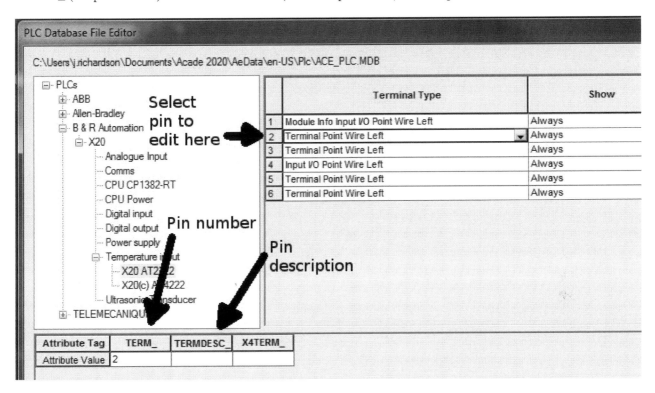

The **TERM_** and **TERMDESC_** also exist for addressable terminals but you may have to scroll to the right, past other columns, to find them.

Set up prompts for rack and slot information

Although we have set up all of the terminals we must still tell AutoCAD to prompt the user for the **Rack** and **Slot** information in the module header.

Click the top terminal to highlight it. You will see the attributes for this terminal at the bottom of the **PLC Database File Editor** window. Under **Line1** you will see that the PLC rack is displayed using the characters **RACK** and the value **%%1**. Similarly value **%%2** under **LINE2** represents the value of the PLC slot.

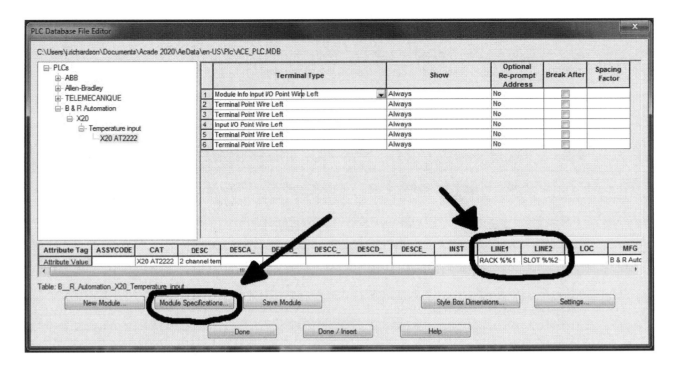

Click the **Module Specifications...** button.

The **Module Specifications** box appears. It allows you to edit some of the settings you made earlier.

Click the **Module Prompts** button. You will see the list of prompts. Currently they are all blank.

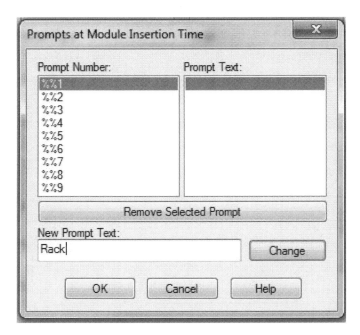

This box can be tricky to use so follow the instructions on where to click and where to type carefully.

Highlight **%%1** in the list. Now click on the **New Prompt Text** box. Type the word **"Rack"** in the **New Prompt Text** box as shown. Click **Change**.

Repeat this with **%%2** using the word **"Slot"** as the prompt. Click **Change**.

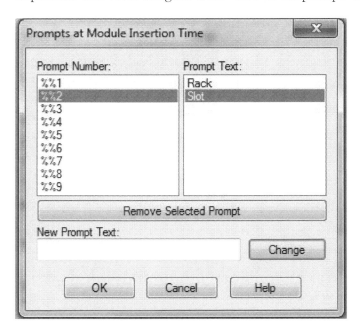

The image above shows the box with the added text. The user will be asked for these values when the symbol is inserted.

Click **OK** to close the **Prompts at Module Insertion Time** box. Then click **OK** again in the **Module Specifications** box to return to the **PLC Database File Editor**.

18

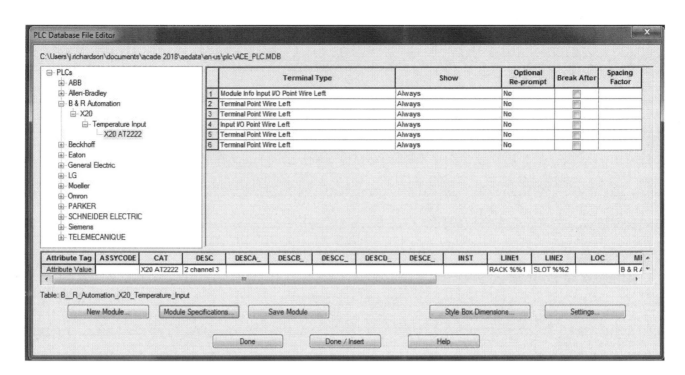

The button **Style Box Dimensions** opens the window below. It lets you adjust the box drawn around the module.

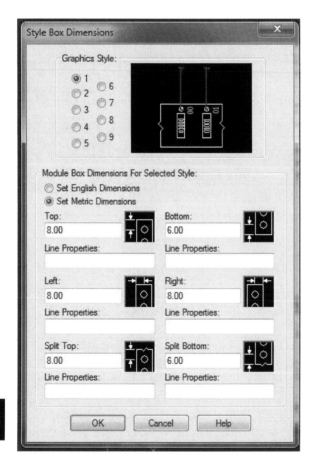

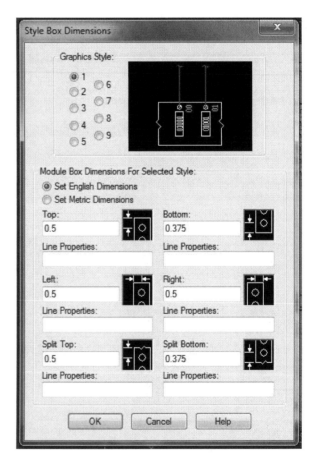

This box contains different settings for **English** and **Metric**. These are actually two separate sets of values and will be used depending on whether your drawing is set to English or metric units.

By selecting **Set English Dimensions** or **Set Metric Dimensions** you can choose which set to display and edit. The defaults for each are shown in the two images above.

The spacing values set in this box define the distance between the border of the PLC card and the terminal nearest to it. If these are set too small your PLC outline will appear as a narrow strip down the middle of the card instead of a box around the outside.

For our example, leave the dimensions unchanged and click **OK**.

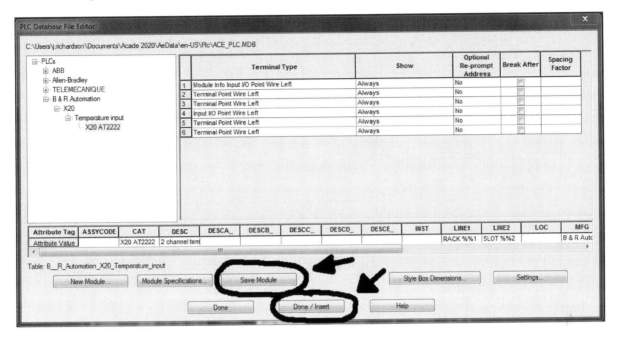

Click **Save Module** in the **PLC Database File Editor** screen. This saves your new PLC module.

Then click **Done/Insert** to close the editor and insert your module. The **PLC Parametric Selection** box will open with your new symbol selected. Click **OK** to insert it.

Click your drawing to place the dotted outline of the card in the centre. You are asked to confirm the spacing.

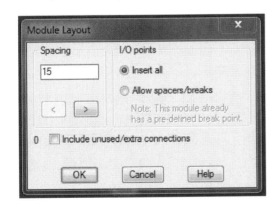

Click **OK** to accept the pre-set value of **15**.

Choose **6** for the rack value and **7** for the slot number and click **OK**.

Enter **I:020** for the starting address. Click **OK**.

Position the card on your drawing. Ensure that the **X** at the top of the outline is level with one of the defined rung positions. This ensures its terminals will line up with any rungs you draw later. The new card will be placed on your drawing.

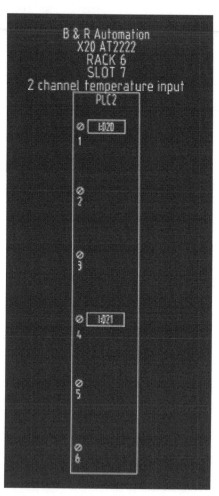

If you go to the **Insert PLC (Parametric)** button you will also find that the new manufacturer, **B & R Automation**, has been added to the catalogue with your new PLC symbol included ready for future use.

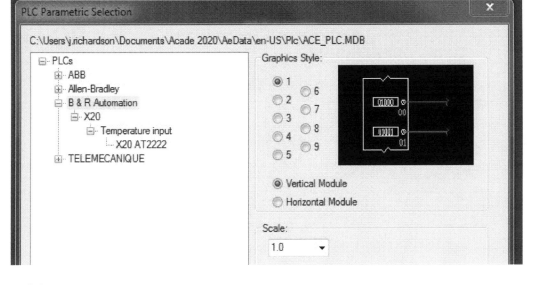

Add some wiring

To complete the drawing with realistic example wiring, you can add some fixed resistors from the **Icon Menu** (under the heading **Miscellaneous > Electronics**) and some wires (using the **Wire** tool) to show some three wire PT100 temperature sensors as shown below. Save your drawings.

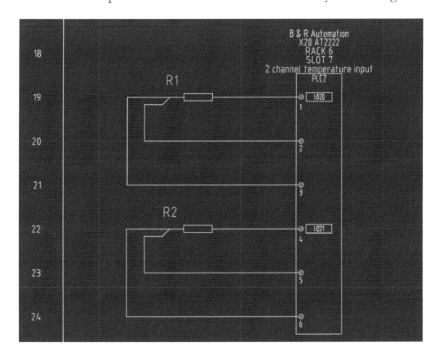

18.4   Editing a symbol

You can use the **PLC Database File Editor** to alter an existing PLC symbol. To do this, open the **PLC Database File Editor** and select the PLC card you wish to edit. You can then alter the **Terminal Type** by right clicking on the table as you did when creating a new symbol. You can also click the **Module Specifications** button to change overall settings for the module.

To delete a PLC module from the catalogue, right click the module name in the tree at the left of the **PLC Database File Editor** window and choose **Delete** from the menu that appears. This menu also contains an option to **Rename** modules.

You can delete an entire manufacturer, including all of their modules, by right clicking on the top level folder and using the **Delete** function.

18

18.5   Further PLC features

This book can only give a brief introduction to PLC drawings. In addition to the parametric PLC tool already discussed, you can also insert PLCs as fixed blocks or as individual IO points.

Open the **Icon Menu** on the **Schematic** tab of the ribbon. Choose the **PLC I/O** folder. You will see the components in the image below.

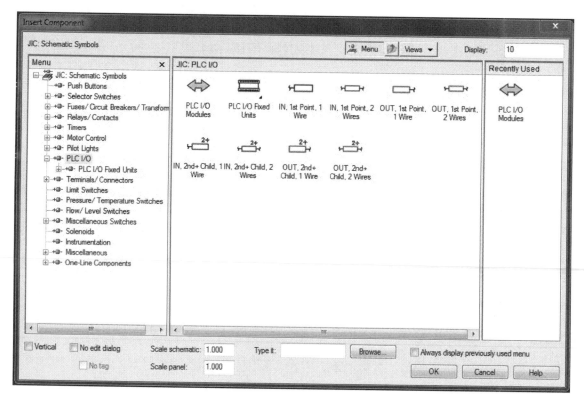

The first item in this menu, **PLC I/O Modules** will open the **Insert PLC (Parametric)** tool we used earlier.

The second item, **PLC I/O Fixed Units**, will open a submenu of PLC cards which you can insert. These fixed PLC components allow for more complicated shapes than the PLC (Parametric) tool. They can also be inserted using the **Insert PLC (Full Units)** button on the ribbon which shares a dropdown menu with the **PLC (Parametric)** tool.

The other components shown allow you to insert a PLC module as separate IO points scattered throughout your drawing. To do this you would choose one **1st Point** component. As with the top terminal in a parametric PLC module, this will carry the part number for the PLC module. Other terminals are then added as child components using the **2nd+ Child** symbols.

18.6   PLC reports

In the **Reports** tool you will find several reports for PLCs, allowing you to display IO signals and connections to other components. PLC cards will also be included in the **Bill of Material** report.

You will find that the **Description** field for the custom PLC card does not show up in the **Bill of Material** report, unlike that for the AB unit entered earlier in the chapter. To fix this you can select the PLC schematic symbol, right click, and choose **Edit Component** from the menu. From this screen you can choose **Lookup** and create a component catalogue entry for the PLC card, as we did for our custom power supply in chapter 15.

The **Bill of Material** report shows the catalogue description the for PLC cards which is different to the description field shown in the **Edit Component** dialogue box.

18

19. Final comments

Congratulations if you have worked through the book to this point. While it was not possible to include every feature of the AutoCAD Electrical software, you should now have sufficient knowledge to produce most electrical schematics.

Our **Testrig1** project is now finished. For completeness you might want to do a **Title Block Update** to update the numbering of the additional sheets. You could then redo the **Drawing List Report** on **sheet 1** to produce a final table of contents.

By copying **SampleProject1**, with the methods described in chapter 6, you can produce blank projects for use in your real work.

Once you have some experience you may wish to alter the files from chapters 4 and 5 to customise the drawing template to your needs. You can also find some useful downloads and resources by visiting the **www.MusselburghPress.com** website.

Solutions to more advanced issues may be found in the AutoCAD online help documentation. The AutoCAD help system also includes questions and posts by users about specific problems. These can be found using the search function.

I would like to thank you for reading my book and hope you have found it worthwhile.

If so I would appreciate it if you could write a short review on Amazon.

James

Index

In

In

In

About the author

James Richardson studied electronics at the University of York. He then spent ten years in the steel industry, working on installation and maintenance of heavy electrical equipment.

He qualified as a Chartered Electrical Engineer and later moved to Scotland to work on the Pelamis wave energy device.

In 2015 he set up James E Richardson (Electrical) Limited, an electrical engineering business, based in Edinburgh.

Working as a contractor?
Setting up a limited company in the UK?

Check out this Amazon bestseller from the same author.

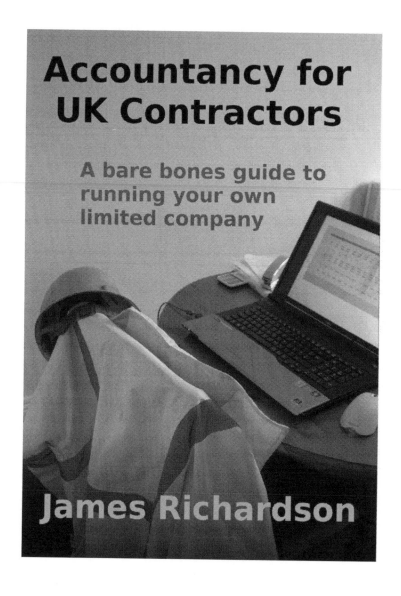

Gibraltar is perfect for a short break but don't skimp on a guidebook.

Save time with this concise guide by the same author. In full colour throughout, with 9 full page maps.

Made in the USA
Columbia, SC
16 February 2022

56282281R10237